INDIANA

GRADE 6

Your online portal to everything you need

connectED.mcgraw-hill.com

Look for these icons to access
exciting digital resources

 Video

 Audio

 Review

 Inquiry

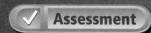 WebQuest

 Assessment

Concepts in Motion

Glencoe

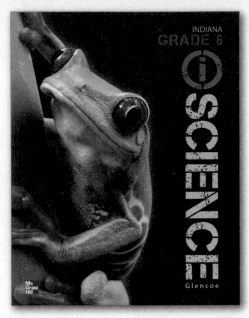

Red-Eyed Tree Frog, *Agalychnis callidryas*
This tiny frog is arboreal—it lives in rain forest trees.
Its diet includes different types of insects. Females
generally are about 6 cm–7.5 cm in length. Males
are slightly smaller. It can be found in Central America,
southern Mexico, and northern Colombia.

The *McGraw·Hill* Companies

 Education

Send all inquiries to:
McGraw-Hill Education
8787 Orion Place
Columbus, OH 43240-4027

ISBN: 978-0-07-888034-6
MHID: 0-07-888034-3

Printed in the United States of America.

3 4 5 6 7 8 9 10 QDB/QDB 15 14 13 12 11

Contents in Brief

Indiana's Academic Standards for Science, Grade 6 Correlated to *Indiana* ⓘ *Science Grade 6*

Process Standards	Pages
The Nature of Science Students gain scientific knowledge by observing the natural and constructed world, performing and evaluating investigations and communicating their findings. These principles should guide student work and be integrated into the curriculum along with the content standards on a daily basis.	
6.NS.1 Make predictions and develop testable questions based on research and prior knowledge.	NOS 6–NOS 7, NOS 22–NOS 29, 194–195, 230–231, 242, 266–267
6.NS.2 Plan and carry out investigations as a class, in small groups or independently often over a period of several class lessons.	NOS 13, 168–169, 194–195, 266–267
6.NS.3 Collect quantitative data with appropriate tools or technologies and use appropriate units to label numerical data.	NOS 14–NOS 16, NOS 18–NOS 19, 13, 19, 27, 41, 53, 56–57, 107, 115, 194–195, 207, 242
6.NS.4 Incorporate variables that can be changed, measured, or controlled.	NOS 23, NOS 27, 47, 81, 122, 182, 194–195, 213
6.NS.5 Use the principles of accuracy and precision when making measurements.	NOS 16, 13, 19, 27, 47, 53, 56–57, 111, 118, 134, 194–195, 207, 242
6.NS.6 Test predictions with multiple trials.	27, 56–57, 81, 122, 207, 213
6.NS.7 Keep accurate records in a notebook during investigations.	NOS 18, NOS 22–NOS 29, 13, 19, 21, 27, 30–31, 41, 44, 47, 53, 56–57, 79, 81, 89, 90, 107, 115, 118, 121, 123, 127, 131, 136–137, 151, 157, 161, 164, 168–169, 179, 182, 187, 191, 194–195, 205, 207, 213, 216, 221, 223, 241, 242, 249, 257, 266–267
6.NS.8 Analyze data, using appropriate mathematical manipulation as required, and use it to identify patterns and make inferences based on these patterns.	NOS 7, NOS 17, NOS 21, 71, 121, 146–147, 207, 221, 230–231, 266–267
6.NS.9 Evaluate possible causes for differing results (valid data).	19, 71, 136–137, 182, 194–195, 207, 213
6.NS.10 Compare the results of an experiment with the prediction.	27, 81, 96–97, 260–261
6.NS.11 Communicate findings using graphs, charts, maps and models through oral and written reports.	NOS 9, 96–97, 136–137, 157, 168–169, 194–195, 221, 223, 230–231, 241, 249, 257, 266–267
The Design Process: As citizens of the constructed world, students will participate in the design process. Students will learn to use materials and tools safely and employ the basic principles of the engineering design process in order to find a solution to a problem.	
6.DP.1 Identify a need or problem that needs to be solved.	NOS 12–NOS 13, 5, 194–195
6.DP.2 Brainstorm potential solutions.	NOS 12–NOS 13, 5, 67, 194–195
6.DP.3 Document the design throughout the entire design process so that it can be replicated in a portfolio/ notebook with drawings including labels.	NOS 12–NOS 13, 5, 67, 194–195

Indiana's Academic Standards for Science, Grade 6 Correlated to *Indiana ⓘ Science Grade 6*

Process Standards	Pages
6.DP.4 Select a solution to the need or problem.	NOS 12–NOS 13, 5, 194–195
6.DP.5 Select the most appropriate materials to develop a solution that will meet the need.	NOS 12–NOS 13, 5, 194–195
6.DP.6 Create a solution through a prototype.	NOS 12–NOS 13, 5, 194–195
6.DP.7 Test and evaluate how well the solution meets the goal.	NOS 12–NOS 13, 5, 194–195
6.DP.8 Evaluate and test the design using measurement.	NOS 12–NOS 13, 194–195
6.DP.9 Present evidence using mathematical representation (graphs, data tables).	NOS 12–NOS 13, 5, 194–195
6.DP.10 Communicate the solution including evidence using mathematical representations (graphs, data tables), drawings or prototype.	NOS 12–NOS 13, 5, 19, 194–195
6.DP.11 Redesign to improve the solution based on how well the solution meets the need.	NOS 12–NOS 13, 5, 194–195

Standard 1: Physical Science	Pages

Core Standard
Explain that all objects and substances in the natural world are composed of matter in different states with different properties.

Core Standard
Understand there are different forms of energy with unique characteristics.

6.1.1 Understand that the properties and behavior of matter can be explained by a model which depicts particles representing atoms or molecules in motion.	11, 22–23
6.1.2 Explain the properties of solids, liquids and gases using drawings and models that represent matter as particles in motion whose state can be represented by the relative positions and movement of the particles.	10–11, 22–23
6.1.3 Using a model in which matter is composed of particles in motion, investigate that when substances undergo a change in state, mass is conserved.	23, 27
6.1.4 Recognize that objects in motion have kinetic energy and objects at rest have potential energy.	42, 45, 47, 50
6.1.5 Describe with examples that potential energy exists in several different forms (gravitational potential energy, elastic potential energy, and chemical potential energy, among others).	42–43

Process Standards	Pages
6.1.6 Compare and contrast potential and kinetic energy and how they can be transformed within a system from one form to another.	42–43, 47, 50, 53
6.1.7 Explain that energy may be manifested as heat, light, electricity, mechanical motion, and sound and is often associated with chemical reactions.	44–45, 52–53

Standard 2: Earth and Space Science	Pages

Core Standard
Understand the relationships between celestial bodies and the force that keeps them in regular and predictable motion.

6.2.1 Describe and model how the position, size and relative motions of the earth, moon, and sun cause day and night, solar and lunar eclipses and phases of the moon.	71–77, 83–85, 89–93, 96–97
6.2.2 Recognize that gravity is a force that keeps celestial bodies in regular and predictable motion, holds objects to earth's surface, and is responsible for ocean tides.	72, 93–94, 108
6.2.3 Understand that the sun, an average star where nuclear reactions occur, is the central and largest body in the solar system.	71, 108–111
6.2.4 Compare and contrast the planets of the solar system with one another and with asteroids and comets with regard to their size, composition, distance from sun, surface features and ability to support life.	108–111, 115–119, 123–127, 131–134, 136–137
6.2.5 Demonstrate that the seasons in both hemispheres are the result of the inclination of the earth on its axis which in turn causes changes in sunlight intensity and length of day.	71–73, 75–77, 79

Standard 3: Life Science	Pages

Core Standard
Describe that all organisms, including humans, are part of complex systems found in all biomes (freshwater, marine, forest, desert, grassland, tundra).

Core Standard
Understand that the major source of energy for ecosystems is light produced by major nuclear reactions in the sun.

6.3.1 Describe specific relationships (predator/prey, consumer/producer or parasite/host) between organisms and determine whether these relationships are competitive or mutually beneficial.	224, 226–228, 230–231
6.3.2 Describe how changes caused by organisms in the habitat where they live can be beneficial or detrimental to themselves or the native plants and animals.	187–192, 206–209, 213–219, 223–228, 242–247, 252–257, 261–264

Standard 3: Life Science	Pages
6.3.3 Describe how certain biotic and abiotic factors, such as predators, quantity of light and water, range of temperatures, and soil composition, can limit the number of organisms that an ecosystem can support.	208, 242–247, 252–257, 261–262
6.3.4 Recognize that plants use energy from the sun to make sugar (glucose) by the process of photosynthesis.	165, 179–183, 224
6.3.5 Describe how all animals, including humans, meet their energy needs by consuming other organisms, breaking down their structures, and using the materials to grow and function.	224–225
6.3.6 Recognize that food provides the energy for the work that cells do and is a source of the molecular building blocks that can be incorporated into a cell's structure or stored for later use.	154, 165–166, 182–183

Standard 4: Science, Engineering and Technology	Pages
Core Standard Apply a form of energy to design and construct a simple mechanical device.	
6.4.1 Understand how to apply potential or kinetic energy to power a simple device.	56–57
6.4.2 Construct a simple device that uses potential or kinetic energy to perform work.	56–57
6.4.3 Describe the transfer of energy amongst energy interactions.	49–53

Author
William D. Rogers, DA
Professor of Biology
Ball State University
Muncie, IN

Consultant
Cheryl Wistrom, PhD
Associate Professor of Chemistry
Saint Joseph's College
Rensselaer, IN

Reviewers
Jane E.M. Buckingham
Teacher
Crispus Attucks Medical Magnet High School
Indianapolis, IN

Ginger Shirley
Our Lady of Providence Junior–Senior High School
Clarksville, IN

Tony Spoors
Switzerland County Middle School
Vevay, IN

Nancy A. Stearns
Switzerland County Middle School
Vevay, IN

Driftwood River, Bartholomew County

Authors and Contributors

Authors

American Museum of Natural History
New York, NY

Michelle Anderson, MS
Lecturer
The Ohio State University
Columbus, OH

Juli Berwald, PhD
Science Writer
Austin, TX

John F. Bolzan, PhD
Science Writer
Columbus, OH

Rachel Clark, MS
Science Writer
Moscow, ID

Patricia Craig, MS
Science Writer
Bozeman, MT

Randall Frost, PhD
Science Writer
Pleasanton, CA

Lisa S. Gardiner, PhD
Science Writer
Denver, CO

Jennifer Gonya, PhD
The Ohio State University
Columbus, OH

Mary Ann Grobbel, MD
Science Writer
Grand Rapids, MI

Whitney Crispen Hagins, MA, MAT
Biology Teacher
Lexington High School
Lexington, MA

Carole Holmberg, BS
Planetarium Director
Calusa Nature Center and
Planetarium, Inc.
Fort Myers, FL

Tina C. Hopper
Science Writer
Rockwall, TX

Jonathan D. W. Kahl, PhD
Professor of Atmospheric Science
University of Wisconsin-
Milwaukee
Milwaukee, WI

Nanette Kalis
Science Writer
Athens, OH

S. Page Keeley, MEd
Maine Mathematics and Science
Alliance
Augusta, ME

Cindy Klevickis, PhD
Professor of Integrated Science
and Technology
James Madison University
Harrisonburg, VA

Kimberly Fekany Lee, PhD
Science Writer
La Grange, IL

Michael Manga, PhD
Professor
University of California, Berkeley
Berkeley, CA

Devi Ried Mathieu
Science Writer
Sebastopol, CA

Elizabeth A. Nagy-Shadman, PhD
Geology Professor
Pasadena City College
Pasadena, CA

William D. Rogers, DA
Professor of Biology
Ball State University
Muncie, IN

Donna L. Ross, PhD
Associate Professor
San Diego State University
San Diego, CA

Marion B. Sewer, PhD
Assistant Professor
School of Biology
Georgia Institute of Technology
Atlanta, GA

Julia Meyer Sheets, PhD
Lecturer
School of Earth Sciences
The Ohio State University
Columbus, OH

Michael J. Singer, PhD
Professor of Soil Science
Department of Land, Air and
Water Resources
University of California
Davis, CA

Karen S. Sottosanti, MA
Science Writer
Pickerington, Ohio

Paul K. Strode, PhD
I.B. Biology Teacher
Fairview High School
Boulder, CO

Jan M. Vermilye, PhD
Research Geologist
Seismo-Tectonic Reservoir
Monitoring (STRM)
Boulder, CO

Judith A. Yero, MA
Director
Teacher's Mind Resources
Hamilton, MT

Dinah Zike, MEd
Author, Consultant, Inventor
of Foldables
Dinah Zike Academy; Dinah-
Might Adventures, LP
San Antonio, TX

Margaret Zorn, MS
Science Writer
Yorktown, VA

Consulting Authors

Alton L. Biggs
Biggs Educational Consulting
Commerce, TX

Ralph M. Feather, Jr., PhD
Assistant Professor
Department of Educational
Studies and Secondary Education
Bloomsburg University
Bloomsburg, PA

Douglas Fisher, PhD
Professor of Teacher Education
San Diego State University
San Diego, CA

Edward P. Ortleb
Science/Safety Consultant
St. Louis, MO

Series Consultants

Science

Solomon Bililign, PhD
Professor
Department of Physics
North Carolina Agricultural and
Technical State University
Greensboro, NC

John Choinski
Professor
Department of Biology
University of Central Arkansas
Conway, AR

Anastasia Chopelas, PhD
Research Professor
Department of Earth and Space
Sciences
UCLA
Los Angeles, CA

David T. Crowther, PhD
Professor of Science Education
University of Nevada, Reno
Reno, NV

A. John Gatz
Professor of Zoology
Ohio Wesleyan University
Delaware, OH

Sarah Gille, PhD
Professor
University of California San
Diego
La Jolla, CA

David G. Haase, PhD
Professor of Physics
North Carolina State University
Raleigh, NC

Janet S. Herman, PhD
Professor
Department of Environmental
Sciences
University of Virginia
Charlottesville, VA

David T. Ho, PhD
Associate Professor
Department of Oceanography
University of Hawaii
Honolulu, HI

Ruth Howes, PhD
Professor of Physics
Marquette University
Milwaukee, WI

**Jose Miguel Hurtado, Jr.,
PhD**
Associate Professor
Department of Geological
Sciences
University of Texas at El Paso
El Paso, TX

Monika Kress, PhD
Assistant Professor
San Jose State University
San Jose, CA

Mark E. Lee, PhD
Associate Chair & Assistant
Professor
Department of Biology
Spelman College
Atlanta, GA

Linda Lundgren
Science writer
Lakewood, CO

Keith O. Mann, PhD
Ohio Wesleyan University
Delaware, OH

Charles W. McLaughlin, PhD
Adjunct Professor of Chemistry
Montana State University
Bozeman, MT

Katharina Pahnke, PhD
Research Professor
Department of Geology and
Geophysics
University of Hawaii
Honolulu, HI

Jesús Pando, PhD
Associate Professor
DePaul University
Chicago, IL

Hay-Oak Park, PhD
Associate Professor
Department of Molecular
Genetics
Ohio State University
Columbus, OH

David A. Rubin, PhD
Associate Professor of Physiology
School of Biological Sciences
Illinois State University
Normal, IL

Toni D. Sauncy
Assistant Professor of Physics
Department of Physics
Angelo State University
San Angelo, TX

Series Consultants, continued

Malathi Srivatsan, PhD
Associate Professor of
Neurobiology
College of Sciences and
Mathematics
Arkansas State University
Jonesboro, AR

Cheryl Wistrom, PhD
Associate Professor of Chemistry
Saint Joseph's College
Rensselaer, IN

Reading

ReLeah Cossett Lent
Author/Educational Consultant
Blue Ridge, GA

Math

Vik Hovsepian
Professor of Mathematics
Rio Hondo College
Whittier, CA

Series Reviewers

Thad Boggs
Mandarin High School
Jacksonville, FL

Catherine Butcher
Webster Junior High School
Minden, LA

Erin Darichuk
West Frederick Middle School
Frederick, MD

Joanne Hedrick Davis
Murphy High School
Murphy, NC

Anthony J. DiSipio, Jr.
Octorara Middle School
Atglen, PA

Adrienne Elder
Tulsa Public Schools
Tulsa, OK

Carolyn Elliott
Iredell-Statesville Schools
Statesville, NC

Christine M. Jacobs
Ranger Middle School
Murphy, NC

Jason O. L. Johnson
Thurmont Middle School
Thurmont, MD

Felecia Joiner
Stony Point Ninth Grade Center
Round Rock, TX

Joseph L. Kowalski, MS
Lamar Academy
McAllen, TX

Brian McClain
Amos P. Godby High School
Tallahassee, FL

Von W. Mosser
Thurmont Middle School
Thurmont, MD

Ashlea Peterson
Heritage Intermediate Grade
Center
Coweta, OK

Nicole Lenihan Rhoades
Walkersville Middle School
Walkersvillle, MD

Maria A. Rozenberg
Indian Ridge Middle School
Davie, FL

Barb Seymour
Westridge Middle School
Overland Park, KS

Ginger Shirley
Our Lady of Providence Junior-
Senior High School
Clarksville, IN

Curtis Smith
Elmwood Middle School
Rogers, AR

Sheila Smith
Jackson Public School
Jackson, MS

Sabra Soileau
Moss Bluff Middle School
Lake Charles, LA

Tony Spoores
Switzerland County Middle
School
Vevay, IN

Nancy A. Stearns
Switzerland County Middle
School
Vevay, IN

Kari Vogel
Princeton Middle School
Princeton, MN

Alison Welch
Wm. D. Slider Middle School
El Paso, TX

Linda Workman
Parkway Northeast Middle
School
Creve Coeur, MO

Online Guide

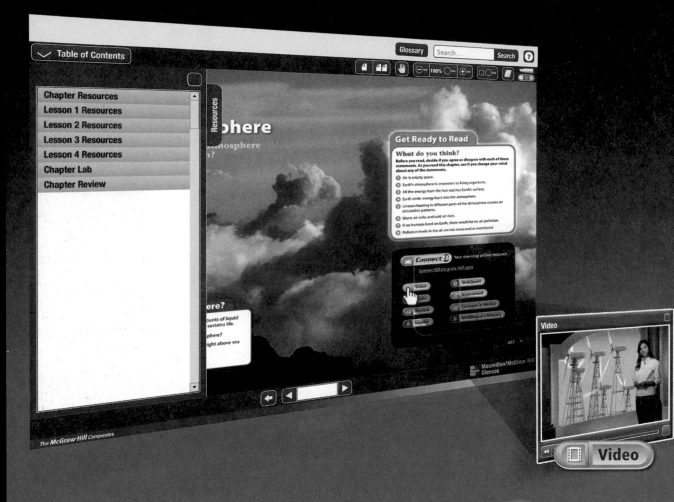

ConnectED

▷ **Your Digital Science Portal**

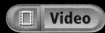 **Video**

 **Audio**

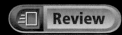 **Review**

 **Inquiry**

 **WebQuest**

See the science in real life through these exciting videos.

Click the link and you can listen to the text while you follow along.

Try these interactive tools to help you review the lesson concepts.

Explore concepts through hands–on and virtual labs.

These web-based challenges relate the concepts you're learning about to the latest news and research.

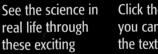

The icons in your online student edition link you to interactive learning opportunities. Browse your online student book to find more.

Review

Personal Tutor

Animation

Concepts in Motion

"It's easy to do my assignments online and quick to find everything I need."

Assessment

Check how well you understand the concepts with online quizzes and practice questions.

Concepts in Motion

The textbook comes alive with animated explanations of important concepts.

Multilingual eGlossary

Read key vocabulary in 13 languages.

Treasure Hunt

Your science book has many features that will aid you in your learning. Some of these features are listed below. You can use the activity at the right to help you find these and other special features in the book.

- **THE BIG IDEA** can be found at the start of each chapter.

- The Reading Guide at the start of each lesson lists 🔑 **Key Concepts**, vocabulary terms, and online supplements to the content.

- **Connect ED** icons direct you to online resources such as animations, personal tutors, math practices, and quizzes.

- **Inquiry** Labs and Skill Practices are in each chapter.

- Your **FOLDABLES** help organize your notes.

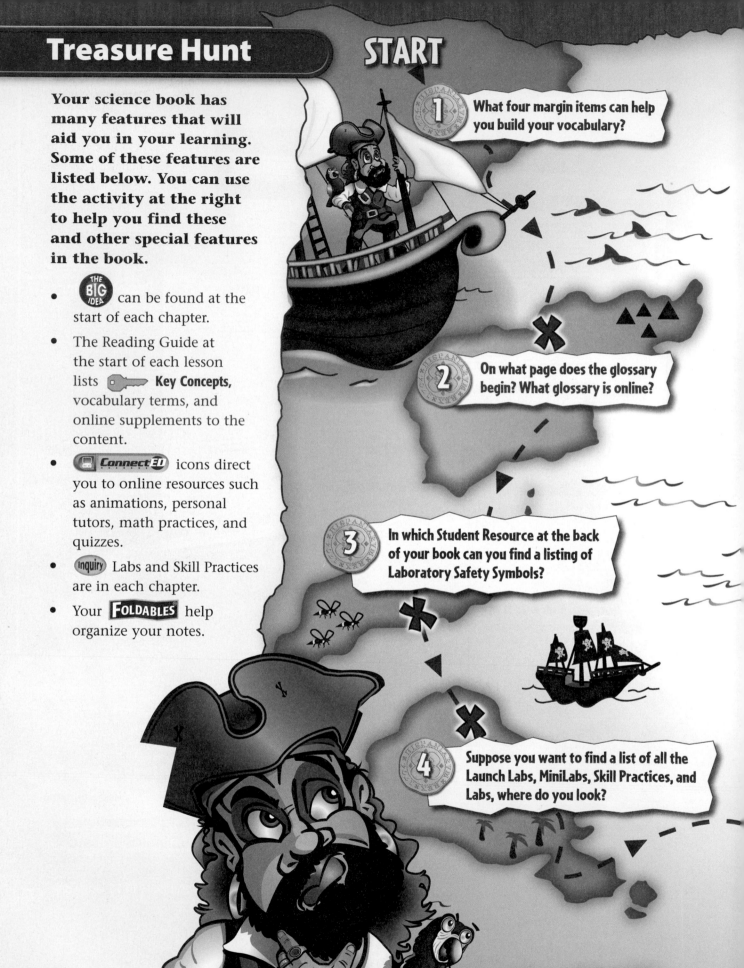

START

1 What four margin items can help you build your vocabulary?

2 On what page does the glossary begin? What glossary is online?

3 In which Student Resource at the back of your book can you find a listing of Laboratory Safety Symbols?

4 Suppose you want to find a list of all the Launch Labs, MiniLabs, Skill Practices, and Labs, where do you look?

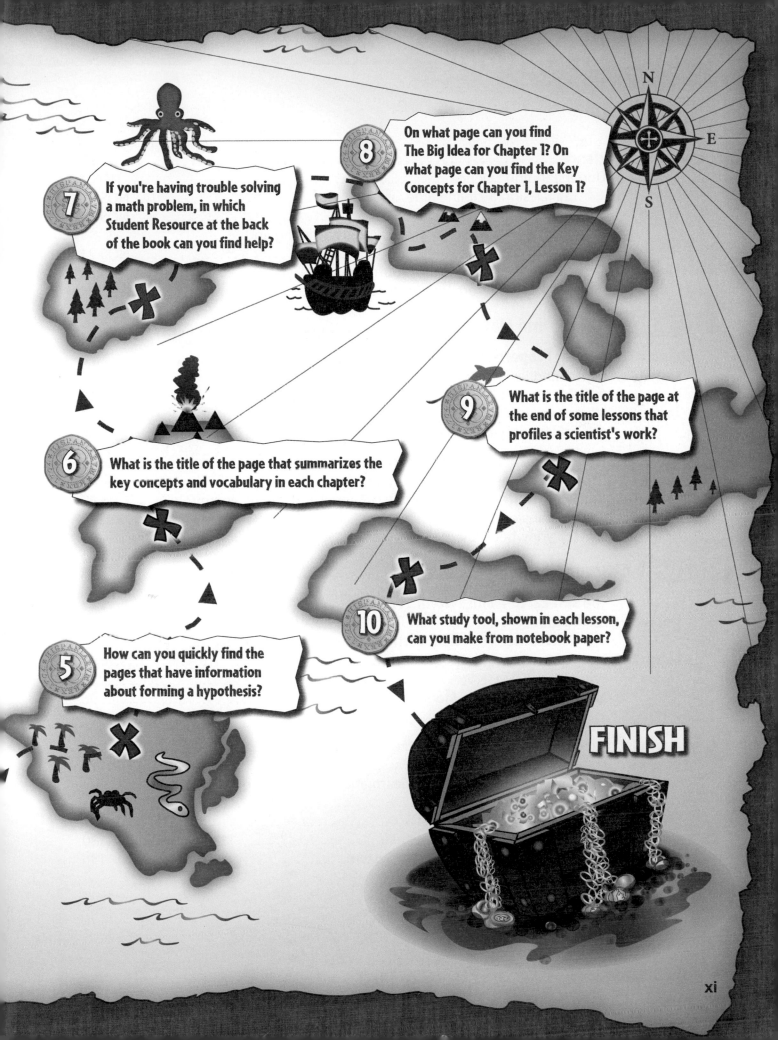

If you're having trouble solving a math problem, in which Student Resource at the back of the book can you find help?

On what page can you find The Big Idea for Chapter 1? On what page can you find the Key Concepts for Chapter 1, Lesson 1?

What is the title of the page that summarizes the key concepts and vocabulary in each chapter?

What is the title of the page at the end of some lessons that profiles a scientist's work?

How can you quickly find the pages that have information about forming a hypothesis?

What study tool, shown in each lesson, can you make from notebook paper?

FINISH

Table of Contents

Table of Contents

Inquiry

Inquiry Launch Labs

Inquiry MiniLabs

Inquiry Skill Practice

Inquiry Labs

Features

GREEN SCIENCE

SCIENCE & SOCIETY

CAREERS in SCIENCE

Science & Engineering

Methods of Science

THE BIG IDEA What processes do scientists use when they perform scientific investigations?

Inquiry Pink Water?

This scientist is using pink dye to measure the speed of glacier water in the country of Greenland. Scientists are testing the hypothesis that the speed of the glacier water is increasing because amounts of meltwater, caused by climate change, are increasing.

- What is a hypothesis?

- What other ways do scientists test hypotheses?

- What processes do scientists use when they perform scientific investigations?

Unit

Nature of SCIENCE

This chapter begins your study of the nature of science, but there is even more information about the nature of science in this book. Each unit begins by exploring an important topic that is fundamental to scientific study. As you read these topics, you will learn even more about the nature of science.

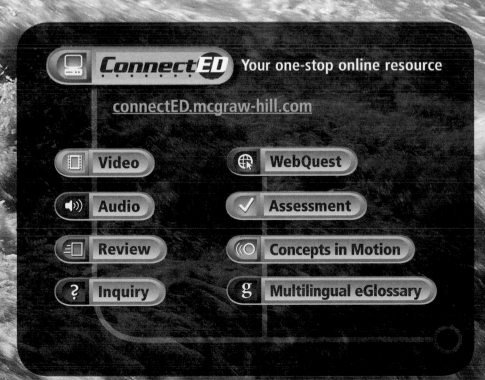

ConnectED Your one-stop online resource

connectED.mcgraw-hill.com

Video   WebQuest

Audio   Assessment

Review   Concepts in Motion

Inquiry   Multilingual eGlossary

Understanding Science

Reading Guide

Key Concepts 🔑
ESSENTIAL QUESTIONS

- What is scientific inquiry?

- How do scientific laws and scientific theories differ?

- What is the difference between a fact and an opinion?

Vocabulary

science p. NOS 4

observation p. NOS 6

inference p. NOS 6

hypothesis p. NOS 6

prediction p. NOS 6

technology p. NOS 8

scientific theory p. NOS 9

scientific law p. NOS 9

critical thinking p. NOS 10

 **Academic Standards for Science**

Covers: 6.NS.1, 6.NS.8, 6.NS.11, 6.DP.2, 6.DP.3, 6.DP.4, 6.DP.5, 6.DP.6, 6.DP.7, 6.DP.8, 6.DP.9, 6.DP.10, 6.DP.11

What is science?

Did you ever hear a bird sing and then look in nearby trees to find the singing bird? Have you ever noticed how the Moon changes from a thin crescent to a full moon each month? When you do these things, you are doing science. **Science** *is the investigation and exploration of natural events and of the new information that results from those investigations.*

For thousands of years, men and women of all countries and cultures have studied the natural world and recorded their observations. They have shared their knowledge and findings and have created a vast amount of scientific information. Scientific knowledge has been the result of a great deal of debate and confirmation within the science community.

People use science in their everyday lives and careers. For example, firefighters, as shown in **Figure 1,** wear clothing that has been developed and tested to withstand extreme temperatures and not catch fire. Parents use science when they set up an aquarium for their children's pet fish. Athletes use science when they use high-performance gear or wear high-performance clothing. Without thinking about it, you use science or the results of science in almost everything you do. Your clothing, food, hair products, electronic devices, athletic equipment, and almost everything else you use are results of science.

Figure 1 Firefighters' clothing, oxygen tanks, and equipment are all results of science.

Branches of Science

There are many different parts of the natural world. Because there is so much to study, scientists often focus their work in one branch of science or on one topic within that branch of science. There are three main branches of science—Earth science, life science, and **physical** science.

WORD ORIGIN · · · · · · · · · · ·

physical
from Latin *physica*, means "study of nature"

Earth Science

The study of Earth, including rocks, soils, oceans, the atmosphere, and surface features is Earth science. This Earth scientist is collecting lava samples for research. Earth scientists might ask other questions such as

- How do different shorelines react to tsunamis?
- Why do planets orbit the Sun?
- What is the rate of climate change?

Life Science

The study of living things is life science, or biology. These biologists are attaching a radio collar to a polar bear and marking it. The mark on a bear's back can be seen from the air, and biologists can tell which bears are being tracked. Biologists also ask questions such as

- Why do some trees lose their leaves in winter?
- How do birds know which direction they are going?
- How do mammals control their body temperature?

Physical Science

The study of matter and energy is physical science. It includes both physics and chemistry. This research chemist is preparing samples of possible new medicines. Physicists and chemists ask other questions such as

- What chemical reactions must take place to launch a spaceship into space?
- Is it possible to travel faster than the speed of light?
- What makes up matter?

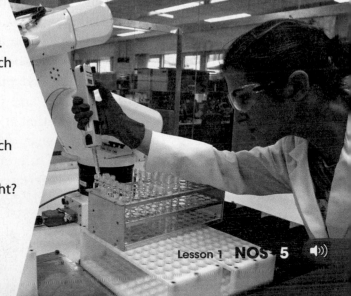

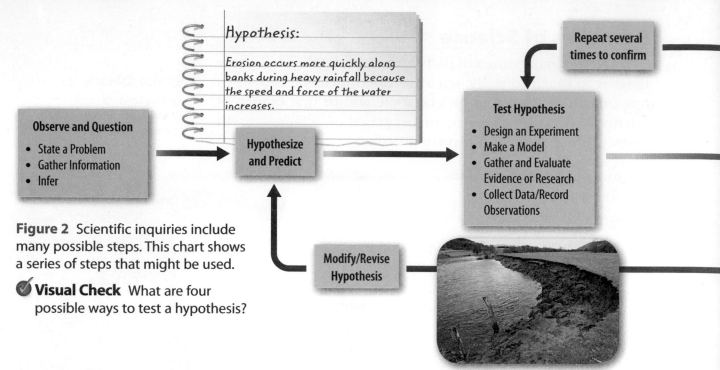

Hypothesis:

Erosion occurs more quickly along banks during heavy rainfall because the speed and force of the water increases.

Observe and Question
- State a Problem
- Gather Information
- Infer

Hypothesize and Predict

Test Hypothesis
- Design an Experiment
- Make a Model
- Gather and Evaluate Evidence or Research
- Collect Data/Record Observations

Repeat several times to confirm

Modify/Revise Hypothesis

Figure 2 Scientific inquiries include many possible steps. This chart shows a series of steps that might be used.

Visual Check What are four possible ways to test a hypothesis?

Scientific Inquiry

When scientists conduct scientific investigations, they use scientific inquiry. Scientific inquiry is a process that uses a set of skills to answer questions or to test ideas about the natural world. There are many kinds of scientific investigations, and there are many ways to conduct them. The series of steps used in each investigation often varies. The flow chart in **Figure 2** shows an example of the skills used in scientific inquiry.

 Key Concept Check What is scientific inquiry?

Ask Questions

One way to begin a scientific investigation is to observe the natural world and ask questions. **Observation** *is the act of using one or more of your senses to gather information and taking note of what occurs.* Suppose you observe that the banks of a river have eroded more this year than in the previous year, and you want to know why. You also note that there was an increase in rainfall this year. After these observations, you make an inference based on these observations. *An* **inference** *is a logical explanation of an observation that is drawn from prior knowledge or experience.*

You infer that the increase in rainfall caused the increase in erosion. You decide to investigate further. You develop a hypothesis and a method to test it.

Hypothesize and Predict

A **hypothesis** *is a possible explanation for an observation that can be tested by scientific investigations.* A hypothesis states an observation and provides an explanation. For example, you might make the following hypothesis: More of the riverbank eroded this year because the amount, the speed, and the force of the river water increased.

When scientists state a hypothesis, they often use it to make predictions to help test their hypothesis. *A* **prediction** *is a statement of what will happen next in a sequence of events.* Scientists make predictions based on what information they think they will find when testing their hypothesis. For example, predictions for the hypothesis above could be: If rainfall increases, then the amount, the speed, and the force of river water will increase. If the amount, the speed, and the force of river water increase, then there will be more erosion.

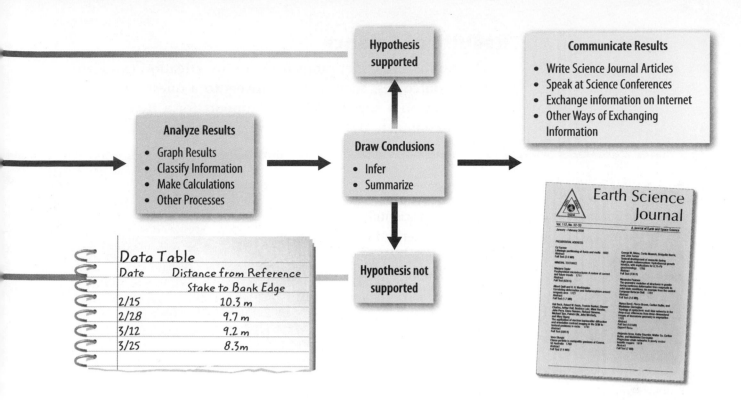

Date	Distance from Reference Stake to Bank Edge
2/15	10.3 m
2/28	9.7 m
3/12	9.2 m
3/25	8.3m

Data Table

Test Hypothesis

When you test a hypothesis, you often test whether your predictions are true. If a prediction is confirmed, then it supports your hypothesis. If your prediction is not confirmed, you might need to modify your hypothesis and retest it.

There are several ways to test a hypothesis when performing a scientific investigation. Four possible ways are shown in **Figure 2.** For example, you might make a model of a riverbank in which you change the speed and the amount of water and record results and observations.

Analyze Results

After testing your hypothesis, you analyze your results using various methods, as shown in **Figure 2.** Often, it is hard to see trends or relationships in data while collecting it. Data should be sorted, graphed, or classified in some way. After analyzing the data, additional inferences can be made.

Draw Conclusions

Once you find the relationships among data and make several inferences, you can draw conclusions.

A conclusion is a summary of the information gained from testing a hypothesis. Scientists study the available information and draw conclusions based on that information.

Communicate Results

An important part of the scientific inquiry process is communicating results. Several ways to communicate results are listed in **Figure 2.** Scientists might share their information in other ways, too. Scientists communicate results of investigations to inform other scientists about their research and the conclusions of their research. Scientists might apply each other's conclusions to their own work to help support their hypotheses.

Further Scientific Inquiry

Scientific inquiry is not completed once one scientific investigation is completed. If predictions are correct and the hypothesis is supported, scientists will retest the predictions several times to make sure the conclusions are the same. If the hypothesis is not supported, any new information gained can be used to revise the hypothesis. Hypotheses can be revised and tested many times.

Results of Science

The results and conclusions from an investigation can lead to many outcomes, such as the answers to a question, more information on a specific topic, or support for a hypothesis. Other outcomes are described below.

Technology

A technical solution can be the answer to a scientific question, such as, "How can the hearing impaired hear better?" After investigation, experimentation, and research, the conclusion might be the development of a new technology. **Technology** *is the practical use of scientific knowledge, especially for industrial or commercial use.* Technology, such as the cochlear implant can help some deaf people hear.

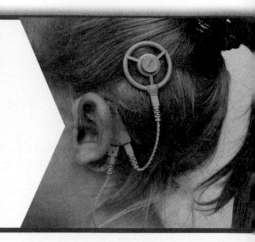

New Materials

Space travel has unique challenges. Astronauts must carry oxygen to breathe. They also must be protected against temperature and pressure extremes, as well as small, high-speed flying objects. The spacesuit consists of 14 layers of material. The outer layer is made of a blend of three materials. One material is waterproof. Another protects against high-speed flying objects. The third material is heat and fire-resistant.

Possible Explanations

Scientists often perform investigations to find explanations as to why or how something happens, such as, "How do stars form?" This photo showing a cloud of gas and dust with newly formed stars was taken by NASA's *Spitzer Space Telescope*.

 Reading Check What are some results of science?

Scientific Theory and Scientific Law

Another outcome of science is the development of scientific theories and laws. Recall that a hypothesis is a possible explanation about an observation that can be tested by scientific investigations. What happens when a hypothesis or a group of hypotheses has been tested many times and has been supported by the repeated scientific investigations? The hypothesis can become a scientific theory.

Scientific Theory

Often, the word *theory* is used in casual conversations to mean an untested idea or an opinion. However, scientists use *theory* differently. *A* **scientific theory** *is an explanation of observations or events that is based on knowledge gained from many observations and investigations.*

Scientists regularly question scientific theories and test them for validity. A scientific theory generally is accepted as true until it is disproved. An example of a scientific theory is the theory of plate tectonics. The theory of plate tectonics explains how Earth's crust moves and why earthquakes and volcanoes occur. Another example of a scientific theory is discussed in **Figure 3.**

▲ **Figure 3** Scientists once believed Earth was the center of the solar system. In the 16th century, Nicolaus Copernicus hypothesized that Earth and the other planets actually revolve around the Sun.

Scientific Law

A scientific law is different from a social law, which is an agreement among people concerning a behavior. *A* **scientific law** *is a rule that describes a pattern in nature.* Unlike a scientific theory that explains why an event occurs, a scientific law only states that an event will occur under certain circumstances. For example, Newton's law of gravitational force implies that if you drop an object, it will fall toward Earth. Newton's law does not explain why the object moves toward Earth when dropped, only that it will.

 Key Concept Check How do scientific laws and theories differ?

New Information

Scientific information constantly changes as new information is discovered or as previous hypotheses are retested. New information can lead to changes in scientific theories, as explained in **Figure 4.** When new facts are revealed, a current scientific theory might be revised to include the new facts, or it might be disproved and rejected.

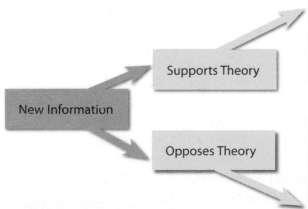

If new information supports a current scientific theory, then the theory is not changed. The information might be published in a scientific journal to show further support of the theory. The new information might also lead to advancements in technology or spark new questions that lead to new scientific investigations.

If new information opposes, or does not support a current scientific theory, the theory might be modified or rejected altogether. Often, new information will lead scientists to look at the original observations in a new way. This can lead to new investigations with new hypotheses. These investigations can lead to new theories.

New Information → Supports Theory
New Information → Opposes Theory

▲ **Figure 4** New information can lead to changes in scientific theories.

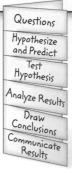
Evaluating Scientific Evidence

Did you ever read an advertisement, such as the one below, that made extraordinary claims? If so, you probably practice **critical thinking**—*comparing what you already know with the information you are given in order to decide whether you agree with it.* To determine whether information is true and scientific or pseudoscience (information incorrectly represented as scientific), you should be skeptical and identify facts and opinions. This helps you evaluate the strengths and weaknesses of information and make informed decisions. Critical thinking is important in all decision making—from everyday decisions to community, national, and international decisions.

 Key Concept Check How do a fact and an opinion differ?

Learn Algebra
While You Sleep!

Have you struggled to learn algebra? Struggle no more.

Math-er-ific's new algebra pillow is scientifically proven to transfer math skills from the pillow to your brain while you sleep. This revolutionary scientific design improved the algebra test scores of laboratory mice by 150 percent.

Dr. Tom Equation says, "I have never seen students or mice learn algebra so easily. This pillow is truly amazing."

For only $19.95, those boring hours spent studying are a thing of the past. So act fast! If you order today, you can get the algebra pillow and the equally amazing geometry pillow for only $29.95. That is a $10 savings!

Skepticism

To be skeptical is to doubt the truthfulness or accuracy of something. Because of skepticism, science can be self-correcting. If someone publishes results or if an investigation gives results that don't seem accurate, a skeptical scientist usually will challenge the information and test the results for accuracy.

Identifying Facts

The prices of the pillows and the savings are facts. A fact is a measurement, observation, or statement that can be strictly defined. Many scientific facts can be evaluated for their validity through investigations.

Identifying Opinions

An opinion is a personal view, feeling, or claim about a topic. Opinions are neither true nor false.

Mixing Facts and Opinions

Sometimes people mix facts and opinions. You must read carefully to determine which information is fact and which is opinion.

Science cannot answer all questions.

Scientists recognize that some questions cannot be studied using scientific inquiry. Questions that deal with opinions, beliefs, values, and feelings cannot be answered through scientific investigation. For example, questions that cannot be answered through scientific investigation might include

• Are comedies the best kinds of movies?

• Is it ever okay to lie?

• Which food tastes best?

The answers to all of these questions are based on opinions, not facts.

Safety in Science

It is very important for anyone performing scientific investigations to use safe practices, such as the student shown in **Figure 5.** You should always follow your teacher's instructions. If you have questions about potential hazards, use of equipment, or the meaning of safety symbols, ask your teacher. Always wear protective clothing and equipment while performing scientific investigations. If you are using live animals in your investigations, provide appropriate care and ethical treatment to them. For more information on practicing safe and ethical science, consult the Science Safety Skill Handbook in the back of this book.

Figure 5 Always use safe lab practices when doing scientific investigations.

ACADEMIC VOCABULARY

potential
(adjective) possible, likely, or probable

Lesson 1 Review

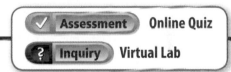

✔ **Assessment**   **Online Quiz**

❓ **Inquiry**   **Virtual Lab**

Use Vocabulary

1. The practical use of science, especially for industrial or commercial use, is _____.

2. **Distinguish** between a hypothesis and a prediction.

3. **Define** *observation* in your own words.

Understand Key Concepts 🔑

4. Which is NOT part of scientific inquiry?
   A. analyze results   **C.** make a hypothesis
   B. falsify results   **D.** make observations

5. **Explain** the difference between a scientific theory and a scientific law. Give an example of each.

6. **Write** an example of a fact and an example of an opinion.

Interpret Graphics

7. **Organize** Draw a graphic organizer similar to the one below. List four ways a scientist can communicate results.

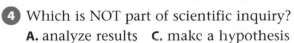

Communicate Results

Critical Thinking

8. **Identify** a real-world problem related to your home, your community, or your school that could be investigated scientifically.

9. **Design** a scientific investigation to test one possible solution to the problem you identified in the previous question.

Science & Engineering

The Design Process

Create a Solution to a Problem

Scientists investigate and explore natural events. Then they interpret data and share information learned from those investigations. How do engineers differ from scientists? Engineers design, construct, and maintain the designed world. Look around you and notice things that do not occur in nature. Schools, roads, submarines, toys, microscopes, medical equipment, amusement park rides, computer programs, and video games all result from engineering. Science involves the practice of scientific inquiry, but engineering involves The Design Process—a set of methods used to create a solution to a problem or need.

From the first snowshoes to modern ski lifts, people have designed solutions to effectively travel in the snow. The term *engineer* may not have existed when the first snowshoes were made. However, The Design Process and the goals of the people who developed snowshoes and ski lifts are similar.

The Design Process

1. Identify a Problem or Need
- Determine a problem or need
- Document all questions, research, and procedures throughout the process

2. Research and Develop Solutions
- Brainstorm possible solutions
- Research any existing solutions that address the problem or need
- Suggest limitations of the solutions

3. Construct a Prototype
- Develop possible solutions
- Estimate materials, costs, resources, and time to develop the solutions
- Select the best possible solution
- Construct a prototype

4. Test and Evaluate Solutions
- Use models to test the solutions
- Use graphs, charts, and tables to evaluate results
- Analyze the process and evaluate strengths and weaknesses of the solution

5. Communicate Results and Redesign
- Communicate your design process and results to others
- Redesign and modify solution
- Construct final solution

It's Your Turn

Design a Zipline Ride

You are a guide for an adventure tour company that specializes in physically challenging activities in natural environments. You have been hired to design an exciting zipline ride near your town.

Identify the Problem

You know nothing about zipline rides or the requirements to construct a fast and safe zipline course. Consider the best location, platform design and construction, maximum angle of descent, length of ride, and materials required. Is it possible to zip too quickly or too slowly? Record your problem and questions with possible solutions in your Science Journal.

Research Existing Solutions

Begin answering your questions by researching existing ziplines, roller coasters, and other similar thrill rides. Note possible limitations to your solutions, such as cost, size, materials, location, time, or other restraints.

Brainstorm Possible Solutions

Continue recording ideas for your zipline ride. Include possible locations for it in your environment, sites for launching and safe-landing platforms, length of zipline, materials and equipment needed for the zipline and rider, estimated costs, and time of development and construction.

Construct a Prototype

Draw several plans to answer your problems. Use simple materials to construct a scale model of your zipline. Check for accurate scale of dimensions and weight for each element to guarantee a fun, fast, and safe ride.

Test and Evaluate Solutions

Test your model many times to guarantee weight, speed, distance, and safe solutions. Use graphs, charts, and tables to evaluate the process and identify strengths and weaknesses in your solutions.

Communicate Your Results and Redesign Your Zipline

Communicate your design process and solution to peers using your visual displays and model. Discuss and critique your working solution. Do further research and testing, if necessary. Redesign and modify your solution to meet design objectives. Finally, construct a model of your solution.

Reading Guide

Key Concepts
ESSENTIAL QUESTIONS

- Why is it important for scientists to use the International System of Units?

- What causes measurement uncertainty?

- What are mean, median, mode, and range?

Vocabulary

description p. NOS 14

explanation p. NOS 14

International System of Units (SI) p. NOS 14

significant digits p. NOS 16

Academic Standards for Science

Covers: 6.NS.3, 6.NS.5, 6.NS.7, 6.NS.8

Measurement and Scientific Tools

Description and Explanation

The scientist in **Figure 6** is observing a volcano. He describes in his journal that the flowing lava is bright red with a black crust, and it has a temperature of about 630°C. A **description** *is a spoken or written summary of observations.* There are two types of descriptions. When making a qualitative description, such as *bright red,* you use your senses (sight, sound, smell, touch, taste) to describe an observation. When making a quantitative description, such as *630°C,* you use numbers and measurements to describe an observation. Later, the scientist might explain his observations. An **explanation** *is an interpretation of observations.* Because the lava was bright red and about 630°C, the scientist might explain that these conditions indicate the lava is cooling and the volcano did not recently erupt.

The International System of Units

At one time, scientists in different parts of the world used different units of measurement. Imagine the confusion when a British scientist measured weight in pounds-force, a French scientist measured weight in Newtons, and a Japanese scientist measured weight in momme (MOM ee). Sharing scientific information was difficult, if not impossible.

In 1960, scientists adopted a new system of measurement to eliminate this confusion. The **International System of Units (SI)** *is the internationally accepted system for measurement.* SI uses standards of measurement, called base units, which are shown in **Table 1** on the next page. A base unit is the most common unit used in the SI system for a given measurement.

Figure 6 Scientists use descriptions and explanations when observing natural events.

Table 1 SI Base Units

Quantity Measured	Unit	Symbol
Length	meter	m
Mass	kilogram	kg
Time	second	s
Electric current	ampere	A
Temperature	Kelvin	K
Amount of substance	mole	mol
Intensity of light	candela	cd

Table 1 You can use SI units to measure the physical properties of objects.

◖◎ Concepts in Motion

Interactive Table

SI Unit Prefixes

In addition to base units, SI uses prefixes to identify the size of the unit, as shown in **Table 2.** Prefixes are used to indicate a fraction of ten or a multiple of ten. In other words, each unit is either ten times smaller than the next larger unit or ten times larger than the next smaller unit. For example, the prefix *deci–* means 10^{-1}, or 1/10. A decimeter is 1/10 of a meter. The prefix *kilo–* means 10^3, or 1,000. A kilometer is 1,000 m.

Converting Between SI Units

Because SI is based on ten, it is easy to convert from one SI unit to another. To convert SI units, you must multiply or divide by a factor of ten. You also can use proportions as shown below in the Math Skills activity.

 Key Concept Check Why is it important for scientists to use the International System of Units (SI)?

Table 2 Prefixes are used in SI to indicate the size of the unit. ▼

Table 2 Prefixes

Prefix	Meaning
Mega- (M)	1,000,000 (10^6)
Kilo- (k)	1,000 (10^3)
Hecto- (h)	100 (10^2)
Deka- (da)	10 (10^1)
Deci- (d)	0.1 (10^{-1})
Centi- (c)	0.01 (10^{-2})
Milli- (m)	0.001 (10^{-3})
Micro- (μ)	0.000 001 (10^{-6})

Math Skills ⁺⁄₌ Use Proportions

A book has a mass of **1.1 kg**. Using a proportion, find the mass of the book in grams.

1 Use the table to determine the correct relationship between the units. One kg is 1,000 times greater than 1 g. So, there are 1,000 g in 1 kg.

2 Then set up a proportion.

$$\left(\frac{x}{1.1 \text{ kg}}\right) = \left(\frac{1,000 \text{ g}}{1 \text{ kg}}\right)$$

$$x = \left(\frac{(1,000 \text{ g})(1.1 \text{ kg})}{1 \text{ kg}}\right) = 1,100 \text{ g}$$

3 Check your units. The answer is 1,100 g.

▤ Review
- **Math Practice**
- **Personal Tutor**

Practice

1. Two towns are separated by 15,328 m. What is the distance in kilometers?

2. A dosage of medicine is 325 mg. What is the dosage in grams?

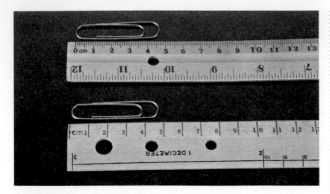

Figure 7 All measurements have some uncertainty.

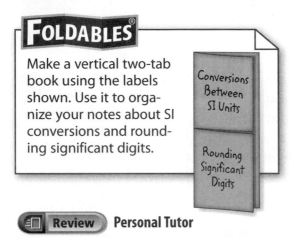
Table 3 Significant Digits Rules

1. All nonzero numbers are significant.

2. Zeros between nonzero digits are significant.

3. One or more final zeros used after the decimal point are significant.

4. Zeros used solely for spacing the decimal point are NOT significant. The zeros only indicate the position of the decimal point.

* The blue numbers in the examples are the significant digits.

Number	Significant Digits	Applied Rules
1.234	4	1
1.02	3	1, 2
0.023	2	1, 4
0.200	3	1, 3
1,002	4	1, 2
3.07	3	1, 2
0.001	1	1, 4
0.012	2	1, 4
50,600	3	1, 2, 4

Measurement and Uncertainty

Have you ever measured an object, such as a paper clip? The tools used to take measurements can limit the accuracy of the measurements. Look at the bottom ruler in **Figure 7.** Its measurements are divided into centimeters. You know that the paper clip is between 4 cm and 5 cm. You might guess that it is 4.5 cm long. Now, look at the top ruler. Its measurements are divided into millimeters. You can say with more certainty that the paper clip is about 4.7 cm long. This measurement is more accurate than the first.

 Key Concept Check What causes measurement uncertainty?

Significant Digits and Rounding

Because scientists duplicate each other's work, they must record numbers with the same degree of precision as the original data. Significant digits allow scientists to do this. **Significant digits** *are the number of digits in a measurement that you know with a certain degree of reliability.* **Table 3** lists the rules for expressing and determining significant digits.

In order to achieve the same degree of precision as a previous measurement, it often is necessary to round a measurement to a certain number of significant digits. Suppose you have the number below, and you need to round it to four significant digits.

$$1{,}348.527 \text{ g}$$

To round to four significant digits, you need to round the 8. If the digit to the right of the 8 is 0, 1, 2, 3, or 4, the digit being rounded (8) remains the same. If the digit to the right of the 8 is 5, 6, 7, 8, or 9, the digit being rounded (8) increases by one. The rounded number is 1,349 g.

What if you need to round 1,348.527 g to two significant digits? You would look at the number to the right of the 3 to determine how to round. 1,348.527 rounded to two significant digits would be 1,300 g. The 4 and 8 become zeros.

Mean, Median, Mode, and Range

A rain gauge measures the amount of rain that falls on a location over a period of time. A rain gauge can be used to collect data in scientific investigations, such as the data shown in **Table 4a.** Scientists often need to analyze their data to obtain information. Four values often used when analyzing numbers are median, mean, mode, and range.

 Key Concept Check What are mean, median, and mode?

Median

The median is the middle number in a data set when the data are arranged in numerical order. The rainfall data are listed in numerical order in Table 4b. If you have an even number of data items, add the two middle numbers together and divide by two to find the median.

$$\text{median} = \frac{8.18 \text{ cm} + 8.84 \text{ cm}}{2}$$

$$= 8.51 \text{ cm}$$

Table 4a
Rainfall Data

January	7.11 cm
February	11.89 cm
March	9.58 cm
April	8.18 cm
May	7.11 cm
June	1.47 cm
July	18.21 cm
August	8.84 cm

Mean

The mean, or average, of a data set is the sum of the numbers in a data set divided by the number of entries in the set. To find the mean, add the numbers in your data set and then divide the total by the number of items in your data set.

$$\text{mean} = \frac{(\text{sum of numbers})}{(\text{number of items})}$$

$$= \frac{72.39 \text{ cm}}{8 \text{ months}}$$

$$= \frac{9.05 \text{ cm}}{\text{month}}$$

Mode

The mode of a data set is the number or item that appears most often. The number in blue in Table 4b appears twice. All other numbers only appear once.

$$\text{mode} = 7.11$$

Table 4b
Rainfall Data
(numerical order)

1.47 cm
7.11 cm
7.11 cm
8.18 cm
8.84 cm
9.58 cm
11.89 cm
18.21 cm

Range

The range is the difference between the greatest number and the least number in the data set.

$$\text{range} = 18.21 - 1.47$$

$$= 16.74$$

Scientific Tools

As you engage in scientific inquiry, you will need tools to help you take quantitative measurements. Always follow appropriate safety procedures when using scientific tools. For more information about the proper use of these tools, see the Science Skill Handbook at the back of this book.

◄ Science Journal

Use a science journal to record observations, questions, hypotheses, data, and conclusions from your scientific investigations. A science journal is any notebook that you use to take notes or record information and data while you conduct a scientific investigation. Keep it organized so you can find information easily. Write down the date whenever you record new information in the journal. Make sure you are recording your data honestly and accurately.

Rulers and Metersticks ►

Use rulers and metersticks to measure lengths and distances. The SI unit of measurement for length is the meter (m). For small objects, such as pebbles or seeds, use a metric ruler with centimeter and millimeter markings. To measure larger objects, such as the length of your bedroom, use a meterstick. To measure long distances, such as the distance between cities, use an instrument that measures in kilometers. Be careful when carrying rulers and metersticks, and never point them at anyone.

◄ Glassware

Use beakers to hold and pour liquids. The lines on a beaker are not very precise measurements, so you should use a graduated cylinder to measure the volume of a liquid. Volume is typically measured in liters (L) or milliliters (mL).

Triple-Beam Balance ▶

Use a triple-beam balance to measure the mass of an object. The mass of a small object is measured in grams. The mass of large object is usually measured in kilograms. Triple-beam balances are instruments that require some care when using. Follow your teacher's instructions so that you do not damage the instrument. Digital balances also might be used.

◀ Thermometer

Use a thermometer to measure the temperature of a substance. Although Kelvin is the SI unit for temperature, you will use a thermometer to measure temperature in degrees Celsius (°C). To use a thermometer, place a room-temperature thermometer into the substance for which you want to measure temperature. Do not let the thermometer touch the bottom of the container that holds the substance or you will get an inaccurate reading. When you finish, remember to place your thermometer in a secure place. Do not lay it on a table, because it can roll off the table. Never use a thermometer as a stirring rod.

Computers and the Internet ▶

Use a computer to collect, organize, and store information about a research topic or scientific investigation. Computers are useful tools to scientists for several reasons. Scientists use computers to record and analyze data, to research new information, and to quickly share their results with others worldwide over the Internet.

Tools Used by Earth Scientists

Binoculars

Binoculars are instruments that enable people to view faraway objects more clearly. Earth scientists use them to view distant landforms, animals, or even incoming weather.

Compass

A compass is an instrument that shows magnetic north. Earth scientists use compasses to navigate when they are in the field and to determine the direction of distant landforms or other natural objects.

Wind Vane and Anemometer

A wind vane is a device, often attached to the roofs of buildings, that rotates to show the direction of the wind. An anemometer, or wind-speed gauge, is used to measure the speed and the force of wind.

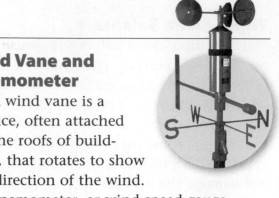

Streak Plate

A streak plate is a piece of hard, unglazed porcelain that helps you identify minerals. When you scrape a mineral along a streak plate, the mineral leaves behind powdery marks. The color of the mark is the mineral's streak.

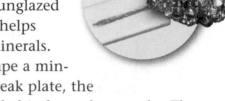

Lesson 2 Review

Use Vocabulary

1 **Distinguish** between description and explanation.

2 **Define** *significant digits* in your own words.

Understand Key Concepts

3 Which base unit is NOT part of the International System of Units?

A. ampere   C. pound

B. meter   D. second

4 **Give an example** of how scientific tools cause measurement uncertainty.

5 **Differentiate** among mean, median, mode, and range.

Interpret Graphics

6 **Change** Copy the graphic organizer below, and change the number shown to have the correct number of significant digits indicated.

124.683

1 significant digit

5 significant digits

3 significant digits

Critical Thinking

7 **Write** a short essay explaining why the United States should consider adopting SI as the measurement system used by supermarkets and other businesses.

Math Skills

Review

Math Practice

8 **Convert** 52 m to kilometers. Explain how you got your answer.

What can you learn by collecting and analyzing data?

People who study ancient cultures often collect and analyze data from soil samples. Soil samples contain bits of pottery, bones, seeds, and other clues to how ancient people lived and what they ate. In this activity, you will separate and analyze a simulated soil sample from an ancient civilization.

Materials

250-mL beaker

large piece of newsprint

1-L containers

forceps

strainer

probe

Also needed: soil mixture, balance, plastic containers

Safety

Learn It

Data includes observations you can make with your senses and observations based on measurements of some kind. **Collecting and analyzing data** includes collecting, classifying, comparing and contrasting, and interpreting (looking for meaning in the data).

Try It

1 Read and complete a lab safety form.

2 Obtain a 200-mL sample of "soil."

3 Spread the newsprint over your workspace. Slowly pour the soil through a strainer over a plastic container. Shake the strainer gently so that all of the soil enters the container.

4 Pour the remaining portion of the soil sample onto the newsprint. Use a probe and forceps to separate objects. Classify different types of objects, and place them into the other plastic containers.

5 Copy the data tables from the board into your Science Journal.

6 Use the balance to measure and record the masses of each group of objects found in your soil sample. Write your group's data in the data table on the board.

7 When all teams have finished, use the class data from the board to find the mean, the median, the mode, and the range for each type of object.

Apply It

8 **Make Inferences** Assuming that the plastic objects represented animal bones, how many different types of animals were indicated by your analysis? Explain.

9 **Evaluate** Archaeologists often include information about the depth at which soil samples are taken. If you received a soil sample that kept the soil and other objects in their original layers, what more might you discover?

10 🔑 **Key Concept** Why didn't everyone in the class get the same data? What were some possible sources of uncertainty in your measurements?

Case Study

Reading Guide

Key Concepts 🔑
ESSENTIAL QUESTIONS

- How are independent variables and dependent variables related?

- How is scientific inquiry used in a real-life scientific investigation?

Vocabulary
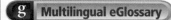
variable p. NOS 23

independent variable
p. NOS 23

dependent variable
p. NOS 23

g Multilingual eGlossary

Academic Standards for Science
Covers: 6.NS.1, 6.NS.4, 6.NS.7

The Iceman's Last Journey

The Tyrolean Alps border western Austria, northern Italy, and eastern Switzerland, as shown in **Figure 8.** They are popular with tourists, hikers, mountain climbers, and skiers. In 1991, two hikers discovered the remains of a man, also shown in **Figure 8,** in a melting glacier on the border between Austria and Italy. They thought the man had died in a hiking accident. They reported their discovery to the authorities.

Initially authorities thought the man was a music professor who disappeared in 1938. However, they soon learned that the music professor was buried in a nearby town. Artifacts near the frozen corpse indicated that the man died long before 1938. The artifacts, as shown in **Figure 9,** were unusual. The man, nicknamed the Iceman, was dressed in leggings, a loincloth, and a goatskin jacket. A bearskin cap lay nearby. He wore shoes made of red deerskin with thick bearskin soles. The shoes were stuffed with grass for insulation. In addition, investigators found a copper ax, a partially constructed longbow, a quiver containing 14 arrows, a wooden backpack frame, and a dagger at the site.

Figure 8 Excavators used jackhammers to free the man's body from the ice, which caused serious damage to his hip. Part of a longbow also was found nearby.

A Controlled Experiment

The identity of the corpse was a mystery. Several people hypothesized about his identify, but controlled experiments were needed to unravel the mystery of who the Iceman was. Scientists and the public wanted to know the identity of the man, why he had died, and when he had died.

Identifying Variables and Constants

When scientists design a controlled experiment, they have to identify factors that might affect the outcome of an experiment. A **variable** *is any factor that can have more than one value.* In controlled experiments, there are two kinds of variables. The **independent variable** *is the factor that you want to test. It is changed by the investigator to observe how it affects a dependent variable.* The **dependent variable** *is the factor you observe or measure during an experiment.* When the independent variable is changed, it causes the dependent variable to change.

A controlled experiment has two groups—an experimental group and a control group. The experimental group is used to study how a change in the independent variable changes the dependent variable. The control group contains the same factors as the experimental group, but the independent variable is not changed. Without a control, it is difficult to know if your experimental observations result from the variable you are testing or from another factor.

Scientists used inquiry to investigate the mystery of the Iceman. As you read the rest of the story, notice how scientific inquiry was used throughout the investigation. The blue boxes in the margins point out examples of the scientific inquiry process. The notebooks in the margin identify what a scientist might have written in a journal.

Figure 9 These models show what the Iceman and the artifacts found with him might have looked like.

Scientific investigations often begin when someone asks a question about something observed in nature.

Observation: A corpse was found buried in ice in the Tyrolean Alps.
Hypothesis: The corpse found in the Tyrolean Alps is the body of a missing music professor because he went missing in 1938.
Observation: Artifacts near the body suggested that the body was much older than the music professor would have been.
Revised Hypothesis: The corpse found was dead long before 1938 because the artifacts found near him date back way before the 1930s.
Prediction: If the artifacts belong to the corpse, then the corpse is not the music professor.

> Inference: Based on its construction, the ax it is at least 4,000 years old.
> Prediction: If the ax is at least 4,000 years old, then the body found near it is also at least 4,000 years old.
> Test Results: Radiocarbon dating showed the man to be 5,300 years old.

After many observations, revised hypotheses, and tests, conclusions often can be made.

> Conclusion: The Iceman is about 5,300 years old. He was a seasonal visitor to the high mountains. He died in autumn. When winter came the Iceman's body became buried and frozen in the snow, which preserved his body.

An Early Conclusion

Konrad Spindler was a professor of archeology at the University of Innsbruck in Austria when the Iceman was discovered. Spindler estimated that the ax, shown in **Figure 10,** was at least 4,000 years old based on its construction. If the ax was that old, then the Iceman was also at least 4,000 years old. Later, radiocarbon dating showed that the Iceman actually lived about 5,300 years ago.

The Iceman's body was in a mountain glacier 3,210 m above sea level. What was this man doing so high in the snow- and ice-covered mountains? Was he hunting for food, shepherding his animals, or looking for metal ore?

Spindler noted that some of the wood used in the artifacts was from trees that grew at lower elevations. He concluded that the Iceman was probably a seasonal visitor to the high mountains.

Spindler also hypothesized that shortly before the Iceman's death, the Iceman had driven his herds from their summer high mountain pastures to the lowland valleys. However, the Iceman soon returned to the mountains where he died of exposure to the cold, wintry weather.

The Iceman's body was extremely well preserved. Spindler inferred that ice and snow covered the Iceman's body shortly after he died. Spindler concluded that the Iceman died in autumn and was quickly buried and frozen, which preserved his body and all his possessions.

Figure 10 This ax, bow and quiver, and dagger and sheath were found with the Iceman's body.

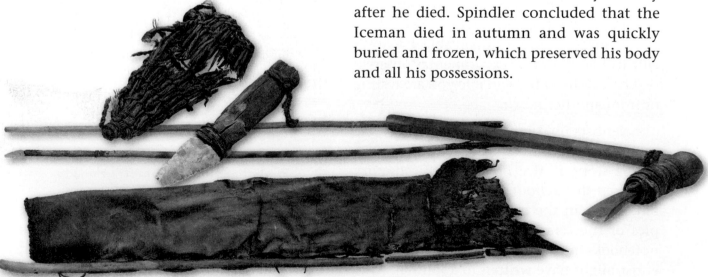

More Observations and Revised Hypotheses

When the Iceman's body was discovered, Klaus Oeggl was an assistant professor of botany at the University of Innsbruck. His area of study was plant life during prehistoric times in the Alps. He was invited to join the research team studying the Iceman.

Upon close examination of the Iceman and his belongings, Professor Oeggl found three plant materials—grass from the Iceman's shoe, as shown in **Figure 11,** a splinter of wood from his longbow, and a tiny fruit called a sloe berry.

Over the next year, Professor Oeggl examined bits of charcoal wrapped in maple leaves that had been found at the discovery site. Examination of the samples revealed the charcoal was from the wood of eight different types of trees. All but one of the trees grew only at lower elevations than where the Iceman's body was found. Like Spindler, Professor Oeggl suspected that the Iceman had been at a lower elevation shortly before he died. From Oeggl's observations, he formed a hypothesis and made some predictions.

Oeggl realized that he would need more data to support his hypothesis. He requested that he be allowed to examine the contents of the Iceman's digestive tract. If all went well, the study would show what the Iceman had swallowed just hours before his death.

> Scientific investigations often lead to new questions.

> Observations: Plant matter near body to study—grass on shoe, splinter from longbow, sloe berry fruit, charcoal wrapped in maple leaves, wood in charcoal from 8 different trees— 7 of 8 types of wood in charcoal grow at lower elevations
> Hypothesis: The Iceman had recently been at lower elevations before he died because the plants identified near him grow only at lower elevations.
> Prediction: If the identified plants are found in the digestive tract of the corpse, then the man actually was at lower elevations just before he died.
> Question: What did the Iceman eat the day before he died?

Figure 11 Professor Oeggl examined the Iceman's belongings along with the leaves and grass that were stuck to his shoe.

Experiment to Test Hypothesis

The research teams provided Professor Oeggl with a tiny sample from the Iceman's digestive tract. He was determined to study it carefully to obtain as much information as possible. Oeggl carefully planned his scientific inquiry. He knew that he had to work quickly to avoid the decomposition of the sample and to reduce the chances of contaminating the samples.

His plan was to divide the material from the digestive tract into four samples. Each sample would undergo several chemical tests. Then, the samples would be examined under an electron microscope to see as many details as possible.

Professor Oeggl began by adding a saline solution to the first sample. This caused it to swell slightly, making it easier to identify particles using the microscope at a relatively low magnification. He saw particles of a wheat grain known as einkorn, which was a common type of wheat grown in the region during prehistoric times. He also found other edible plant material in the sample.

Oeggl noticed that the sample also contained pollen grains, as shown in the inset of **Figure 12**. To see the pollen grains more clearly, he used a chemical that separated unwanted substances from the pollen grains. He washed the sample a few times with alcohol. After each wash, he examined the sample under a microscope at a high magnification. The pollen grains became more visible. Many more microscopic pollen grains could now be seen. Professor Oeggl identified these pollen grains as those from a hop hornbeam tree.

There is more than one way to test a hypothesis. Scientists might gather and evaluate evidence, collect data and record their observations, create a model, or design and perform an experiment. They also might perform a combination of these skills.

Test Plan:
- Divide a sample of the Iceman's digestive tract into four sections.
- Examine the pieces under microscopes.
- Gather data from observations of the pieces and record observations.

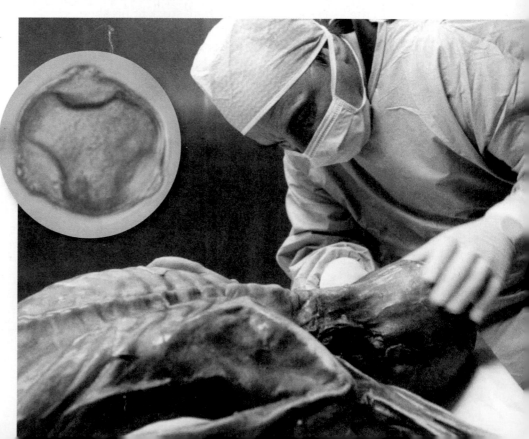

Figure 12 Eventually, Professor Oeggl identified pollen grains from hop hornbeam trees.

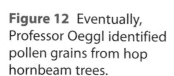

Analyzing Results

Professor Oeggl observed that the hop-hornbeam pollen grains had not been digested. Therefore, the Iceman must have swallowed them within hours before his death. But, hop hornbeam trees only grow in lower valleys. Oeggl was confused. How could pollen grains from trees at low elevations be ingested within few hours of this man dying in high, snow-covered mountains? Perhaps the samples from the Iceman's digestive tract had been contaminated. Oeggl knew he needed to investigate further.

Further Experimentation

Oeggl realized that the most likely source of contamination would be Oeggl's own laboratory. He decided to test whether his lab equipment or saline solution contained hop-hornbeam pollen grains. To do this, he prepared two identical, sterile slides with saline solution. Then, on one slide, he placed a sample from the Iceman's digestive tract. The slide with the sample was the experimental group. The slide without the sample was the control group.

The independent variable, or the variable that Oeggl changed, is the presence of the sample on the slide. The dependent variable, or the variable the Oeggl was testing, was whether hop-hornbeam pollen grains show up on the slides. Oeggl examined the slides carefully.

Analyzing Additional Results

The experiment showed that the control group (the slide without the digestive tract sample) contained no hop-hornbeam pollen grains. Therefore, the pollen grains had not come from his lab equipment or solutions. Each sample from the Iceman's digestive tract was closely re-examined. All of the samples contained the same hop-hornbeam pollen grains. The Iceman had indeed swallowed the hop-hornbeam pollen grains.

Error is common in scientific research. Scientists are careful to document procedures and any unanticipated factors or accidents. They also are careful to document uncertainty in their measurements.

Procedure:
- Sterilize laboratory equipment.
- Prepare saline slides.
- View saline slides under electron microscope. Results: no hop-hornbeam pollen grains
- Add digestive tract sample to one slide.
- View this slide under electron microscope. Result: hop hornbeam pollen grains present.

Controlled experiments contain two types of variables.

Dependent Variables: amount of hop-hornbeam pollen grains found on slide
Independent Variable: digestive tract sample on slide

Without a control group, it is difficult to determine the origin of some observations.

Control Group: sterilized slide
Experimental Group: sterilized slide with digestive tract sample

Observation: The Iceman's digestive tract contains pollen grains from the hop hornbeam tree and other plants that bloom in spring.

Inference: Knowing the rate at which food and pollen decompose after swallowed, it can be inferred that the Iceman ate three times on the day that he died.

Prediction: The Iceman died in the spring within hours of digesting the hop-hornbeam pollen grains.

Mapping the Iceman's Journey

The hop-hornbeam pollen grains were helpful in determining the season the Iceman died. Because the pollen grains were whole, Professor Oeggl inferred that the Iceman swallowed the pollen grains during their blooming season. Therefore, the Iceman must have died between March and June.

After additional investigation, Professor Oeggl was ready to map the Iceman's final trek up the mountain. Because Oeggl knew the rate at which food travels through the digestive system, he inferred that the Iceman had eaten three times in the final day and a half of his life. From the digestive tract samples, Oeggl estimated where the Iceman was located when he ate.

First, the Iceman ingested pollen grains native to higher mountain regions. Then he swallowed hop-hornbeam pollen grains from the lower mountain regions several hours later. Last, the Iceman swallowed other pollen grains from trees of higher mountain areas again. Oeggl proposed the Iceman traveled from the southern region of the Italian Alps to the higher, northern region as shown in **Figure 13**, where he died suddenly. He did this all in a period of about 33 hours.

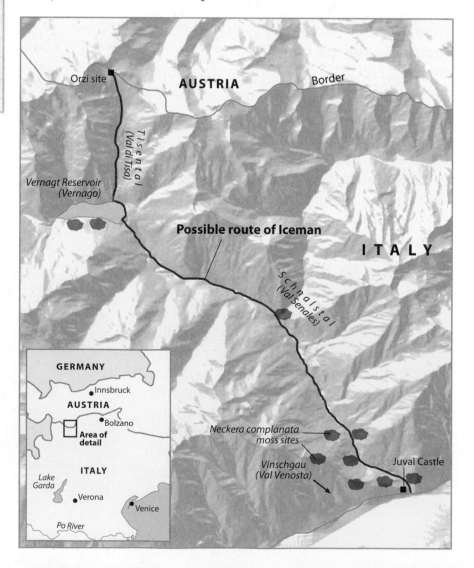

Figure 13 By examining the contents of the Iceman's digestive tract, Professor Oeggl was able to reconstruct the Iceman's last journey.

Conclusion

Researchers from around the world worked on different parts of the Iceman mystery and shared their results. Analysis of the Iceman's hair revealed his diet usually contained vegetables and meat. Examining the Iceman's one remaining fingernail, scientists determined that he had been sick three times within the last six months of his life. X-rays revealed an arrowhead under the Iceman's left shoulder. This suggested that he died from that serious injury rather than from exposure.

Finally, scientists concluded that the Iceman traveled from the high alpine region in spring to his native village in the lowland valleys. There, during a conflict, the Iceman sustained a fatal injury. He retreated back to the higher elevations, where he died. Scientists recognize their hypotheses can never be proved, only supported or not supported. However, with advances in technology, scientists are able to more thoroughly investigate mysteries of nature.

> Scientific investigations may disprove early hypotheses or conclusions. However, new information can cause a hypothesis or conclusion to be revised many times.

> Revised Conclusion: In spring, the Iceman traveled from the high country to the valleys. After he was involved in a violent confrontation, he climbed the mountain into a region of permanent ice where he died of his wounds.

Lesson 3 Review

✔ Assessment   Online Quiz

Use Vocabulary

1. A factor that can have more than one value is a(n) _____ .

2. **Differentiate** between independent and dependent variables.

Understand Key Concepts 🔑

3. Which part of scientific inquiry was NOT used in this case study?
   A. Draw conclusions.
   B. Make observations.
   C. Hypothesize and predict.
   D. Make a computer model.

4. **Determine** which is the control group and which is the experimental group in the following scenario: Scientists are testing a new kind of aspirin to see whether it will relieve headaches. They give one group of volunteers the aspirin. They give another group of volunteers pills that look like aspirin but are actually sugar pills.

Interpret Graphics

5. **Summarize** Copy and fill in the flow chart below summarizing the sequence of scientific inquiry steps that was used in one part of the case study. Draw the number of boxes needed for your sequence.

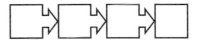

6. **Explain** What is the significance of the hop-hornbeam pollen found in the Iceman's digestive tract?

Critical Thinking

7. **Formulate** more questions about the Iceman. What would you want to know next?

8. **Evaluate** the hypotheses and conclusions made during the study of the Iceman. Do you see anything that might be an assumption? Are there holes in the research?

Inferring from Indirect Evidence

Materials

owl pellet

bone identification chart

dissecting needle

forceps

magnifying lens

Also needed:
toothpicks, small brush, paper plate, ruler

Safety

In the case study about the Iceman, you learned how scientists used evidence found in or near the body to learn how the Iceman might have lived and what he ate. In this investigation, you will use similar indirect evidence to learn more about an owl.

An owl pellet is a ball of fur and feathers that contains bones, teeth, and other undigested parts of animals eaten by the owl. Owls and other birds, such as hawks and eagles, swallow their prey whole. Stomach acids digest the soft parts of the food. Skeletons and body coverings are not digested and form a ball. When the owl coughs up the ball, it might fall to the ground. Feathers, straw, or leaves often stick to the moist ball when it strikes the ground.

Ask a Question

What kinds of information can I learn about an owl by analyzing an owl pellet?

Make Observations

1. Read and complete a lab safety form.

2. Carefully measure the length, the width, and the mass of your pellet. Write the data in your Science Journal.

3. Gently examine the outside of the pellet using a magnifying lens. Do you see any sign of fur or feathers? What other substances can you identify? Record your observations.

4. Use a dissecting needle, toothpicks, and forceps to gently pull apart the pellet. Try to avoid breaking any of the tiny bones. Spread out the parts on a paper plate.

5. Copy the table into your Science Journal. Use the bone identification chart to identify each of the bones and other materials found in your pellet. Make a mark in the table for each part you identify.

Bone Identification Chart		
Bone	**Animal**	**Number**
Skull		
Jaw		
Shoulder blade		
Forelimb		
Hind limb		
Hip/pelvis		
Rib		
Vertebrae		
Insect parts		

Analyze and Conclude

6. **Assemble** the bones you find into a skeleton. You may need to locate pictures of rodents, shrews, moles, and birds.

7. **Discuss** with your teammates why parts of an animal skeleton might be missing.

8. **Write** a report that includes your data and conclusions about the owl's diet.

9. **Identify Cause and Effect** Is every bone you found in the pellet necessarily from the owl's prey? Why or why not?

10. **Analyze** What conclusions can you reach about the diet of the particular owl from which your pellet came? Can you extend this conclusion to the diets of all owls? Why or why not?

11. 🅱️ **The Big Idea** How did the scientific inquiry you used in the investigation compare to those used by the scientists studying the Iceman? In what ways were they the same? In what ways were they different?

Communicate Your Results

Compare your results with those of several other teams. Discuss any evidence to support that the owl pellets did or did not come from the same area.

Inquiry Extension

Put your data on the board. Use the class data to determine a mean, median, mode, and range for each type of bone.

☑ When using your forceps, squeeze the sides very lightly so that you don't crush fragile bones.

☑ Use the brush to clean each bone. Try rotating the bones as you match them to the chart.

☑ Lay the bones on the matching box on the chart as you separate them. Then count them when you are finished.

4

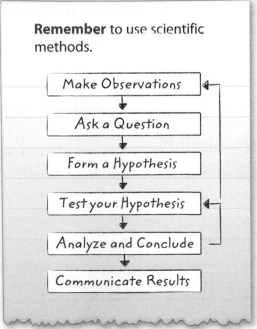

Remember to use scientific methods.

```
Make Observations  ◄─┐
      ↓              │
 Ask a Question      │
      ↓              │
 Form a Hypothesis   │
      ↓              │
Test your Hypothesis ◄┐
      ↓              ││
Analyze and Conclude ─┘│
      ↓               │
Communicate Results   │
```

Chapter Study Guide and Review

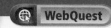 **WebQuest**

 THE BIG IDEA Scientists use the process of scientific inquiry to perform scientific investigations.

Key Concepts Summary 🔑

Lesson 1: Understanding Science

- Scientific inquiry is a process that uses a set of skills to answer questions or to test ideas about the natural world.
- A **scientific law** is a rule that describes a pattern in nature. A **scientific theory** is an explanation of things or events that is based on knowledge gained from many **observations** and investigations.
- Facts are measurements, observations, and theories that can be evaluated for their validity through objective investigation. Opinions are personal views, feelings, or claims about a topic that cannot be proven true or false.

Lesson 2: Measurement and Scientific Tools

- Scientists worldwide use the **International System of Units** because their work is easier to confirm and repeat by their peers.
- Measurement uncertainty occurs because no scientific tool can provide a perfect measurement.
- Mean, median, mode, and range are statistical calculations that are used to evaluate sets of data.

Lesson 3: Case Study: The Iceman's Last Journey

- The **independent variable** is the factor a scientist changes to observe how it affects a **dependent variable.** A dependent variable is the factor a scientist measures or observes during an experiment.
- Scientific inquiry was used throughout the investigation of the Iceman when hypotheses, predictions, tests, analysis, and conclusions were developed.

Vocabulary

science p. NOS 4
observation p. NOS 6
inference p. NOS 6
hypothesis p. NOS 6
prediction p. NOS 6
technology p. NOS 8
scientific theory p. NOS 9
scientific law p. NOS 9
critical thinking p. NOS 10

description p. NOS 14
explanation p. NOS 14
International System of Units (SI) p. NOS 14
significant digits p. NOS 16

variable p. NOS 23
independent variable p. NOS 23
dependent variable p. NOS 23

Use Vocabulary

Replace each underlined term with the correct vocabulary word.

1 A <u>description</u> is an interpretation of observations.

2 The <u>means</u> are the numbers of digits in a measurement that you know with a certain degree of reliability.

3 The act of watching something and taking note of what occurs is a(n) <u>inference</u>.

4 A <u>scientific theory</u> is a rule that describes a pattern in nature.

Understand Key Concepts

5 In the diagram of the process of scientific inquiry, which skill is missing from the Test Hypothesis box?

> **Test Hypothesis**
> - Design an Experiment
> - Gather and Evaluate Evidence
> - Collect Data/Record Observations

A. Analyze results.

B. Communicate results.

C. Make a model.

D. Make observations.

6 You have the following data set: 2, 3, 4, 4, 5, 7, and 8. Is 6 the mean, the median, the mode, or the range of the data set?

A. mean

B. median

C. mode

D. range

7 Which best describes an independent variable?

A. It is a factor that is not in every test.

B. It is a factor the investigator changes.

C. It is a factor you measure during a test.

D. It is a factor that stays the same in every test.

Critical Thinking

8 **Predict** what would happen if every scientist tried to use all the skills of scientific inquiry in the same order in every investigation.

9 **Assess** the role of measurement uncertainty in scientific investigations.

10 **Evaluate** the importance of having a control group in a scientific investigation.

Writing in Science

11 **Write** a five-sentence paragraph explaining why the International System of Units (SI) is an easier system to use than the English system of measurement. Be sure to include a topic sentence and a concluding sentence in your paragraph.

REVIEW THE BIG IDEA

12 What process do scientists use to perform scientific investigations? List and explain three of the skills involved.

13 Infer the purpose of the pink dye in the scientific investigation shown in the photo.

Math Skills

 Review
—— Math Practice ——

Use Numbers

14 Convert 162.5 hg to grams.

15 Convert 89.7 cm to millimeters.

Unit 1

ENERGY AND MATTER

1950   1975   2000

? Inquiry

Visit ConnectED for this unit's STEM activity.

1945
American-led atomic bomb attacks on the Japanese cities of Hiroshima and Nagasaki bring about the end of World War II.

1954
Obninsk Nuclear Power Plant, located in the former USSR, begins operating as the world's first nuclear power plant to generate electricity for a power grid. It produces around 5 megawatts of electric power.

2007
Fourteen percent of the world's electricity now comes from nuclear power.

Models

Have you ridden on an amusement park roller coaster such as the one in **Figure 1?** As you were going down the steepest hill or hanging upside down in a loop, did you think to yourself, "I hope I don't fly off this thing"? Before construction begins on a roller coaster, engineers build different models of the thrill ride to ensure proper construction and safety. A **model** is a representation of an object, an idea, or a system that is similar to the physical object or idea being studied.

Using Models in Physical Science

Models are used to study things that are too big or too small, happen too quickly or too slowly, or are too dangerous or too expensive to study directly. Different types of models serve different purposes. Roller-coaster engineers might build a physical model of their idea for a new, daring coaster. Using mathematical and computer models, the engineers can calculate the measurements of hills, angles, and loops to ensure a safe ride. Finally, the engineers might create another model called a blueprint, or drawing, that details the construction of the ride. Studying the various models allows engineers to predict how the actual roller coaster will behave when it travels through a loop or down a giant hill.

Figure 1 Engineers use various models to design roller coasters.

Types of Models

Physical Model

A physical model is a model that you can see and touch. It shows how parts relate to one another, how something is built, or how complex objects work. Physical models often are built to scale. A limitation of a physical model is that it might not reflect the physical behavior of the full-size object. For example, this model will not accurately show how wind will affect the ride.

Mathematical Model

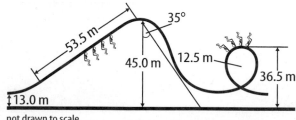

53.5 m   35°
45.0 m   12.5 m
13.0 m   36.5 m
not drawn to scale

A mathematical model uses numerical data and equations to model an event or idea. Mathematical models often include input data, constants, and output data. When designing a thrill ride, engineers use mathematical models to calculate the heights, the angles of loops and turns, and the forces that affect the ride. One limitation of a mathematical model is that you cannot use it to model how different parts are assembled.

Making Models

An important factor in making a model is determining its purpose. You might need a model that physically represents an object. Or, you might need a model that includes only important elements of an object or a process. When you build a model, first determine the function of the model. What variables need to change? What materials should you use? What do you need to communicate to others? **Figure 2** shows two models of a glucose molecule, each with a different purpose.

Limitations of Models

It is impossible to include all the details about an object or an idea into one model. All models have limitations. When using models to design a structure, an engineer must be aware of the information each model does and does not provide. For example, a blueprint of a roller coaster does not show the maximum weight that a car can support. However, a mathematical model would include this information. Scientists and engineers consider the purpose and the limitations of the model they use to ensure they draw accurate conclusions from models.

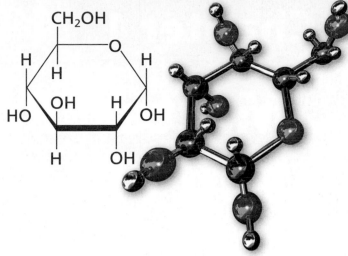

Figure 2 The model on the left is used to represent how the atoms in a glucose molecule bond together. The model on the right is a 3-D representation of the molecule, which shows how atoms might interact.

Computer Simulation

A computer simulation is a model that combines large amounts of data and mathematical models with computer graphic and animation programs. Simulations can contain thousands of complex mathematical models. When roller coaster engineers change variables in mathematical models, they use computer simulation to view the effects of the change.

Inquiry MiniLab

30 minutes

Can you model a roller coaster?

You are an engineer with an awesome idea for a new roller coaster—the car on your roller coaster makes a jump and then lands back on the track. You model your idea to show it to managers at a theme park in hopes that you can build it.

1 Read and complete a lab safety form.

2 Create a blueprint of your roller coaster. Include a scale and measurements.

3 Follow your blueprint to build a scaled physical model of your roller coaster. Use **foam hose insulation, tape,** and other **craft supplies.**

4 Use a **marble** as a model for a roller-coaster car. Test your model. Record your observations in your Science Journal.

Analyze and Conclude

1. **Compare** your blueprint and physical model.

2. **Evaluate** After you test your physical model, list the design changes would make to your blueprint.

3. **Identify** What are the limitations of each of your models?

Chapter 1

Matter: Properties and Changes

THE BIG IDEA

What gives a substance its unique identity?

Inquiry · What properties does it have?

When designing a safe airplane, choosing materials with specific properties is important. Notice how the metal used in the outer shell of this airplane is curved, yet it is strong enough to hold its shape. Think about how properties of the airplane's materials are important to the conditions in which it flies.

- What properties would be important to consider when constructing the outer shell of an airplane?

- Why is metal used for electrical wiring and plastic used for interior walls of an airplane?

- Why do different substances have different properties?

Get Ready to Read

What do you think?

Before you read, decide if you agree or disagree with each of these statements. As you read this chapter, see if you change your mind about any of the statements.

1 The particles in a solid object do not move.

2 Your weight depends on your location.

3 The particles in ice are the same as the particles in liquid water.

4 Mixing powdered drink mix with water causes a new substance to form.

5 If you combine two substances, bubbling is a sign that a new type of substance might be forming.

6 If you stir salt into water, the total amount of matter decreases.

ConnectED Your one-stop online resource

connectED.mcgraw-hill.com

- Video
- WebQuest
- Audio
- Assessment
- Review
- Concepts in Motion
- Inquiry
- Multilingual eGlossary

Lesson 1

Reading Guide

Key Concepts
ESSENTIAL QUESTIONS

- How do particles move in solids, liquids, and gases?
- How are physical properties different from chemical properties?
- How are properties used to identify a substance?

Vocabulary

volume p. 10

solid p. 10

liquid p. 10

gas p. 10

physical property p. 12

mass p. 12

density p. 13

solubility p. 14

chemical property p. 15

 Multilingual eGlossary

 Video BrainPOP®

Academic Standards for Science

6.1.1 Understand that the properties and behavior of matter can be explained by a model which depicts particles representing atoms or molecules in motion.

Also covers: 6.1.2, 6.NS.3, 6.NS.5, 6.NS.7, 6.NS.9, 6.DP.10

Matter and Its Properties

Inquiry What makes this possible?

White-water rafting is a lot of fun, but you have to be prepared. The ride down the rapids can be dangerous, and you need good equipment. What properties must the helmets, the raft, the oars, and the life vests have to make a safe white-water ride possible?

How can you describe a substance?

Think about the different ways you can describe a type of matter. Is it hard? Can you pour it? What color is it? Answering questions like these can help you describe the properties of a substance. In this lab, you will observe how the properties of a mixture can be very different from the properties of the substances it is made from.

1. Read and complete a lab safety form.

2. Using a **small plastic spoon,** measure two spoonfuls of **cornstarch** into a **clear plastic cup.** What does the cornstarch look like? What does it feel like?

3. Slowly stir one spoonful of **water** into the cup containing the cornstarch. Gently roll the new substance around in the cup with your finger.

Think About This

1. What were some properties of the cornstarch and water before they were mixed?

2. 🔑 **Key Concept** How were the properties of the mixture different from the original properties of the cornstarch and water?

What is matter?

Imagine the excitement of white-water rafting through a mountain pass. As your raft plunges up and down through the rushing water, you grip your oar. You hope that the powerful current will lead you safely past the massive boulders. Only after you reach a quiet pool of water can you finally take a breath and enjoy the beautiful surroundings.

Imagine looking around and asking yourself, "What is matter?" Trees, rocks, water, and all the things you might see on a rafting trip are matter because they have mass and take up space. Air, even though you can't see it, is also matter because it has mass and takes up space. Light from the Sun is not matter because it does not have mass and does not take up space. Sounds, forces, and energy also are not matter.

Think about the properties of matter you would see on your white water rafting trip. The helmet you wear is hard and shiny. The rubber raft is soft and flexible. The water is cool and clear. Matter has many different properties. You will learn about some physical properties and chemical properties of matter in this chapter. You will also read about how these properties help to identify many types of matter.

REVIEW VOCABULARY

matter
anything that has mass and takes up space

States of Matter

One property that is useful when you are describing different materials is the state of matter. Three familiar states of matter are solids, liquids, and gases. You can determine a material's state of matter by answering the following questions:

• Does it have a definite shape?

• Does it have a definite volume?

Volume *is the amount of space a sample of matter occupies.* As shown in **Table 1,** a material's state of matter determines whether its shape and its volume change when it is moved from one container to another.

Solids, Liquids, and Gases

Notice in **Table 1** that *a solid is a state of matter with a definite shape and volume.* The shape and volume of a solid do not change regardless of whether it is inside or outside a container. *A* **liquid** *is a state of matter with a definite volume but not a definite shape.* A liquid changes shape if it is moved to another container, but its volume does not change. *A state of matter without a definite shape or a definite volume is a* **gas.** A gas changes both shape and volume depending on the size and shape of its container.

✓ **Reading Check** Which state of matter has a definite shape and a definite volume?

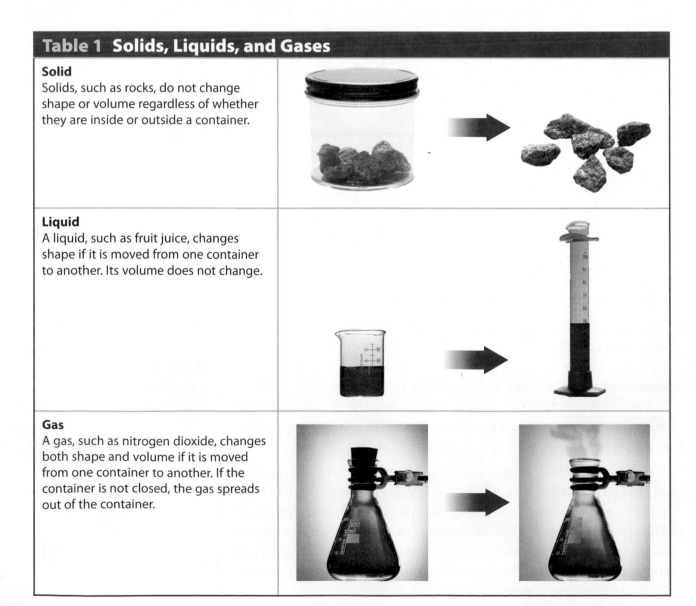

Table 1 Solids, Liquids, and Gases	
Solid Solids, such as rocks, do not change shape or volume regardless of whether they are inside or outside a container.	
Liquid A liquid, such as fruit juice, changes shape if it is moved from one container to another. Its volume does not change.	
Gas A gas, such as nitrogen dioxide, changes both shape and volume if it is moved from one container to another. If the container is not closed, the gas spreads out of the container.	

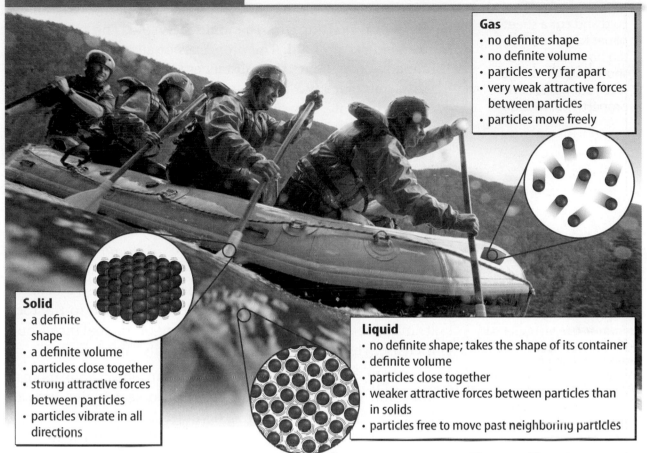

Particles of Matter 🔑

Gas
- no definite shape
- no definite volume
- particles very far apart
- very weak attractive forces between particles
- particles move freely

Solid
- a definite shape
- a definite volume
- particles close together
- strong attractive forces between particles
- particles vibrate in all directions

Liquid
- no definite shape; takes the shape of its container
- definite volume
- particles close together
- weaker attractive forces between particles than in solids
- particles free to move past neighboring particles

Figure 1 The movement and attraction between particles are different in solids, liquids, and gases.

✅ **Visual Check** How does the force between particles differ in a solid, a liquid, and a gas?

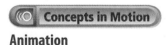 **Concepts in Motion**

Animation

Moving Particles

All matter is made of tiny particles that are constantly moving. Notice in **Figure 1** how the movement of particles is different in each state of matter. In solids, particles vibrate back and forth in all directions. However, particles in a solid cannot move from place to place. In liquids, the distance between particles is greater. Particles in liquids can slide past one another, similar to the way marbles in a box slide around. In a gas, particles move freely rather than staying close together.

 Key Concept Check How do particles move in solids, liquids, and gases?

Attraction Between Particles

Particles of matter that are close together exert an attractive force, or pull, on each other. The strength of the attraction depends on the distance between particles. Think about how this attraction affects the properties of the objects in **Figure 1**. A strong attraction holds particles of a solid close together in the same position. Liquids can flow because forces between the particles are weaker. Particles of a gas are so spread apart that they are not held together by attractive forces.

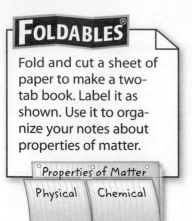
What are physical properties?

Think again about the properties of matter you might observe on a rafting trip. The water feels cold. The raft is heavy. The helmets are hard. The properties of all materials, or types of matter, depend on the substances that make them up. Recall that a substance is a type of matter with a composition that is always the same. *Any characteristic of matter that you can observe without changing the identity of the substances that make it up is a* **physical property.** **State** of matter, temperature, and the size of an object are all examples of physical properties.

Mass and Weight

Some physical properties of matter, such as mass and weight, depend on the size of the sample. **Mass** *is the amount of matter in an object.* Weight is the gravitational pull on the mass of an object. To measure the mass of a rock, you can use a balance, as shown in **Figure 2.** If more particles were added to the rock, its mass would increase, and the reading on the balance would increase. The weight of the rock would also increase.

Weight depends on the location of an object, but its mass does not. For example, the mass of an object is the same on Earth as it is on the Moon. The object's weight, however, is greater on Earth because the gravitational pull on the object is greater on Earth than on the Moon.

 Reading Check How do mass and weight differ?

Figure 2 You can measure a material's mass and volume and then calculate its density.

Review   Personal Tutor

Mass, Volume, and Density

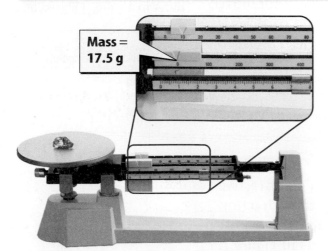

Mass =
17.5 g

Mass
A balance measures an object's mass by comparing it to the known mass of the slides on the balance. Common units for measuring mass are the kilogram (kg) and the gram (g).

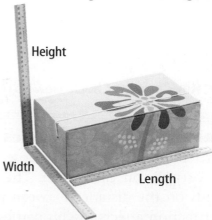

Volume = length × width × height

Height

Width

Length

Volume of a Rectangular-Shaped Solid
If a solid has a rectangular shape, you can find its volume by multiplying its length, its width, and its height together. A common unit of volume for a solid is the cubic centimeter (cm^3).

Volume

Another physical property of matter that depends on the amount or size of the sample is volume. You can measure the volume of a liquid by pouring it into a graduated cylinder or a measuring cup and reading the volume mark. Two ways to measure the volume of a solid are shown in **Figure 2.** If a solid has a regular geometric shape, you can calculate its volume by using the correct formula. If a solid has an irregular shape, you can use the displacement method to measure its volume.

Density

Density is a physical property of matter that does not depend on the size or amount of the sample. **Density** *is the mass per unit volume of a substance.* Density is useful when identifying unknown substances because it is constant for a given substance, regardless of the size of the sample. For example, imagine hiking in the mountains and finding a shiny yellow rock. Is it gold? Suppose you calculate that the density of the rock is 5.0 g/cm^3. This rock cannot be gold because the density of gold is 19.3 g/cm^3. A sample of pure gold, regardless of the size, will always have a density of 19.3 g/cm^3.

 **MiniLab**   **10 minutes**

How can you find an object's mass and volume?

1. Read and complete a lab safety form.

2. Obtain a small sample of **modeling clay.**

3. Using a **balance,** find the mass of the sample. Record it in your Science Journal.

4. Add exactly 25 mL of **tap water** to a **50-mL graduated cylinder.**

5. Shape the clay so that it can be placed into the graduated cylinder.

6. Slide the clay into the graduated cylinder. Record the new volume of the water.

Analyze and Conclude

1. **Compare** the volume of the water with the total volume of the water and the clay. What is the volume of the clay?

2. **Key Concept** Why are mass and volume considered physical properties?

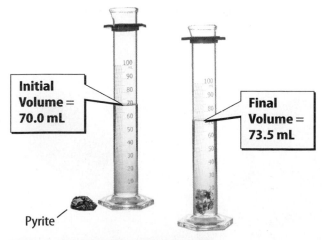

Initial Volume = 70.0 mL

Final Volume = 73.5 mL

Pyrite

Volume of an Irregular-Shaped Solid
The volume of an irregular-shaped object can be measured by displacement. The volume of the object is the difference between the water level before and after placing the object in the water. The common unit for liquid volume is the milliliter (mL).

Density Equation

$$\text{Density (in g/mL)} = \frac{\text{mass (in g)}}{\text{volume (in mL)}}$$

$$D = \frac{m}{V}$$

To find the density of the rock, first determine the mass and the volume of the rock:

mass: $m = 17.5 \text{ g}$
volume: $V = 73.5 \text{ mL} - 70.0 \text{ mL} = 3.5 \text{ mL}$

Then, divide the mass by the volume:

$$D = \frac{17.5 \text{ g}}{3.5 \text{ mL}} = 5.0 \text{ g/mL}$$

Density Calculation
Density can be calculated using the density equation. The common units of density are grams per milliliter (g/mL) or grams per cubic centimeter (g/cm^3). $1 \text{ mL} = 1 \text{ cm}^3$.

| Drink Mix | Sand |

Figure 3 The drink mix is soluble in water. The sand is not soluble in water.

WORD ORIGIN
solubility
from Latin *solubilis*, means "capable of being dissolved"

Solubility

You can observe another physical property of matter if you stir a powdered drink mix into water. The powder dissolves, or mixes evenly, in the water. **Solubility** *is the ability of one material to dissolve in another.* You cannot see the drink mix powder in the left glass in **Figure 3** because the powder is soluble in water. The liquid is red because of the food coloring in the powder. The sand settles in the glass because it is not soluble in water.

Melting and Boiling Point

Melting point and boiling point also are physical properties. The melting point is the temperature at which a solid changes to a liquid. Ice cream, for example, melts when it warms enough to reach its melting point. The boiling point is the temperature at which a liquid changes to a gas. If you heat a pan of water, the water will boil, or change to a gas, at its boiling point. Different materials have different melting and boiling points. These temperatures do not depend on the size or amount of the material.

 Reading Check How does a substance change at its melting point and at its boiling point?

Additional Physical Properties

Several other physical properties—magnetism, malleability, and electrical conductivity—are shown in **Figure 4.** Notice how the physical properties of each material make it useful. Can you think of other examples of materials chosen for certain uses because of their physical properties?

Physical Properties 🔑

Figure 4 Physical properties include magnetism, malleability, and electrical conductivity.

Magnetism is a physical property that allows some materials to attract certain metals.

A malleable material, such as aluminum foil used in cooking, is useful because it can be hammered or rolled into thin sheets.

Some metals, such as copper, are used in electrical wire because of their high electrical conductivity.

Figure 5 Flammability and the ability to rust are examples of chemical properties.

Flammability
In 1937 the airship *Hindenburg* caught fire and crashed. It was filled with hydrogen, a highly flammable gas.

Ability to rust
The metal parts of an old car soon rust because the metal contains iron. The ability to rust is a chemical property of iron.

What are chemical properties?

Have you ever seen an apple turn brown? When you bite into or cut open apples or other fruits, substances that make up the fruit react with oxygen in the air. When substances react with each other, their particles combine to form a new, different substance. The ability of substances in fruit to react with oxygen is a chemical property of the substances. *A chemical property is the ability or inability of a substance to combine with or change into one or more new substances.* A chemical property is a characteristic of matter that you observe as it reacts with or changes into a different substance. For example, copper on the roof of a building turns green as it reacts with oxygen in the air. The ability to react with oxygen is a chemical property of copper. Two other chemical properties—flammability and the ability to rust— are shown in **Figure 5.**

 Key Concept Check How do chemical properties and physical properties differ?

Flammability

Flammability is the ability of a type of matter to burn easily. Suppose you are on a camping trip and want to light a campfire. You see rocks, sand, and wood. Which would you choose for your fire? Wood is a good choice because it is flammable. Rocks and sand are not flammable.

Materials are often chosen for certain uses based on flammability. For example, gasoline is used in cars because it burns easily in engines. Materials that are used for cooking pans must not be flammable. The tragedy shown in **Figure 5** resulted when hydrogen, a highly flammable gas, was used in the airship *Hindenburg.* Today, airships are filled with helium, a nonflammable gas.

Ability to Rust

You have probably seen old cars that have begun to rust like the one in **Figure 5.** You might also have seen rust on bicycles or tools left outside. Rust is a substance that forms when iron reacts with water and oxygen in the air. The ability to rust is a chemical property of iron or metals that contain iron.

Table 2 Identifying an Unknown Material by its Physical Properties 🔑

Substance		Color	Mass (g)	Melting Point (°C)	Density (g/cm³)
Table salt		white	14.5	801	2.17
Sugar		white	11.5	148	1.53
Baking soda		white	16.0	50	2.16
Unknown		white	16.0	801	2.17

Identifying Matter Using Physical Properties

Physical properties are useful for describing types of matter, but they are also useful for identifying unknown substances. For example, look at the substances in **Table 2.** Notice how their physical properties are alike and how they are different. How can you use these properties to identify the unknown substance?

You cannot identify the unknown substance by its color. All of the substances are white. You also cannot identify the unknown substance by its mass or volume. Mass and volume are properties of matter that change with the amount of the sample present. However, recall that melting point and density are properties of matter that do not depend on the size or the amount of the sample. They are more reliable for identifying an unknown substance. Notice that both the melting point and the density of the unknown substance match those of table salt. The unknown substance must be table salt.

When you identify matter using physical properties, consider how the properties are alike and how they are different from known types of matter. It is important that the physical properties you use to identify an unknown type of matter are properties that do not change for any sample size. A cup of salt and a spoonful of salt will have the same melting point and density even though the mass and volume for each will be different. Therefore, melting point and density are physical properties that are reliable when identifying an unknown substance.

 Key Concept Check How are properties used to identify a substance?

Sorting Materials Using Properties

Both physical properties and chemical properties are useful for sorting materials. The beads in **Figure 6** are sorted by color and shape—two physical properties. When you bring groceries home from the store, you might put crackers in a cupboard, but you probably put milk and yogurt in the refrigerator to keep them from spoiling. The tendency to spoil is a chemical property of the milk and yogurt. You probably often sort other types of matter by physical or chemical properties without realizing it.

Separating Mixtures Using Physical Properties

Physical properties are useful for separating different types of matter that are mixed. For example, suppose you have a frozen juice pop on a stick. How could you separate the frozen juice from the stick? If you set the freezer pop on a counter, the frozen juice will melt and separate from the stick. The melting point of the juice is much lower than the melting point of the stick. Melting point is a physical property you can use to separate mixtures. Other ways that you can use physical properties to separate mixtures are shown in **Figure 7.**

 Reading Check How could you separate a mixture of sand and small pebbles?

▲ **Figure 6** These beads are sorted by color and shape.

Figure 7 Physical properties, such as state of matter, boiling point, and magnetism, can be used to separate mixtures. ▼

Separating Mixtures

Separation by State of Matter	Separation by Boiling Point	Separation by Magnetism

▲ Water can flow through the holes in the strainer because it is a liquid. The spaghetti noodles cannot flow through because they are solid and too large.

▲ If you boil a mixture of salt and water, the liquid water changes to a gas when it reaches its boiling point. The salt is left behind.

▲ Iron filings, which have the property of magnetism, can be separated from the sand using a magnet. The magnet attracts the iron filings but not the sand.

☑ **Visual Check** How could you separate a mixture of salt, sand, and iron filings?

Lesson 1 Review

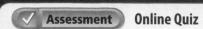

Visual Summary

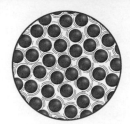

The movement of particles is different in a solid, a liquid, and a gas.

Physical properties and chemical properties are used to describe types of matter.

Physical properties such as magnetism can be used to separate mixtures.

FOLDABLES

Use your lesson Foldable to review the lesson. Save your Foldable for the project at the end of the chapter.

What do you think NOW?

You first read the statements below at the beginning of the chapter.

1. The particles in a solid object do not move.

2. Your weight depends on your location.

3. The particles in ice are the same as the particles in liquid water.

Did you change your mind about whether you agree or disagree with the statements? Rewrite any false statements to make them true.

Use Vocabulary

1 A state of matter that has a definite volume but not a definite shape is a _____.

2 **Distinguish** between a physical property and a chemical property.

Understand Key Concepts

3 **Analyze** Which can be used to identify an unknown substance: mass, melting point, density, volume, state of matter?

4 **Contrast** the movement of particles in a solid, a liquid, and a gas.

5 Which of these is a chemical property?
  A. boiling point   **C.** flammability
  B. density   **D.** solubility

Interpret Graphics

6 **Explain** Use the drawing to explain why a gas has no definite shape or volume.

7 **Calculate** Copy the table below and calculate the density of each object.

Object	Mass	Volume	Density
1	6.50 g	1.25 cm³	
2	8.65 g	2.50 mL	

Critical Thinking

8 **Design** an investigation you could use to find the density of a penny.

Math Skills Review
—— Math Practice ——

9 The mass of a mineral is 9.6 g. The mineral is placed in a graduated cylinder containing 8.0 mL of water. The water level rises to 16.0 mL. What is the mineral's density?

How can you calculate density?

metal block

100-mL
graduated
cylinder

metric ruler

triple-beam
balance

Safety

Density is the mass per unit volume of a substance. In this lab, you will measure the mass of a solid block. Next you will measure the volume in two different ways. Then you will calculate the density of the block for each volume measurement.

Learn It

Scientists take measurements when collecting data. In this lab, you will **measure** mass and volume, then use these data to calculate density.

Try It

1 Read and complete a lab safety form.

2 Copy the data table in your Science Journal. Use a triple beam balance to measure the mass of the metal block. Record your measurements.

3 Use a ruler to measure the length, width, and height of the block. Record your measurements.

4 Pour 30 mL of water into a 100-mL graduated cylinder. Record the volume of the water.

5 Carefully slide the metal block into the graduated cylinder. Record the total volume.

6 Using the measurements from step 3, determine the volume of the block using this equation:
volume = length × width × height

7 Calculate the volume of the block using displacement. Subtract the volume of the water in step 4 from the volume of the water and block in step 5.

Apply It

8 **Calculate** Using the mass and each volume measurement of the block, calculate the density of the block.

9 **Compare** the density of the block calculated by the two different volumes. *Hint:* $1 \text{ mL} = 1 \text{ cm}^3$. Are they the same? Why or why not?

10 **Key Concept** Why is density a physical property of the block?

Measurements	
Mass (g)	
Length (cm)	
Width (cm)	
Height (cm)	
Volume of water (mL)	
Volume of water and block (mL)	

Reading Guide

Key Concepts
ESSENTIAL QUESTIONS

- How are physical changes different from chemical changes?

- How do physical and chemical changes affect mass?

Vocabulary

physical change p. 22

chemical change p. 24

law of conservation of mass p. 27

 Multilingual eGlossary

Video BrainPOP®

Academic Standards for Science

6.1.1 Understand that the properties and behavior of matter can be explained by a model which depicts particles representing atoms or molecules in motion.

6.1.2 Explain the properties of solids, liquids and gases using drawings and models that represent matter as particles in motion whose state can be represented by the relative positions and movement of the particles.

6.1.3 Using a model in which matter is composed of particles in motion, investigate that when substances undergo a change in state, mass is conserved.

Also covers: 6.NS.3, 6.NS.5, 6.NS.6, 6.NS.7, 6.NS.10

Matter and Its Changes

Inquiry Why is it orange?

Streams are usually filled with clear freshwater. What happened to this water? Chemicals from a nearby mine seeped through rocks before flowing into the stream. These chemicals combined with metals in the rocks, causing orange rust to form in the water.

What does a change in the color of matter show?

Matter has many different properties. Chemical properties can only be observed if the matter changes from one type to another. How can you tell if a chemical property has changed? Sometimes a change in the color of matter shows that its chemical properties have changed.

1. Read and complete a lab safety form.

2. Obtain the **red indicator sponge** and the **red acid solution** from your teacher. Predict what will happen if the red acid solution touches the red sponge.

3. Use a **dropper** to remove a few drops of acid solution from the **beaker.** Place the drops on the sponge. ⚠ *Be careful not to splash the liquid onto yourself or your clothing.*

4. Record your observations in your Science Journal.

Think About This

1. **Compare** the properties of the sponge before and after you placed the acid solution onto the sponge. Was your prediction correct?

2. 🔑 **Key Concept** How do you know that physical properties and chemical properties changed?

Changes of Matter

Imagine going to a park in the spring and then going back to the same spot in the fall. What changes do you think you might see? The changes would depend on where you live. An example of what a park in the fall might look like in many places is shown in **Figure 8.** Leaves that are soft and green in the spring might turn red, yellow, or brown in the fall. The air that was warm in the spring might be cooler in the fall. If you visit the park early on a fall morning, you might notice a thin layer of frost on the leaves. Matter, such as the things you see at a park, can change in many ways. These changes can be either physical or chemical.

 Reading Check What are some examples of matter changing in winter?

Figure 8 The physical and chemical properties of matter change in a park throughout the year.

What are physical changes?

A change in the size, shape, form, or state of matter that does not change the matter's identity is a **physical change**. You can see an example of a physical change in **Figure 9**. Recall that mass is an example of a physical property. Notice that the mass of the modeling clay is the same before and after its shape was changed. When a physical change occurs, the chemical properties of the matter stay the same. The substances that make up matter are exactly the same both before and after a physical change.

Dissolving

One of the physical properties you read about in Lesson 1 was solubility—the ability of one material to dissolve, or mix evenly, in another. Dissolving is a physical change because the identities of the substances do not change when they are mixed. As shown in **Figure 10**, the identities of the water molecules and the sugar molecules do not change when sugar crystals dissolve in water.

Reading Check Explain why dissolving is classified as a physical change.

Figure 9 Changing the shape of the modeling clay does not change its mass.

Dissolving—A Physical Change

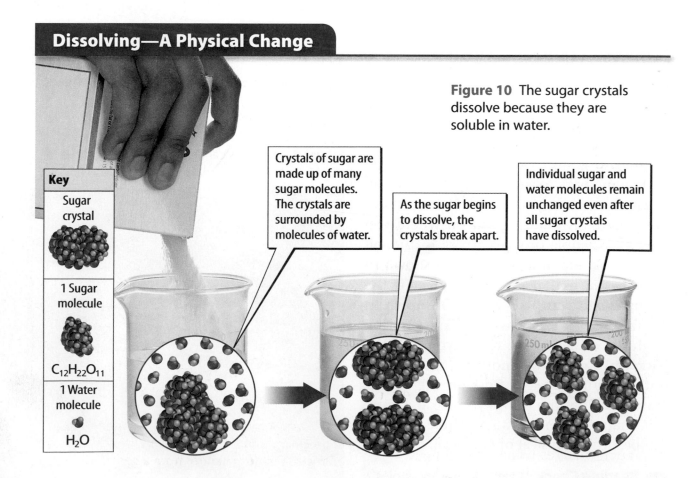

Figure 10 The sugar crystals dissolve because they are soluble in water.

Crystals of sugar are made up of many sugar molecules. The crystals are surrounded by molecules of water.

As the sugar begins to dissolve, the crystals break apart.

Individual sugar and water molecules remain unchanged even after all sugar crystals have dissolved.

Key

Sugar crystal

1 Sugar molecule

$C_{12}H_{22}O_{11}$

1 Water molecule

H_2O

Changing State

In Lesson 1 you read about three states of matter—solid, liquid, and gas. Can you think of examples of matter changing from one state to another? A layer of ice might form on a lake in the winter. A glassblower melts glass into a liquid so that it can be formed into shapes. Changes in the state of matter are physical changes.

Melting and Boiling If you heat ice cubes in a pot on the stove, the ice will melt, forming water that soon begins to boil. When a material melts, it changes from a solid to a liquid. When it boils, it changes from a liquid to a gas. The substances that make up the material do not change during a change in the state of matter, as shown in **Figure 11**. The particles that make up ice (solid water) are the same as the particles that make up water as a liquid or as a gas.

Energy and Change In State The energy of the particles and the distances between the particles are different for a solid, a liquid, and a gas. Changes in energy cause changes in the state of matter. For example, energy must be added to a substance to change it from a solid to a liquid or from a liquid to a gas. Adding energy to a substance can increase its temperature. When the temperature reaches the substance's melting point, the solid changes to a liquid. At the boiling point, the liquid changes to a gas.

What would happen if you changed the rate at which you add energy to a substance? For example, what would happen if you heated an ice cube in your hand instead of in a pot on the stove? The ice would reach its melting point more slowly in your hand. The rate at which one state of matter changes to another depends on the rate at which energy is added to or taken away from the substance.

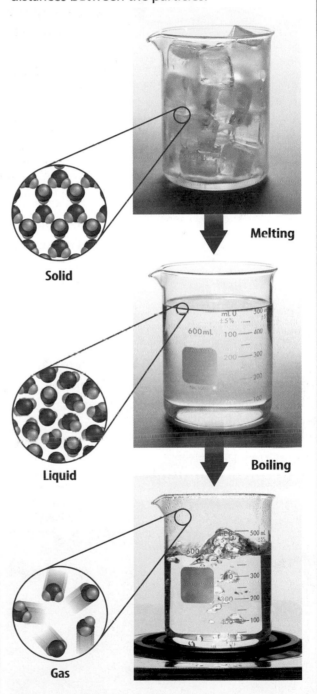

Figure 11 The particles that make up ice (solid water), liquid water, and water vapor (water in the gaseous state) are the same. Changing from one state to another changes only the amount of energy of the particles and the distances between the particles.

Solid

Melting

Liquid

Boiling

Gas

✔ **Visual Check** Describe the change in the energy and motion of particles of a substance if the substance changes from a gas to a liquid.

Physical Changes | Chemical Changes

What are chemical changes?

Some changes in matter involve more than just changing physical properties. *A* **chemical change** *is a change in matter in which the substances that make up the matter change into other substances with different chemical and physical properties.* Recall that a chemical property is the ability or inability of a substance to combine with or change into one or more new substances. During a physical change, only the physical properties of matter change. However, the new substance produced during a chemical change has different chemical and physical properties. Another name for a chemical change is a chemical reaction. The particles that make up two or more substances react, or combine, with each other and form a new substance.

Key Concept Check How are chemical changes different from physical changes?

Signs of a Chemical Change

How can you tell that the burning of the trees in **Figure 12** is a chemical change? The reaction produces two gases—carbon dioxide and water vapor—even though you cannot see them. After the fire, you can see that any part of the trees that remains is black, and you can see ash—another new substance. But with some changes, the only new substance formed is a gas you cannot see. As trees burn in a forest fire, light and heat are signs of a chemical change. For many reactions, changes in physical properties, such as color or state of matter, are signs that a chemical change has occurred. However, the only sure sign of a chemical change is the formation of a new substance.

Figure 12 A forest fire causes a chemical change in the trees, producing new substances.

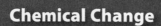
Chemical Change

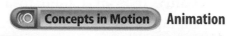
Concepts in Motion Animation

Light and heat during a forest fire are signs that a chemical change is occurring.

After the fire, the formation of new substances shows that a chemical change has taken place.

Visual Check Why is the smoke produced during a forest fire a sign of a chemical change?

Formation of Gas Bubbles of gas can form during both a physical change and a chemical change. When you heat a substance to its boiling point, the bubbles show that a liquid is changing to a gas—a physical change. When you combine substances, such as the medicine tablet and the water in **Figure 13,** gas bubbles show that a chemical change is occurring. Sometimes you cannot see the gas produced, but you might be able to smell it. The aroma of freshly baked bread, for example, is a sign that baking bread causes a chemical reaction that produces a gas.

 Reading Check How can you determine whether the formation of bubbles is the result of a physical change or a chemical change?

Formation of a Precipitate Some chemical reactions result in the formation of a precipitate (prih SIH puh tut). As shown in the middle photo in **Figure 13,** a precipitate is a solid that sometimes forms when two liquids combine. When a liquid freezes, the solid formed is not a precipitate. A precipitate is not a state change from a liquid to a solid. Instead, the particles that make up two liquids react and form the particles that make up the solid precipitate, a new substance.

Color Change Suppose you want your room to be a different color. You would simply apply paint to the walls. The change in color is a physical change because you have only covered the wall. A new substance does not form. But notice the color of the precipitate in the middle photo of **Figure 13.** In this case, the change in color is a sign of a chemical change. The photo in the bottom of the figure shows that marshmallows change from white to brown when they are toasted. The change in the color of the marshmallows is also a sign of a chemical change.

 Reading Check What are some signs that a chemical change has occurred?

Figure 13 Formation of a gas, formation of a precipitate, and color change are all signs of a chemical change.

Formation of gas bubbles

Formation of a precipitate

Color change

✔ **Visual Check** What is a sign besides color change that indicates that the marshmallow is under-going a chemical change?

▲ **Figure 14** The flames, the light, and the sound of a fireworks display are signs of a chemical change.

Energy and Chemical Change

Think about a fireworks show. Again and again, you hear loud bangs as the fireworks burst into a display of colors, as in **Figure 14.** The release of thermal energy, light, and sound are signs that the fireworks result from chemical changes. All chemical reactions involve energy changes.

Thermal energy is often needed for a chemical reaction to take place. Suppose you want to bake pretzels, as shown in **Figure 15.** What would happen if you placed one pan of unbaked pretzel dough in the oven and another pan of unbaked pretzel dough on the kitchen counter? Only the dough in the hot oven would become pretzels. Thermal energy is needed for the chemical reactions to occur that bake the pretzels.

Energy in the form of light is needed for other chemical reactions. Photosynthesis is a chemical reaction by which plants and some unicellular organisms produce sugar and oxygen. This process only occurs if the organisms are **exposed** to light. Many medicines also undergo chemical reactions when exposed to light. You might have seen some medicines stored in orange bottles. If the medicines are not stored in these light-resistant bottles, the ingredients can change into other substances.

ACADEMIC VOCABULARY

expose
(verb) to uncover; to make visible

Figure 15 Thermal energy is needed for the chemical reactions that take place when baking pretzels. ▶

Can changes be reversed?

Think again about the way matter changes form during a fireworks display. Once the chemicals combine and cause the explosions, you cannot get back the original chemicals. Like most chemical changes, the fireworks display cannot be reversed.

Grating a carrot and cutting an apple are physical changes, but you cannot reverse these changes either. Making a mixture by dissolving salt in a pan of water is also a physical change. You can reverse this change by boiling the mixture. The water will change to a gas, leaving the salt behind in the pan. Some physical changes can be easily reversed, but others cannot.

 Reading Check Identify one physical change that can be reversed and one that cannot be reversed.

Conservation of Mass

Physical changes do not affect the mass of substances. When ice melts, for example, the mass of the ice equals the mass of the resulting liquid water. If you cut a piece of paper into strips, the total mass of the paper remains the same. Mass is conserved, or unchanged, during a physical change.

Mass is also conserved during a chemical change. Antoine Lavoisier (AN twon · luh VWAH zee ay) (1743–1794), a French chemist, made this discovery. Lavoisier carefully measured the masses of materials before and after chemical reactions. His discovery is now a scientific law. *The* **law of conservation of mass** *states that the total mass before a chemical reaction is the same as the total mass after the chemical reaction.* Weight also is the same because it depends on mass. For example, the mass of an unburned match plus the mass of the oxygen it reacts with equals the mass of the ashes plus the masses of all the gases given off when the match burns.

 Key Concept Check How do physical and chemical changes affect mass?

inquiry MiniLab   10 minutes

Is mass conserved during a chemical reaction?

If you have ever seen the glow of a light stick, you have observed a chemical change. How does the chemical reaction affect the mass of the light stick?

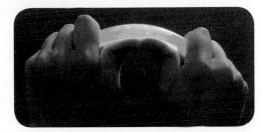

1. Read and complete a lab safety form.
2. Obtain a **light stick** from your teacher. Carefully remove it from the packaging.
3. Observe the structure of the light stick. Record your observations in your Science Journal.
4. Measure and record the mass of the light stick using a **balance.**
5. Grasp the ends of the light stick. Gently bend it to break the inner vial. Shake the stick gently to start the reaction.
6. Use a **stopwatch** to time the reaction for 3 minutes. Record your observations.
7. Repeat step 4.

Analyze and Conclude

1. **Explain** the purpose of the inner vial in the light stick.
2. **Describe** what occurred when the inner vial was broken.
3. **Key Concept** What effect did the chemical reaction have on the mass? Why?

WORD ORIGIN ·································

conservation
from Latin *conservare*, means "to keep, preserve"

Comparing Physical and Chemical Changes

Suppose you want to explain to a friend the difference between a physical change and a chemical change. What would you say? You could explain that the identity of matter does not change during a physical change, but the identity of matter does change during a chemical change. However, you might not be able to tell just by looking at a substance whether its identity changed. You cannot tell whether the particles that make up the matter are the same or different.

Sometimes deciding if a change is physical or chemical is easy. Often, however, identifying the type of change is like being a detective. You have to look for clues that will help you figure out whether the identity of the substance has changed. For example, look at the summary of physical changes and chemical changes in **Table 3.** A change in color can occur during a chemical change or when substances are mixed (a physical change). Bubbles might indicate the formation of gas (a chemical change) or boiling (a physical change). You must consider many factors when comparing physical and chemical changes.

Table 3 Chemical changes produce a new substance, but physical changes do not.

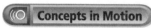
Interactive Table

Reading Check What are some clues you can use to decide if a change is a physical change or a chemical change?

Table 3 Comparing Physical and Chemical Changes		
Type of Change	**Examples**	**Characteristics**
Physical change	• melting • boiling • changing shape • mixing • dissolving • increasing or decreasing in temperature	• Substance is the same before and after the change. • Only physical properties change.
Chemical change	• changing color • burning • rusting • formation of gas • formation of a precipitate • spoiling food • tarnishing silver • digesting food	• Substance is different after the change. • Both physical and chemical properties change.

Physical change

Chemical change

Lesson 2 Review

Visual Summary

The identity of a substance does not change during a physical change such as a change in the state of matter.

A new substance is produced during a chemical change.

The law of conservation of mass states that the mass of a material does not change during a chemical change.

FOLDABLES

Use your lesson Foldable to review the lesson. Save your Foldable for the project at the end of the chapter.

What do you think NOW?

You first read the statements below at the beginning of the chapter.

4. Mixing powdered drink mix with water causes a new substance to form.

5. If you combine two substances, bubbling is a sign that a new type of substance might be forming.

6. If you stir salt into water, the total amount of mass decreases.

Did you change your mind about whether you agree or disagree with the statements? Rewrite any false statements to make them true.

Use Vocabulary

1 The particles that make up matter do not change during a(n) _____.

Understand Key Concepts 🗝

2 **Explain** how physical and chemical changes affect the mass of a material.

3 Which is a physical change?
A. burning wood   C. rusting iron
B. melting ice   D. spoiling food

Interpret Graphics

4 **Analyze** Suppose you mix 12.8 g of one substance with 11.4 g of another. The picture shows the mass you measure for the mixture. Is this reasonable? Explain.

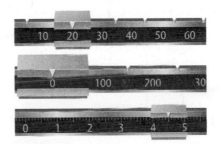

5 **Organize Information** Copy the graphic organizer below, and list an example of each type of change.

Type of Change	Examples
Physical change with formation of bubbles	
Chemical change with formation of bubbles	

Critical Thinking

6 **Consider** Suppose you mix baking soda and white vinegar. What signs might indicate that a chemical change occurs?

7 **Evaluate** You read that a physical change is a change in physical properties, and a chemical change is a change in chemical properties. Do you agree? Explain your answer.

Identifying Unknown Minerals

Materials

mineral samples

nail

100-mL graduated cylinder

triple-beam balance

Safety

Imagine you are a geologist digging for minerals. You find one that you would like to identify. What properties of the mineral would help you? Geologists consider many physical properties of a mineral when determining its identification.

Question

How can you use physical properties to identify unknown minerals?

Procedure

1. Read and complete the lab safety form.
2. Select a mineral sample to observe. Record its color in your Science Journal.
3. Observe the hardness of your mineral.
   a. Scratch your mineral with your fingernail. If it scratches, then your mineral has a low hardness. Go to step 4. If it does not scratch, go to step 3b.
   b. Scratch your mineral with a nail. If it scratches, it has a moderate hardness. If it does not scratch, it has a high hardness.
4. Compare the properties of your mineral with the properties in the chart.

Physical Properties of Minerals			
Mineral	Color	Typical Density (g/cm³)	Hardness
Fluorite	white or light green	3.1	moderate
Gypsum	white or brown	2.3	fairly soft
Hornblende	black or grayish brown	3.2	moderate
Magnetite (iron ore)	dark gray	5.2	moderate
Quartz	white or colorless	2.6	fairly hard
Sphalerite (zinc ore)	black or reddish brown	4.1	fairly soft

5 Think about the properties you observed so far. Are you able to determine which mineral you have based on your initial observations? Explain why or why not in your Science Journal.

6 Look back through the chapter to review the physical property *density*.

7 Design an experiment using mass and volume to determine the density of your mineral.

8 Share your procedure with your teacher for approval before conducting your experiment.

9 Compare your results with information in the Physical Properties of Minerals table.

Analyze and Conclude

10 **Infer** the identity of your mineral sample.

11 **The Big Idea** Which physical property was most useful in identifying the mineral? Why?

12 **Predict** Suppose you have another sample of the same mineral. What properties would you expect to be the same? What properties would be different?

Lab Tips

☑ To measure the water in a cylinder accurately, first put your eye at the level of the liquid. Then observe the level at the meniscus (the center or bottom of the curve in the surface of the liquid).

☑ 1 mL = 1 cm^3

Communicate Your Results

In a small group, share your experiences and your results. How did you collect and record data? What was successful? Did others use different techniques or get different results? Did anything surprise you?

 **Extension**

Choose a different unknown sample to test that looks similar to the one you tested. Which properties might be different? Test your sample in the same way you tested the first one. Were the results the same or different? What can you conclude from this?

Remember to use scientific methods.

Make Observations

Ask a Question

Form a Hypothesis

Test your Hypothesis

Analyze and Conclude

Communicate Results

Chapter 1 Study Guide

Physical and chemical properties give a substance its unique identity.

Key Concepts Summary	Vocabulary
Lesson 1: Matter and Its Properties  • Particles of a **solid** vibrate about a definite position. Particles of a **liquid** can slide past one another. Particles of a **gas** move freely within their container. • A **physical property** is a characteristic of matter that you can observe without changing the identity of the substances that make it up. A **chemical property** is the ability or inability of a substance to combine with or change into one or more new substances. • Some properties of matter do not depend on size or amount of the sample. You can identify a substance by comparing these properties to those of other known substances.	**volume** p. 10 **solid** p. 10 **liquid** p. 10 **gas** p. 10 **physical property** p. 12 **mass** p. 12 **density** p. 13 **solubility** p. 14 **chemical property** p. 15
Lesson 2: Matter and Its Changes • A change in the size, shape, form, or state of matter in which the identity of the matter stays the same is a **physical change.** A change in matter in which the substances that make it up change into other substances with different chemical and physical properties is a **chemical change.** • The **law of conservation of mass** states that the total mass before a chemical reaction is the same as the total mass after the reaction.	**physical change** p. 22 **chemical change** p. 24 **law of conservation of mass** p. 27

FOLDABLES® Chapter Project

Assemble your lesson Foldables as shown to make a Chapter Project. Use the project to review what you have learned in this chapter.

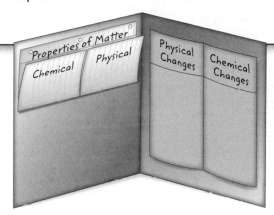

Use Vocabulary

1 A state of matter with a definite volume and a definite shape is a _____.

2 Flammability is an example of a _____ of wood because when wood burns, it changes to different materials.

3 A drink mix dissolves in water because of its _____ in water.

4 The rusting of a metal tool left in the rain is an example of a _____.

5 According to the _____, the mass of an untoasted marshmallow equals its mass after it is toasted plus the mass of any gases produced as it was toasting.

6 Slicing an apple into sections is an example of a _____ that cannot be reversed.

Link Vocabulary and Key Concepts

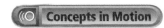 **Concepts in Motion** **Interactive Concept Map**

Copy this concept map, and then use vocabulary terms from the previous page to complete the concept map.

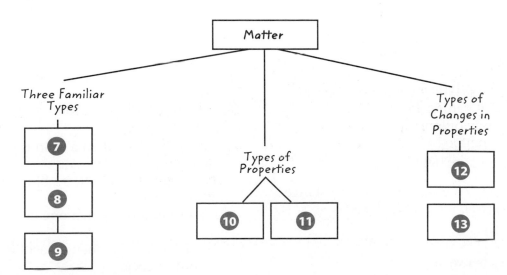

Chapter 1 Review

Understand Key Concepts

1 Which is a property of all solids?
- A. Particles are far apart.
- B. Particles vibrate in all directions.
- C. Volume and shape can easily change.
- D. Weak forces exist between particles.

2 Which characteristic is a chemical property?
- A. highly flammable
- B. mass of 15 kg
- C. woolly texture
- D. golden color

3 Which property of an object depends on its location?
- A. density
- B. mass
- C. volume
- D. weight

4 How are the particles of a gas different from the particles of a liquid shown here?

- A. They move more slowly.
- B. They are farther apart.
- C. They have less energy.
- D. They have stronger attractions.

5 Which is a physical change?
- A. burning natural gas
- B. chopping onions
- C. digesting food
- D. exploding dynamite

6 Which stays the same when a substance changes from a liquid to a gas?
- A. density
- B. mass
- C. forces between particles
- D. distance between particles

7 Which is a chemical change?
- A. boiling water
- B. copper turning green in air
- C. freezing fruit juice
- D. slicing a potato

8 Which would be most useful for identifying an unknown liquid?
- A. density
- B. mass
- C. volume
- D. weight

9 What mass is measured on this balance?

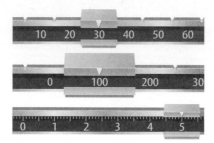

- A. 35 g
- B. 45 g
- C. 135 g
- D. 145 g

10 What causes a chemical reaction when you prepare scrambled eggs?
- A. removing the eggs from the shells
- B. mixing the egg yolks and the egg whites together
- C. heating the eggs in a pan
- D. sprinkling pepper onto the cooked eggs

11 Which describes the formation of a precipitate?
- A. A gas forms when a solid is placed in a liquid.
- B. A liquid forms when a block of metal is heated.
- C. A solid forms when one liquid is poured into another.
- D. Bubbles form when an acid is poured onto a rock.

Critical Thinking

12 **Apply** Suppose you find a gold-colored ring. Explain why you could use some physical properties but not others to determine whether the ring is actually made of gold.

13 **Reason** You make lemonade by mixing lemon juice, sugar, and water. Is this a physical change or a chemical change? Explain.

14 **Give an example** of a physical change you might observe at your school that is reversible and a physical change that is not reversible.

15 **Defend** A classmate defines a liquid as any substance that can be poured. Use the picture below to explain why this is not an acceptable definition.

16 **Suggest** a way that you could use displacement to determine the volume of a rock that is too large to fit into a graduated cylinder.

17 **Hypothesize** A scientist measures the mass of two liquids before and after combining them. The mass after combining the liquids is less than the sum of the masses before. Where is the missing mass?

Writing in Science

18 **Write** a four-sentence description of an object in your home or classroom. Be sure to identify both physical properties and chemical properties of the object.

REVIEW THE BIG IDEA

19 What gives a substance its unique identity?

20 What are some physical and chemical properties that an airplane manufacturer must consider when choosing materials to be used in constructing the shell of the aircraft shown below?

Math Skills

Review
Math Practice

21 Use what you have learned about density to complete the table below. Then, determine the identities of the two unknown metals.

Metal	Mass (g)	Volume (cm³)	Density (g/cm³)
Iron	42.5	5.40	
Lead	28.8	2.55	
Tungsten	69.5	3.60	
Zinc	46.4	6.50	
	61.0	5.40	
	46.4	2.40	

Record your answers on the answer sheet provided by your teacher or on a sheet of paper.

Multiple Choice

1 Which describes the particles in a substance with no definite volume or shape?

   A Particles are close but can move freely.

   B Particles are close but can vibrate in all directions.

   C Particles are far apart and cannot move.

   D Particles are far apart and move freely.

2 Which diagram shows a chemical change?

   A

   B

   C

   D

3 Which is NOT true about firewood that burns completely?

   A Ashes and gases form from the substances in the wood.

   B Oxygen from the air combines with substances in the wood.

   C The total mass of substances in this process decreases.

   D The wood gives off thermal energy and light.

Use the diagram below to answer question 4.

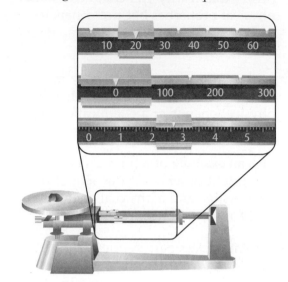

4 What is the mass of the object on the balance scale?

   A 22 g

   B 22.5 g

   C 22.7 g

   D 30 g

5 Which is true when an ice cube melts?

   A Volume and mass increase.

   B Volume and mass do not change.

   C Volume decreases, but mass does not change.

   D Volume increases, but mass decreases.

6 What is the BEST way to separate and save the parts of a sand-and-water mixture?

   A Boil the mixture and collect the steam.

   B Pour the mixture through a filter that only the water can pass through.

   C Lift the sand out of the mix with a spoon.

   D Pour a strong acid into the mixture to dissolve the sand.

Use the table below to answer questions 7 and 8.

Action	Time	Result
Heated	30 minutes	solid
Heated	60 minutes	liquid
Not heated	30 minutes	solid
Not heated	60 minutes	solid

7 Based on the results of this experiment, what can you conclude about heating this unknown substance?

  A Heating melted it in 30 minutes.

  B Heating melted it in 60 minutes.

  C Heating made it solid in 60 minutes.

  D Heating caused no changes.

8 What can you conclude about the original state of the substance?

  A It is part solid and part liquid.

  B It is a liquid.

  C It is a solid.

  D It is part liquid and part gas.

9 Which is a sign of a physical change?

  A Bread gets moldy with age.

  B Ice forms on a puddle in winter.

  C The metal on a car starts to rust.

  D Yeast causes bread dough to rise.

Constructed Response

Use the table below to answer questions 10–13.

Properties	Substance 1	Substance 2	Substance 3
Color	yellow	yellow	yellow
State	solid	solid	solid
Mass	217 g	217 g	75 g
Melting point	505°C	230°C	505°C
Density	3.78 g/cm^3	2.76 g/cm^3	3.78 g/cm^3
Flammable	yes	yes	yes

10 Identify each property of the unknown substances as either chemical or physical. Explain your reasoning.

11 Of the three unknown substances tested, two are the same substance and one is different. Which two substances do you think are the same? Explain your reasoning.

12 Which properties in the table helped you determine your answer in number 11? Which properties were not helpful? Explain your reasoning.

13 What additional physical and chemical properties of substances might the table have included?

NEED EXTRA HELP?												
If You Missed Question...	1	2	3	4	5	6	7	8	9	10	11	12	13
Go to Lesson...	1	2	2	1	1,2	1	2	2	2	1	1	1	1

Energy and Energy Transformations

THE BIG IDEA What is energy, and what are energy transformations?

Inquiry Which objects have energy?

If your answer is everything in the photo, you are right. All objects contain energy. Some objects contain more energy than other objects. The Sun contains so much energy that it is considered an energy resource.

- From where do you think the energy that powers the cars comes?

- Do you think the energy in the Sun and the energy in the green plants are related?

- What do the terms *energy* and *energy transformations* mean to you?

Get Ready to Read

What do you think?

Before you read, decide if you agree or disagree with each of these statements. As you read this chapter, see if you change your mind about any of the statements.

1 A fast-moving baseball has more kinetic energy than a slow-moving baseball.

2 A large truck and a small car moving at the same speed have the same kinetic energy.

3 A book sitting on a shelf has no energy.

4 Energy can change from one form to another.

5 Energy is destroyed when you apply the brakes on a moving bicycle or a moving car.

6 The Sun releases radiant energy.

 Your one-stop online resource

connectED.mcgraw-hill.com

 Video    WebQuest

 Audio    Assessment

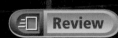 Review    Concepts in Motion

 Inquiry   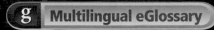 Multilingual eGlossary

Forms of Energy

Reading Guide

Key Concepts
ESSENTIAL QUESTIONS

- What is energy?
- What are potential and kinetic energy?
- How is energy related to work?
- What are different forms of energy?

Vocabulary

energy p. 41

kinetic energy p. 42

potential energy p. 42

work p. 44

mechanical energy p. 45

sound energy p. 45

thermal energy p. 45

electric energy p. 45

radiant energy p. 45

nuclear energy p. 45

 Multilingual eGlossary

Video BrainPOP®

 Academic Standards for Science

Covers: 6.1.4, 6.1.5, 6.1.6, 6.1.7, 6.NS.3, 6.NS.4, 6.NS.5, 6.NS.7

Inquiry **Why is this cat glowing?**

A camera that detects temperature made this image. Dark colors represent cooler temperatures, and light colors represent warmer temperatures. Temperatures are cooler where the cat's body emits less radiant energy and warmer where the cat's body emits more radiant energy.

Can you change matter? 🖐️ 🧪

You observe many things changing. Birds change their positions when they fly. Bubbles form in boiling water. The filament in a lightbulb glows when you turn on a light. How can you cause a change in matter?

1 Read and complete the lab safety form.

2 Half-fill a **foam cup** with **sand.** Place the bulb of a **thermometer** about halfway into the sand. *Do not stir.* Record the temperature in your Science Journal.

3 Remove the thermometer and place a **lid** on the cup. Hold down the lid and shake the cup vigorously for 10 min.

4 Remove the lid. Measure and record the temperature of the sand.

Think About This

1. What change did you observe in the sand?

2. How could you change your results?

3. 🔑 **Key Concept** What do you think caused the change you observed in the sand?

What is energy?

It might be exciting to watch a fireworks display, such as the one shown in **Figure 1.** Over and over, you hear the crack of explosions and see bursts of colors in the night sky. Fireworks release energy when they explode. **Energy** *is the ability to cause change.* The energy in the fireworks causes the changes you see as bursting flashes of light and hear as loud booms.

Energy also causes other changes. The plant in **Figure 1** uses the energy from the Sun and makes food that it uses for growth and other processes. Energy can cause changes in the motions and positions of objects, such as the nail in **Figure 1.** Can you think of other ways energy might cause changes?

🔑 **Key Concept Check** What is energy?

WORD ORIGIN · · · · · · · · · ·

energy
from Greek *energeia*, means "activity"

  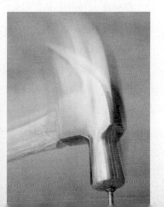

Figure 1 The explosion of fireworks, the growth of a plant, and the motion of a hammer all involve energy.

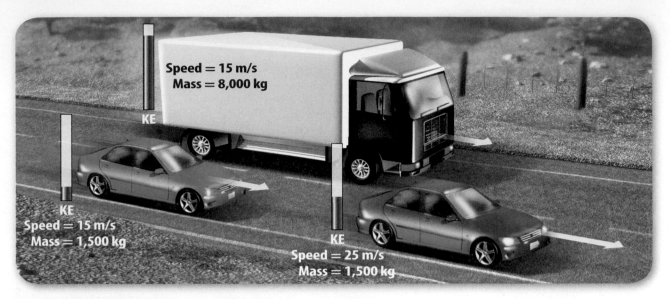

Speed = 15 m/s
Mass = 8,000 kg

KE

KE
Speed = 15 m/s
Mass = 1,500 kg

KE
Speed = 25 m/s
Mass = 1,500 kg

Figure 2 The kinetic energy (KE) of an object depends on its speed and its mass. The vertical bars show the kinetic energy of each vehicle.

Kinetic Energy—Energy of Motion

Have you ever been to a bowling alley? When you rolled the ball and it hit the pins, a change occurred—the pins fell over. This change occurred because the ball had a form of energy called kinetic (kuh NEH tik) energy. **Kinetic energy** *is energy due to motion.* All moving objects have kinetic energy.

Kinetic Energy and Speed

An object's kinetic energy depends on its speed. The faster an object moves, the more kinetic energy it has. For example, the blue car has more kinetic energy than the green car in **Figure 2** because the blue car is moving faster.

Kinetic Energy and Mass

A moving object's kinetic energy also depends on its mass. If two objects move at the same speed, the object with more mass has more kinetic energy. For example, the truck and the green car in **Figure 2** are moving at the same speed, but the truck has more kinetic energy because it has more mass.

✔ **Key Concept Check** What is kinetic energy?

Potential Energy—Stored Energy

Energy can be present even if objects are not moving. If you hold a ball in your hand and then let it go, the gravitational interaction between the ball and Earth causes a change to occur. Before you dropped the ball, it had a form of energy called potential (puh TEN chul) energy. **Potential energy** *is stored energy due to the interactions between objects or particles.* Gravitational potential energy, elastic potential energy, and chemical potential energy are all forms of potential energy.

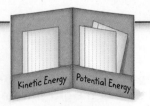

Gravitational Potential Energy

Even when you are just holding a book, gravitational potential energy is stored between the book and Earth. The girl shown in **Figure 3** increases the gravitational potential energy between her backpack and Earth by lifting the backpack higher from the ground.

The gravitational potential energy stored between an object and Earth depends on the object's weight and height. Dropping a bowling ball from a height of 1 m causes a greater change than dropping a tennis ball from 1 m. Similarly, dropping a bowling ball from 3 m causes a greater change than dropping the same bowling ball from only 1 m.

 Reading Check What factors determine the gravitational potential energy stored between an object and Earth?

Elastic Potential Energy

When you stretch a rubber band, as in **Figure 3,** another form of potential energy, called elastic (ih LAS tik) potential energy, is being stored in the rubber band. Elastic potential energy is energy stored in objects that are compressed or stretched, such as springs and rubber bands. When you release the end of a stretched rubber band, the stored elastic potential energy is transformed into kinetic energy. This transformation is obvious when it flies across the room.

Chemical Potential Energy

Food, gasoline, and other substances are made of atoms joined together by chemical bonds. Chemical potential energy is energy stored in the chemical bonds between atoms, as shown in **Figure 3.** Chemical potential energy is released when chemical reactions occur. Your body uses the chemical potential energy in foods for all its activities. People also use the chemical potential energy in gasoline to power cars and buses.

 Key Concept Check In what way are all forms of potential energy the same?

Figure 3 There are different forms of potential energy.

Gravitational Potential Energy
Gravitational potential energy increases when the girl lifts her backpack.

Elastic Potential Energy
The rubber band's elastic potential energy increases when it is stretched.

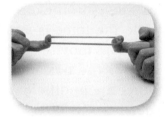

Chemical Potential Energy
Foods and other substances, including glucose, have chemical potential energy stored in the bonds between atoms.

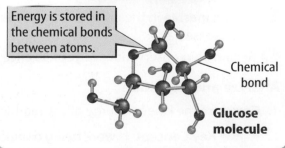
Energy is stored in the chemical bonds between atoms.

Chemical bond

Glucose molecule

Figure 4 The girl does work on the box as she lifts it and increases its gravitational potential energy. The colored bars show the work that the girl does (W) and the box's potential energy (PE).

Energy and Work

You can transfer energy by doing work. **Work** *is the transfer of energy that occurs when a force makes an object move in the direction of the force while the force is acting on the object.* For example, as the girl lifts the box onto the shelf in **Figure 4,** she transfers energy from herself to the box. She does work only while the box moves in the direction of the force and while the force is applied to the box. If the box stops moving, the force is no longer applied, or the box movement and the applied force are in different directions, work is not done on the box.

 Key Concept Check How is energy related to work?

An object that has energy also can do work. For example, when a bowling ball collides with a bowling pin, the bowling ball does work on the pin. Some of the ball's kinetic energy is transferred to the bowling pin. Because of this connection between energy and work, energy is sometimes described as the ability to do work.

Other Forms of Energy

Some other forms of energy are shown in **Table 1.** All energy can be measured in joules (J). A softball dropped from a height of about 0.5 m has about 1 J of kinetic energy just before it hits the floor.

---

inquiry MiniLab

20 minutes

Can a moving object do work?
Is work done when a moving object hits another object?

1. Read and complete a lab safety form.

2. **Tape** one end of a **30-cm grooved ruler** to the edge of a stack of **books** about 8 cm high. Put the lower end of the ruler in a **paper cup** lying on its side.

3. Place a **marble** in the groove at the top end of the ruler and release it.

4. Record your observations in your Science Journal.

Analyze and Conclude

1. **Compare** the kinetic energy of the marble just before and after it hit the cup.

2. **Key Concept** Is work being done on the cup? Explain your answer.

Table 1 Forms of Energy 🔑

Mechanical Energy

The sum of potential energy and kinetic energy in a system of objects is **mechanical energy.** For example, the mechanical energy of a basketball increases when a player shoots the basketball. Both the kinetic energy and gravitational potential energy of the ball increases in the player-ball-ground system.

Sound Energy

When you pluck a guitar string, the string vibrates and produces sound. *The energy that sound carries is* **sound energy.** Vibrating objects emit sound energy. However, sound energy cannot travel through a vacuum, such as the space between Earth and the Sun.

Thermal Energy

All objects and materials are made of particles that have energy. **Thermal energy** *is the sum of kinetic energy and potential energy of the particles that make up an object.* Mechanical energy is due to large-scale motions and interactions in a system and thermal energy is due to atomic-scale motions and interactions of particles. Thermal energy moves from warmer objects, such as burning logs, to cooler objects, such as air.

Electric Energy

An electrical fan uses another form of energy—electric energy. When you turn on a fan, there is an electric current through the fan's motor. **Electric energy** *is the energy an electric current carries.* Electrical appliances, such as fans and dishwashers, change electric energy into other forms of energy.

Radiant Energy—Light Energy

The Sun gives off energy that travels to Earth as electromagnetic waves. Unlike sound waves, electromagnetic waves can travel through a vacuum. Light waves, microwaves, and radio waves are all electromagnetic waves. *The energy that electromagnetic waves carry is* **radiant energy.** Radiant energy sometimes is called light energy.

Nuclear Energy

At the center of every atom is a nucleus. **Nuclear energy** *is energy that is stored and released in the nucleus of an atom.* In the Sun, nuclear energy is released when nuclei join together. In a nuclear power plant, nuclear energy is released when the nuclei of uranium atoms are split apart.

 Key Concept Check Describe three forms of energy.

Lesson 1 Review

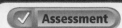

Visual Summary

Energy is the ability to cause change.

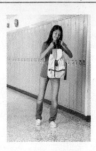

The gravitational potential energy between an object and Earth increases when you lift the object.

You do work on an object when you apply a force to that object over a distance.

FOLDABLES

Use your lesson Foldable to review the lesson. Save your Foldable for the project at the end of the chapter.

What do you think NOW?

You first read the statements below at the beginning of the chapter.

1. A fast-moving baseball has more kinetic energy than a slow-moving baseball.

2. A large truck and a small car moving at the same speed have the same kinetic energy.

3. A book sitting on a shelf has no energy.

Did you change your mind about whether you agree or disagree with the statements? Rewrite any false statements to make them true.

Use Vocabulary

1 **Distinguish** between kinetic energy and potential energy.

2 **Write** a definition of work.

Understand Key Concepts

3 Which type of energy increases when you compress a spring?
   A. elastic potential energy
   B. kinetic energy
   C. radiant energy
   D. sound energy

4 **Infer** How could you increase the gravitational potential energy between yourself and Earth?

5 **Infer** how a bicycle's kinetic energy changes when that bicycle slows down.

6 **Compare and contrast** radiant energy and sound energy.

Interpret Graphics

7 **Identify** Copy and fill in the graphic organizer below to identify three types of potential energy.

Potential Energy

8 **Describe** where chemical potential energy is stored in the molecule shown below.

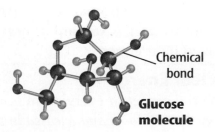

Chemical bond

Glucose molecule

Critical Thinking

9 **Analyze** Will pushing on a car always change the car's mechanical energy? What must happen for the car's kinetic energy to increase?

Can you identify potential and kinetic energy?

Materials

string

paper clip

three large washers

meterstick

tape

small box

ruler

Safety

Have you ever watched the pendulum move in a grandfather clock? The pendulum has energy because it causes change as it moves back and forth. What kind of energy does a moving pendulum have? Can it do work on an object? In this lab, you will analyze the movement and energy of a pendulum.

Learn It

Before you can draw valid conclusions from any scientific experiment, you must **analyze the results** of that experiment. This means you must look for patterns in the results.

Try It

1. Read and complete a lab safety form.

2. Use the photo below as a guide to make a pendulum. Hang one washer on a paper clip. Place a box so it will block the swinging pendulum. Mark the position of the box with tape.

3. Pull the pendulum back until the bottom of the washer is 15 cm from the floor. Release the pendulum. Measure and record the distance the box moves in your Science Journal. Repeat two more times.

4. Repeat step 3 using pendulum heights of 30 cm and 45 cm.

5. Repeat steps 3 and 4 with two washers, then with three washers.

Apply It

6. Does the pendulum have potential energy? Explain.

7. Does it have kinetic energy? How do you know?

8. How does the gravitational potential energy depend on the pendulum's weight and height?

9. How does the distance the box travels depend on the initial gravitational potential energy?

10. Does the pendulum do work on the box? Explain your answer.

11. 🔑 **Key Concept** Determine when the pendulum had maximum potential energy and maximum kinetic energy. Explain your reasoning.

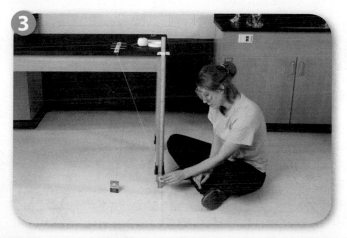

Lesson 2

Energy Transformations

Reading Guide

Key Concepts 🔑
ESSENTIAL QUESTIONS

- What is the law of conservation of energy?
- How does friction affect energy transformations?
- How are different types of energy used?

Vocabulary
law of conservation of energy p. 50

friction p. 51

g Multilingual eGlossary

Academic Standards for Science

6.1.4 Recognize that objects in motion have kinetic energy and objects at rest have potential energy.

6.1.5 Describe with examples that potential energy exists in several different forms (gravitational potential energy, elastic potential energy, and chemical potential energy, among others).

Also covers: 6.1.6, 6.1.7, 6.4.1, 6.4.2, 6.4.3, 6.NS.3, 6.NS.5, 6.NS.6, 6.NS.7

Inquiry | What's that sound?

Blocks of ice breaking off the front of this glacier can be bigger than a car. Imagine the loud rumble they make as they crash into the sea. But after the ice falls into the sea, it will melt gradually. All of these processes involve energy transformations—energy changing from one form to another.

Is energy lost when it changes form?

Energy can have different forms. What happens when energy changes from one form to another?

1. Read and complete a lab safety form.

2. Three students should sit in a circle. One student has 30 **buttons,** one has 30 **pennies,** and one has 30 **paper clips.**

3. Each student should exchange 10 items with the student to the right and 10 items with the student to the left.

4. Repeat step 3.

Think About This

1. If the buttons, the pennies, and the paper clips represent different forms of energy, what represents changes from one form of energy to another?

2. 🔑 **Key Concept** If each button, penny, and paper clip represents one unit of energy, does the total amount of energy increase, decrease, or stay the same? Explain your answer.

Changes Between Forms of Energy

It is the weekend and you are ready to make some popcorn in the microwave and watch a movie. Energy changes form when you make popcorn and watch TV. As shown in **Figure 5,** a microwave changes electric energy into **radiant** energy. Radiant energy changes into thermal energy in the popcorn kernels.

The changes from electric energy to radiant energy to thermal energy are called energy transformations. As you watch the movie, energy transformations also occur in the television. A television transforms electric energy into sound energy and radiant energy.

SCIENCE USE v. COMMON USE

radiant

Science Use energy transmitted by electromagnetic waves

Common Use bright and shining; glowing

Figure 5 Energy changes from one form to another when you use a microwave oven to make popcorn.

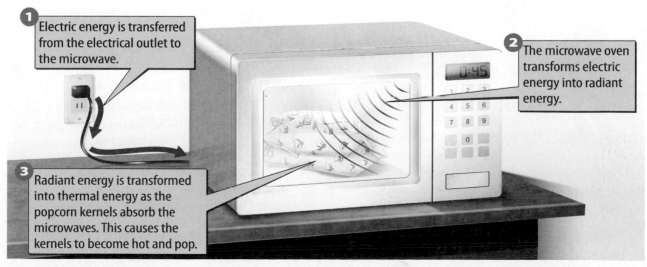

1 Electric energy is transferred from the electrical outlet to the microwave.

2 The microwave oven transforms electric energy into radiant energy.

3 Radiant energy is transformed into thermal energy as the popcorn kernels absorb the microwaves. This causes the kernels to become hot and pop.

Concepts in Motion   Animation

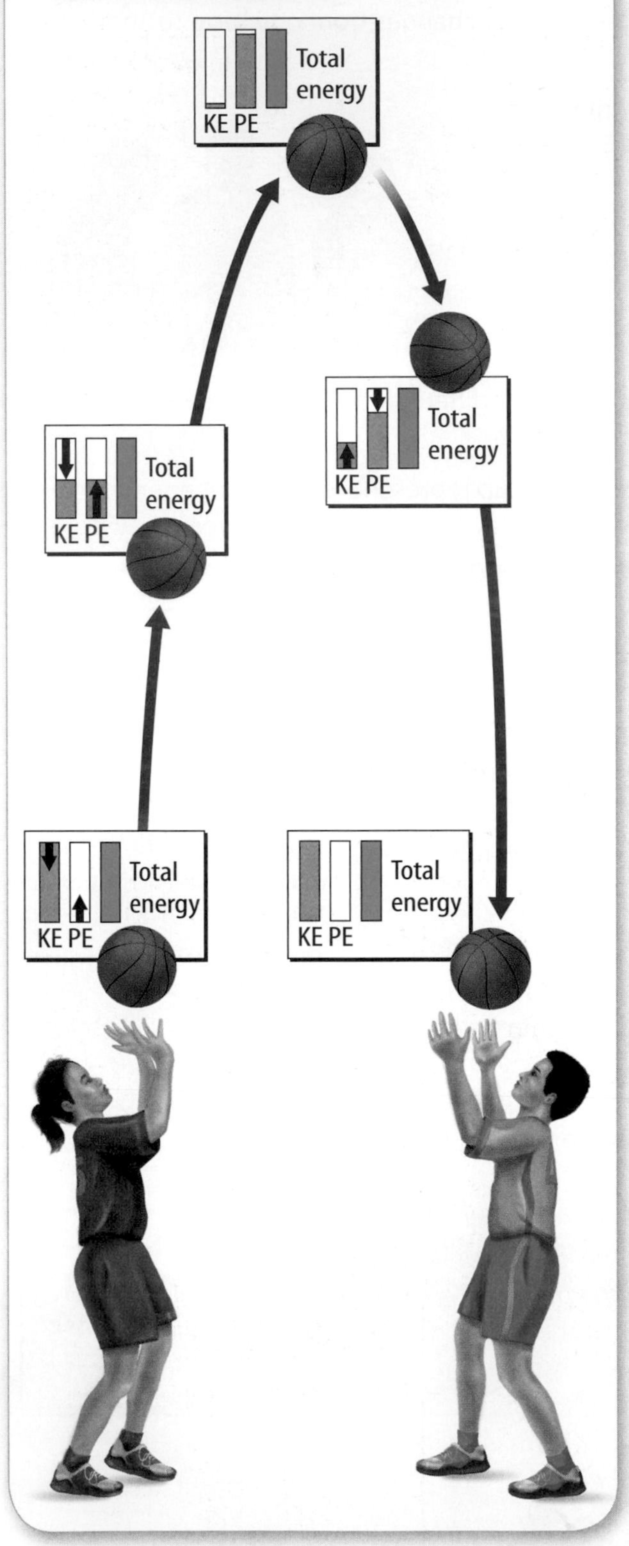

Total energy
KE PE

Total energy
KE PE

Total energy
KE PE

Total energy
KE PE

Total energy
KE PE

Figure 6 The ball's kinetic energy (KE) and potential energy (PE) change as it moves.

✔ **Visual Check** When is the gravitational potential energy the greatest?

Changes Between Kinetic and Potential Energy

Energy transformations also occur when you toss a ball upward, as shown in **Figure 6.** The ball slows down as it moves upward and then speeds up as it moves downward. The ball's speed and height change as energy changes from one form to another.

Kinetic Energy to Potential Energy

The ball is moving fastest and has the most kinetic energy as it leaves your hand, as shown in **Figure 6.** As the ball moves upward, its speed and kinetic energy decrease. However, the potential energy is increasing because the ball's height is increasing. Kinetic energy is changing into potential energy. At the ball's highest point, the gravitational potential energy is at its greatest, and the ball's kinetic energy is at its lowest.

Potential Energy to Kinetic Energy

As the ball moves downward, its potential energy decreases. At the same time, the ball's speed increases. Therefore, the ball's kinetic energy increases. Potential energy is transformed into kinetic energy. When the ball reaches the other player's hand, its kinetic energy is at the maximum value again.

✔ **Reading Check** Why does the potential energy decrease as the ball falls?

The Law of Conservation of Energy

The total energy in the universe is the sum of all the different forms of energy everywhere. *According to the* **law of conservation of energy,** *energy can be transformed from one form into another or transferred from one region to another, but energy cannot be created or destroyed.* The total amount of energy in the universe does not change.

Key Concept Check What is the law of conservation of energy?

Friction and the Law of Conservation of Energy

Sometimes it may seem as if the law of conservation of energy is not accurate. Imagine riding a bicycle, as in **Figure 7.** The moving bicycle has mechanical energy. What happens to this mechanical energy when you apply the brakes and the bicycle stops?

When you apply the brakes, the bicycle's mechanical energy is not destroyed. Instead the bicycle's mechanical energy is transformed into thermal energy, as shown in **Figure 7.** The total amount of energy never changes. The additional thermal energy causes the brakes, the wheels, and the air around the bicycle to become slightly warmer.

Friction between the bicycle's brake pads and the moving wheels transforms mechanical energy into thermal energy. **Friction** *is a force that resists the sliding of two surfaces that are touching.*

 Key Concept Check How does friction affect energy transformations?

There is always some friction between any two surfaces that are rubbing against each other. As a result, some mechanical energy always is transformed into thermal energy when two surfaces rub against each other.

It is easier to pedal a bicycle if there is less friction between the bicycle's parts. With less friction, less of the bicycle's mechanical energy is transformed into thermal energy. One way to reduce friction is to apply a lubricant, such as oil, grease, or graphite, to surfaces that rub against each other.

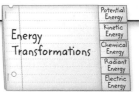
WORD ORIGIN

friction
from Latin *fricare*, means "to rub"

Friction and Thermal Energy

Review **Personal Tutor**

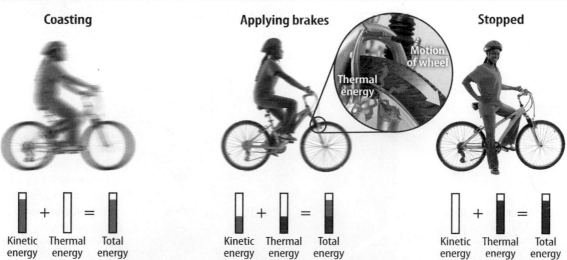

Figure 7 When the girl applies the brakes, friction between the bicycle's brake pads and its wheels transforms mechanical energy into thermal energy. As mechanical energy changes into thermal energy, the bicycle slows down. The total amount of energy does not change.

Using Energy

Every day you use different forms of energy to do different things. You might use the radiant energy from a lamp to light a room, or you might use the chemical energy stored in your body to run a race. When you use energy, you usually change it from one form into another. For example, the lamp changes electric energy into radiant energy and thermal energy.

Using Thermal Energy
All forms of energy can be transformed into thermal energy. People often use thermal energy to cook food or provide warmth. A gas stove transforms the chemical energy stored in natural gas into the thermal energy that cooks food. An electric space heater transforms the electric energy from a power plant into the thermal energy that warms a room. In a jet engine, burning fuel releases thermal energy that the engine transforms into mechanical energy.

Using Chemical Energy
During photosynthesis, a plant transforms the Sun's radiant energy into chemical energy that it stores in chemical compounds. Some of these compounds become food for other living things. Your body transforms the chemical energy from your food into the kinetic energy necessary for movement. Your body also transforms chemical energy into the thermal energy necessary to keep you warm.

Using Radiant Energy
The cell phone in **Figure 8** sends and receives radiant energy using microwaves. When you are listening to someone on a cell phone, that cell phone is transforming radiant energy into electric energy and then into sound energy. When you are speaking into a cell phone, it is transforming sound energy into electric energy and then into radiant energy.

Figure 8 A cell phone changes sound energy into radiant energy when you speak.

Sound waves carry energy into the cell phone.

The cell phone converts the energy carried by sound waves into radiant energy that is carried away by microwaves.

Using Electric Energy

Many of the devices you might use every day, such as handheld video games, MP3 players, and hair dryers, use electric energy. Some devices, such as hair dryers, use electric energy from electric power plants. Other appliances, such as handheld video games, transform the chemical energy stored in batteries into electric energy.

 Key Concept Check How are different types of energy used?

Waste Energy

When energy changes form, some thermal energy is always released. For example, a lightbulb converts some electric energy into radiant energy. However, the lightbulb also transforms some electric energy into thermal energy. This is what makes the lightbulb hot. Some of this thermal energy moves into the air and cannot be used.

Scientists often refer to thermal energy that cannot be used as waste energy. Whenever energy is used, some energy is transformed into useful energy and some is transformed into waste energy. For example, we use the chemical energy in gasoline to make cars, such as those in **Figure 9,** move. However, most of that chemical energy ends up as waste energy—thermal energy that moves into the air.

 Reading Check What is waste energy?

How does energy change form?

When an object falls, energy changes form. How can you compare energies for falling objects?

1. Read and complete a lab safety form.
2. Place a piece of **clay** about 10 cm wide and 3 cm thick on a **small paper plate.**
3. Drop a **marble** onto the clay from a height of about 20 cm, and measure the depth of the depression caused by the marble. Record the measurement in your Science Journal.
4. Repeat step 3 with a heavier marble.

Analyze and Conclude

1. **Infer** Which marble had more kinetic energy just before it hit the clay? Explain your answer.
2. **Key Concept** For which marble was the potential energy greater just before the marble fell? Explain your answer using the law of conservation of energy.

Figure 9 Cars transform most of the chemical energy in gasoline into waste energy.

Lesson 2 Review

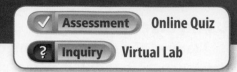
Visual Summary

Energy can change form, but according to the law of conservation of energy, energy can never be created or destroyed.

Friction transforms mechanical energy into thermal energy.

Different forms of energy, such as sound and radiant energy, are used when someone talks on a cell phone.

FOLDABLES

Use your lesson Foldable to review the lesson. Save your Foldable for the project at the end of the chapter.

What do you think NOW?

You first read the statements below at the beginning of the chapter.

4. Energy can change from one form to another.

5. Energy is destroyed when you apply the brakes on a moving bicycle or a moving car.

6. The Sun releases radiant energy.

Did you change your mind about whether you agree or disagree with the statements? Rewrite any false statements to make them true.

Use Vocabulary

1 **Use the term** *friction* in a complete sentence.

Understand Key Concepts

2 **Explain** the law of conservation of energy in your own words.

3 **Describe** the energy transformations that occur when a piece of wood burns.

4 **Identify** the energy transformation that takes place when you apply the brakes on a bicycle.

5 Which energy transformation occurs in a toaster?
- **A.** chemical to electric
- **B.** electric to thermal
- **C.** kinetic to chemical
- **D.** thermal to potential

Interpret Graphics

6 **Organize Information** Copy and fill in the graphic organizer below to show how kinetic and potential energy change when a ball is thrown straight up and then falls down.

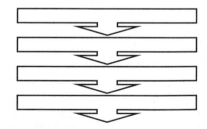

Critical Thinking

7 **Judge** An advertisement states that a machine with moving parts will continue moving forever without having to add any energy. Can this be correct? Explain.

Math Skills

— Review —

Math Practice

8 **Calculate** If you use a 1,000-W microwave for 0.15 h, how much electric energy do you use?

Fossil Fuels and Rising CO_2

Investigate the link between energy use and carbon dioxide in the atmosphere.

You use energy every day—when you ride in a car or on a bus, turn on a television or a radio, and even when you send an e-mail.

Much of the energy that produces electricity, heats and cools buildings, and powers engines, comes from burning fossil fuels—coal, oil, and natural gas. When fossil fuels burn, the carbon in them combines with oxygen in the atmosphere and forms carbon dioxide gas (CO_2). Carbon dioxide is a greenhouse gas. Greenhouse gases absorb energy. This causes the atmosphere and Earth's surface to become warmer. Greenhouse gases make Earth warm enough to support life. Without greenhouse gases, Earth's surface would be frozen.

However, over the past 150 years, the amount of CO_2 in the atmosphere has increased faster than at any time in the past 800,000 years. Most of this increase is the result of burning fossil fuels. More carbon dioxide in the atmosphere might cause average global temperatures to increase. As temperatures increase, weather patterns worldwide could change. More storms and heavier rainfall could occur in some areas, while other regions could become drier. Increased temperatures could also cause more of the polar ice sheets to melt and raise sea levels. Higher sea levels would cause more flooding in coastal areas.

Developing other energy sources such as geothermal, solar, nuclear, wind, and hydroelectric power would reduce the use of fossil fuels and slow the increase in atmospheric CO_2.

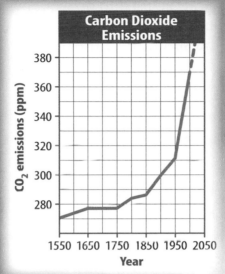

Carbon Dioxide Emissions

(graph: CO_2 emissions (ppm) vs. Year, y-axis from 280 to 380, x-axis from 1550 to 2050)

It's Your Turn

MAKE A LIST How can CO_2 emissions be reduced? Work with a partner. List five ways people in your home, school, or community could reduce their energy consumption. Combine your list with your classmates' lists to make a master list.

300 Years OF CARBON DIOXIDE

1712
A new invention, the steam engine, is powered by burning coal that heats water to produce steam.

Early 1800s
Coal-fired steam engines, able to pull heavy trains and power steamboats, transform transportation.

1882
Companies make and sell electricity from coal for everyday use. Electricity is used to power the first lightbulbs, which give off 20 times the light of a candle.

1908
The first mass-produced automobiles are made available. By 1915, Ford is selling 500,000 cars a year. Oil becomes the fuel of choice for car engines.

Late 1900s
Electrical appliances transform the way we live, work, and communicate. Most electricity is generated by coal-burning power plants.

2007
There are more than 800 million cars and light trucks on the world's roads.

Pinwheel Power

Materials

round pencil with unused eraser

metal washers

cardboard container

sand or small rocks

three-speed hair dryer

stopwatch

Also needed:
manila folder, metric ruler, scissors, hole punch, thread, pushpin

Safety

Moving air, or wind, is an energy source. In some places, wind turbines transform the kinetic energy of wind into electric energy. This electric energy can be used to do work by making an object move. In this lab, you will construct a pinwheel turbine and observe how changes in wind speed affect the rate at which your wind turbine does work.

Ask a Question

How does wind speed affect the rate at which a wind turbine does work?

Make Observations

1 Read and complete a lab safety form.

2 Construct a pinwheel from a manila folder using the diagram below.

3 Use a plastic pushpin to carefully attach the pinwheel to the eraser of a pencil.

4 Use a hole punch to make holes on opposite sides of the top of a container. Use your ruler to make sure the holes are exactly opposite each other. Weigh down the container with sand or small rocks.

5 Put the pencil through the holes, and make sure the pinwheel spins freely. Blow against the blades of the pinwheel with varying amounts of force to observe how the pinwheel moves. Record your observations in your Science Journal.

6 Measure and cut 100 cm of thread. Tie two washers to one end of the thread. Tape the other end of the thread to the pencil.

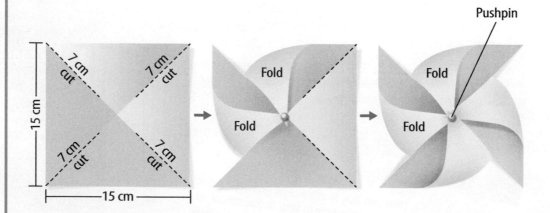

Form a Hypothesis

7 Use your observations from step 5 to form a hypothesis about how wind speed will affect the rate at which the wind turbine does work.

Test Your Hypothesis

8 Work with two other students to test your hypothesis. One person will use the hair dryer to model a slow wind speed. Another person will stop the pencil's movement after 5 seconds on the stopwatch. The third person will measure the length of thread remaining between the pencil and the top of the washers. Then someone will unwind the thread and the group will repeat this procedure four more times with the dryer on low. Record all data in your Science Journal.

9 Repeat step 8 with the dryer on medium.

10 Repeat step 8 with the dryer on high.

Analyze and Conclude

11 **Interpret Data** Did your hypothesis agree with your data and observations? Explain.

12 **Sequence** Describe how energy was transformed from one form into another in this lab.

13 **Draw Conclusions** What factors might have affected the rate at which your pinwheel turbine did work?

14 **The Big Idea** Explain how wind is used as an energy resource.

Communicate Your Results

Use your data and observations to write a paragraph explaining how wind speed affects the rate at which a wind turbine can do work.

 **Extension**

Research the designs of real wind generators. Create a model of a real wind generator. Write a short explanation of its advantages and disadvantages compared to other real wind generators.

Lab Tips

☑ You measure the rate at which the wind turbine does work by measuring how fast the turbine lifts the metal washers.

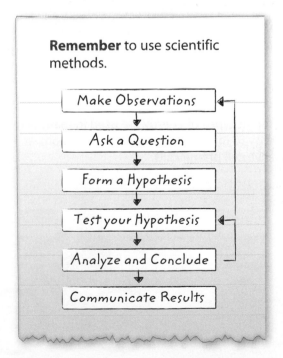

Remember to use scientific methods.

Make Observations
↓
Ask a Question
↓
Form a Hypothesis
↓
Test your Hypothesis
↓
Analyze and Conclude
↓
Communicate Results

Chapter 2 Study Guide

Energy is the ability to cause change. Energy transformations occur when one form of energy changes into another form of energy.

Key Concepts Summary 🔑	Vocabulary
Lesson 1: Forms of Energy • **Energy** is the ability to cause change. • **Kinetic energy** is the energy an object has because of its motion. **Potential energy** is stored energy. • **Work** is the transfer of energy that occurs when a force makes an object move in the direction of the force while the force is acting on the object. • Different forms of energy include **thermal energy** and **radiant energy.** 	**energy** p. 41 **kinetic energy** p. 42 **potential energy** p. 42 **work** p. 44 **mechanical energy** p. 45 **sound energy** p. 45 **thermal energy** p. 45 **electric energy** p. 45 **radiant energy** p. 45 **nuclear energy** p. 45
Lesson 2: Energy Transformations • According to the **law of conservation of energy,** energy can be transformed from one form into another or transferred from one region to another, but energy cannot be created or destroyed. • **Friction** transforms mechanical energy into thermal energy. • Different types of energy are used in many ways including providing energy to move your body, to light a room, and to make and to receive cell phone calls. 	**law of conservation of energy** p. 50 **friction** p. 51

FOLDABLES® Chapter Project

Assemble your Lesson Foldables as shown to make a Chapter Project. Use the project to review what you have learned in this chapter.

Use Vocabulary

Each of the following sentences is false. Make the sentence true by replacing the italicized word with a vocabulary term.

1 *Thermal energy* is the form of energy carried by an electric current.

2 The *chemical potential energy* of an object depends on its mass and its speed.

3 *Friction* is the transfer of energy that occurs when a force is applied over a distance.

4 A lubricant, such as oil, grease, or graphite, reduces *radiant energy* between rubbing objects.

5 *Radiant energy* is energy that is stored in the nucleus of an atom.

Link Vocabulary and Key Concepts

Concepts in Motion **Interactive Concept Map**

Copy this concept map, and then use vocabulary terms from the previous page to complete the concept map.

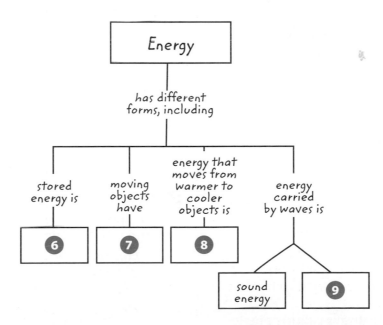

Chapter 2 Review

Understand Key Concepts

1 What factors determine an object's kinetic energy?

A. its height and its mass
B. its mass and its speed
C. its size and its weight
D. its speed and its height

2 The gravitational potential energy stored between an object and Earth depends on

A. the object's height and weight.
B. the object's mass and speed.
C. the object's size and weight.
D. the object's speed and height.

3 When a ball is thrown upward, where does it have the least kinetic energy?

A. at its highest point
B. at its lowest point when it is moving downward
C. at its lowest point when it is moving upward
D. midway between its highest point and its lowest point

4 Which type of energy is released when the string in the photo below is plucked?

A. electric energy
B. nuclear energy
C. radiant energy
D. sound energy

5 According to the law of conservation of energy, which is always true?

A. Energy can never be created or destroyed.
B. Energy is always converted to friction in moving objects.
C. The universe is always gaining energy in many different forms.
D. Work is done when a force is exerted on an object.

6 Which energy transformation is occurring in the food below?

A. chemical energy to mechanical energy
B. electric energy to radiant energy
C. nuclear energy to thermal energy
D. radiant energy to thermal energy

7 In which situation would the gravitational potential energy between you and Earth be greatest?

A. You are running down a hill.
B. You are running up a hill.
C. You stand at the bottom of a hill.
D. You stand at the top of a hill.

8 When you speak into a cell phone which energy conversion occurs?

A. chemical energy to radiant energy
B. mechanical energy to chemical energy
C. sound energy to radiant energy
D. thermal energy to sound energy

9 Which type of energy is released when a firecracker explodes?

A. chemical potential energy
B. elastic potential energy
C. electric energy
D. nuclear energy

10 Inside the engine of a gasoline-powered car, chemical energy is converted primarily to which kind of energy?

A. electric
B. potential
C. sound
D. waste

Critical Thinking

11 **Determine** if work is done on the nail shown below if a person pulls the handle to the left, and the handle moves. Explain.

12 **Contrast** the energy transformations that occur in a electrical toaster oven and in an electrical fan.

13 **Infer** A red box and a blue box are on the same shelf. There is more gravitational potential energy between the red box and Earth than between the blue box and Earth. Which box weighs more? Explain your answer.

14 **Infer** Juanita moves a round box and a square box from a lower shelf to a higher shelf. The gravitational potential energy for the round box increases by 50 J. The gravitational potential energy for the square box increases by 100 J. On which box did Juanita do more work? Explain your reasoning.

15 **Explain** why a skateboard coasting on a flat surface slows down and comes to a stop.

16 **Describe** how energy is conserved when a basketball is thrown straight up into the air and falls back into your hands.

17 **Decide** Harold stretches a rubber band and lets it go. The rubber band flies across the room. Harold says this demonstrates the transformation of kinetic energy to elastic potential energy. Is Harold correct? Explain.

Writing in Science

18 **Write** a short essay explaining the energy transformations that occur in an incandescent lightbulb.

REVIEW **THE BIG IDEA**

19 Write an explanation of energy and energy transformations for a fourth grader who has never heard of these terms.

20 Identify five energy transformations occurring in the photo below.

Math Skills ×÷

 Review

— Math Practice —

Solve One-Step Equations

21 An electrical water heater is rated at 5,500 W and operates for 106 h per month. How much electric energy in kWh does the water heater use each month?

22 A family uses 1,303 kWh of electric energy in a month. If the power company charges $0.08 cents per kilowatt hour, what is the total electric energy bill for the month?

Standardized Test Practice

Record your answers on the answer sheet provided by your teacher or on a sheet of paper.

Multiple Choice

1 Which is true when a player throws a basketball toward a hoop?

   A Kinetic energy is constant.

   B Potential energy is constant.

   C Work is done on the player.

   D Work is done on the ball.

Use the diagram below to answer questions 2 and 3.

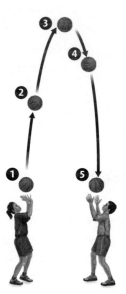

2 At which points is the kinetic energy of the basketball greatest?

   A 1 and 5

   B 2 and 3

   C 2 and 4

   D 3 and 4

3 At which point is the gravitational potential energy at its maximum?

   A 1

   B 2

   C 3

   D 4

Use the table below to answer question 4.

Vehicle	Mass	Speed
Car 1	1,200 kg	20 m/s
Car 2	1,500 kg	20 m/s
Truck 1	4,800 kg	20 m/s
Truck 2	6,000 kg	20 m/s

4 Which vehicle has the most kinetic energy?

   A car 1

   B car 2

   C truck 1

   D truck 2

5 When you compress a spring, which type of energy increases?

   A kinetic

   B nuclear

   C potential

   D radiant

6 Sound energy cannot travel through

   A a vacuum.

   B a wooden table.

   C polluted air.

   D pond water.

7 A bicyclist uses brakes to slow from 3 m/s to a stop. What stops the bike?

   A friction

   B gravity

   C kinetic energy

   D thermal energy

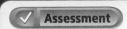

Use the diagram below to answer question 8.

8 The work being done in the diagram above transfers energy to

   A the box.

   B the floor.

   C the girl.

   D the shelf.

9 Which is true of energy?

   A It cannot be created or destroyed.

   B It cannot change form.

   C Most forms cannot be conserved.

   D Most forms cannot be traced to a source.

10 Which energy transformation occurs when you light a gas burner?

   A chemical to thermal

   B electric to chemical

   C nuclear to chemical

   D radiant to thermal

Constructed Response

Use the table below to answer questions 11 and 12.

Form of Energy	Definition

11 Copy the table above, and list six forms of energy. Briefly define each form.

12 Provide real-life examples of each of the listed forms of energy.

Use the diagram below to answer question 13.

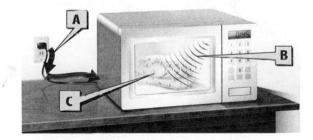

13 Describe the energy transformations that occur at locations A, B, and C.

NEED EXTRA HELP?													
If You Missed Question...	1	2	3	4	5	6	7	8	9	10	11	12	13
Go to Lesson...	1	2	2	1	1	1	2	1	2	2	1	2	2

Unit 2

UNDERSTANDING THE UNIVERSE

"IF YOU LOOK TO YOUR RIGHT, YOU'LL SEE OUR CLOSEST NEIGHBOR, THE ANDROMEDA GALAXY..."

"ONLY 2.5 MILLION LIGHT-YEARS AWAY."

"NEXT, WE HAVE A DYING STAR THAT HAS EXPANDED INTO A RED GIANT."

2000 B.C.   1600   1700   1800

1600 B.C.
Babylonian texts show records of people observing Venus without the aid of technology. Its appearance is recorded for 21 years.

265 B.C.
Greek astronomer Timocharis makes the first recorded observation of Mercury.

1610
Galileo Galilei observes the four largest moons of Jupiter through his telescope.

1613
Galileo records observations of the planet Neptune but mistakes it for a star.

1655
Astronomer Christiaan Huygens observes Saturn and discovers its rings, which were previously thought to be large moons on each side.

1781
William Herschel discovers the planet Uranus.

1900

1930
Clyde Tombaugh discovers Pluto, making him the first American to discover a planet.

1971
Mariner 9 visits Mars and becomes the first human-made object to orbit a planet other than Earth.

2000

2006
After research and consideration, the International Astronomical Union votes to remove Pluto from the list of planets in the solar system.

? Inquiry
Visit ConnectED for this unit's **STEM** activity.

Systems

You have probably heard about a computer's operating system, a weather system, and the system of government in the United States. What exactly is a system? A **system** is a collection of parts that influence or interact with one another. Systems often are used to achieve a goal or are developed with a specific purpose in mind. Like most systems, a milk-bottling manufacturing system is described in terms of the system's input, processing, output, and feedback, as shown in **Figure 1.**

Some systems, such as ecosystems and solar systems, are natural systems. Political, educational, and health-care systems are social systems that involve interactions among people. Transportation, communication, and manufacturing systems are designed systems that provide services or products.

Subsystems and Their Interactions

Large systems often are made of groups of smaller subsystems. Subsystems within a large system interact. **Figure 2** shows specialized transportation subsystems that are a part of an overall transportation system. These subsystems interact with one another, moving people and goods from place to place.

Input—things, such as milk, lids, labels, energy, and information, that enter a system to achieve a goal

Processing—the changes that the system makes to the inputs, such as fastening lids to milk jugs

Output—material, information, or energy that leaves the system, such as sealed and labeled milk jugs

Feedback—information a system uses to regulate the input, process, and output.

▲ **Figure 1** Many systems are designed to achieve a goal.

Figure 2 The subsystems within a transportation system interact with one another. ▼

Waterways transport ships and boats on rivers, lakes, and oceans.

Roadways conveniently transport cars, buses, and trucks on highways, streets, and roads.

Airways quickly transport people and materials long distances.

Pipelines transport large amounts of fluids, such as oil, through a network of pipes.

Railways transport trains and subways on rail lines between stations, at relatively low cost.

Bike paths and sidewalks transport people and packages over short distances at low cost.

The Earth and the Moon are a subsystem of our solar system.

Our solar system is a subsystem of the Milky Way galaxy.

▲ **Figure 3** Natural systems, such as the Milky Way galaxy, consist of subsystems.

Natural Systems

Like a designed system, natural systems have interacting subsystems. As shown in **Figure 3,** Earth and the Moon are a subsystem of our solar system. Our solar system is a subsystem of the Milky Way galaxy. The interactions among these subsystems depend on the gravitational forces that affect the motions of planets, stars, moons, and other objects in space.

Most natural systems constantly change. For example, gravity between Earth and the Moon causes tides. The movements of water against seafloors is altered by friction. This friction affects the tilt of Earth on its axis, if only just a little. The tilt of the Earth is important because it causes the seasons and influences weather patterns. As shown in **Figure 4,** the northern hemisphere is warmer during summer because of the tilt of Earth.

Thinking in Terms of Systems

If you think of the world as one system made up of interacting subsystems, you will better understand the effects of your choices. For example, when people choose to disrupt an ecosystem in one part of the world by clearing huge areas of forests, the resulting climate change affects the weather system in another part of the world. This in turn affects the agricultural system and, therefore, the cost of food. Actions you take locally affect everyone globally.

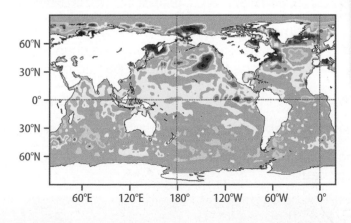

Figure 4 The darker reds show that the temperatures are warmer in the northern hemisphere in summer. ▶

The Sun-Earth-Moon System

THE BIG IDEA

What natural phenomena do the motions of Earth and the Moon produce?

Inquiry Sun Bites?

Look at this time-lapse photograph. The "bites" out of the Sun occurred during a solar eclipse. The Sun's appearance changed in a regular, predictable way as the Moon's shadow passed over a part of Earth.

• How does the Moon's movement change the Sun's appearance?

• What predictable changes does Earth's movement cause?

• What other natural phenomena do the motions of Earth and the Moon cause?

Get Ready to Read

What do you think?

Before you read, decide if you agree or disagree with each of these statements. As you read this chapter, see if you change your mind about any of the statements.

1 Earth's movement around the Sun causes sunrises and sunsets.

2 Earth has seasons because its distance from the Sun changes throughout the year.

3 The Moon was once a planet that orbited the Sun between Earth and Mars.

4 Earth's shadow causes the changing appearance of the Moon.

5 A solar eclipse happens when Earth moves between the Moon and the Sun.

6 The gravitational pull of the Moon and the Sun on Earth's oceans causes tides.

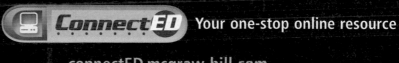 Your one-stop online resource

connectED.mcgraw-hill.com

 Video

 Audio

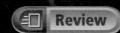 Review

 Inquiry

 WebQuest

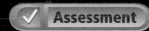 Assessment

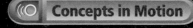 Concepts in Motion

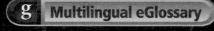 Multilingual eGlossary

Earth's Motion

Reading Guide

Key Concepts
ESSENTIAL QUESTIONS

- How does Earth move?
- Why is Earth warmer at the equator and colder at the poles?
- Why do the seasons change as Earth moves around the Sun?

Vocabulary

orbit p. 72

revolution p. 72

rotation p. 73

rotation axis p. 73

solstice p. 77

equinox p. 77

g Multilingual eGlossary

Academic Standards for Science

6.2.1 Describe and model how the position, size and relative motions of the earth, moon, and sun cause day and night, solar and lunar eclipses and phases of the moon.

6.2.2 Recognize that gravity is a force that keeps celestial bodies in regular and predictable motion, holds objects to earth's surface, and is responsible for ocean tides.

Also covers: 6.2.3, 6.2.5, 6.NS.7, 6.NS.8, 6.NS.9, 6.NS.11

Inquiry Floating in Space?

From the International Space Station, Earth might look like it is just floating, but it is actually traveling around the Sun at more than 100,000 km/h. What phenomena does Earth's motion cause?

Does Earth's shape affect temperatures on Earth's surface?

Temperatures near Earth's poles are colder than temperatures near the equator. What causes these temperature differences?

1. Read and complete a lab safety form.
2. Inflate a **spherical balloon** and tie the balloon closed.
3. Using a **marker,** draw a line around the balloon to represent Earth's equator.
4. Using a **ruler**, place a lit **flashlight** about 8 cm from the balloon so the flashlight beam strikes the equator straight on.
5. Using the marker, trace around the light projected onto the balloon.
6. Have someone raise the flashlight vertically 5–8 cm without changing the direction that the flashlight is pointing. Do not change the position of the balloon. Trace around the light projected onto the balloon again.

Think About This

1. Compare and contrast the shapes you drew on the balloon.

2. At which location on the balloon is the light more spread out? Explain your answer.

3. 🔑 **Key Concept** Use your model to explain why Earth is warmer near the equator and colder near the poles.

Earth and the Sun

If you look outside at the ground, trees, and buildings, it does not seem like Earth is moving. Yet Earth is always in motion, spinning in space and traveling around the Sun. As Earth spins, day changes to night and back to day again. The seasons change as Earth travels around the Sun. Summer changes to winter because Earth's motion changes how energy from the Sun spreads out over Earth's surface.

The Sun

The nearest star to Earth is the Sun, which is shown in **Figure 1**. The Sun is approximately 150 million km from Earth. Compared to Earth, the Sun is enormous. The Sun's diameter is more than 100 times greater than Earth's diameter. The Sun's mass is more than 300,000 times greater than Earth's mass.

Deep inside the Sun, nuclei of atoms combine, releasing huge amounts of energy. This process is called nuclear fusion. The Sun releases so much energy from nuclear fusion that the temperature at its core is more than 15,000,000°C. Even at the Sun's surface, the temperature is about 5,500°C. A small part of the Sun's energy reaches Earth as light and thermal energy.

Figure 1 The Sun is a giant ball of hot gases that emits light and energy.

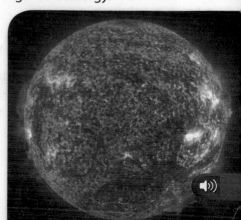

What keeps Earth in orbit?

Why does Earth move around the Sun and not fly off into space?

1. Read and complete a lab safety form.
2. Tie a piece of **strong thread** securely to a **plastic, slotted golf ball.**
3. Swing the ball in a horizontal circle above your head.

Analyze and Conclude

1. **Predict** what would happen if you let go of the thread.

2. 🗝 **Key Concept** Which part of the experiment represents the force of gravity between Earth and the Sun?

Earth's Orbit

As shown in **Figure 2,** Earth moves around the Sun in a nearly circular path. *The path an object follows as it moves around another object is an* **orbit.** *The motion of one object around another object is called* **revolution.** Earth makes one complete revolution around the Sun every 365.24 days.

The Sun's Gravitational Pull

Why does Earth orbit the Sun? The answer is that the Sun's gravity pulls on Earth. The pull of gravity between two objects depends on the masses of the objects and the distance between them. The more mass either object has, or the closer together they are, the stronger the gravitational pull.

The Sun's effect on Earth's motion is illustrated in **Figure 2.** Earth's motion around the Sun is like the motion of an object twirled on a string. The string pulls on the object and makes it move in a circle. If the string breaks, the object flies off in a straight line. In the same way, the pull of the Sun's gravity keeps Earth revolving around the Sun in a nearly circular orbit. If the gravity between Earth and the Sun were to somehow stop, Earth would fly off into space in a straight line.

🗝 **Key Concept Check** What produces Earth's revolution around the Sun?

Figure 2 🗝 Earth moves in a nearly circular orbit. The pull of the Sun's gravity on Earth causes Earth to revolve around the Sun.

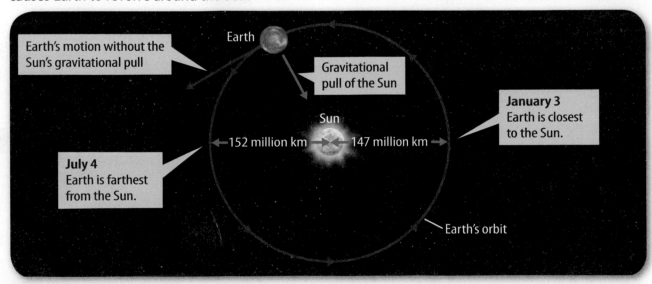

Earth's motion without the Sun's gravitational pull

Earth

Gravitational pull of the Sun

January 3 Earth is closest to the Sun.

Sun

← 152 million km → ← 147 million km →

July 4 Earth is farthest from the Sun.

Earth's orbit

September

Earth's orbit

N S

Sun

N S June

December

Rotation axis

Earth

N S

N S March

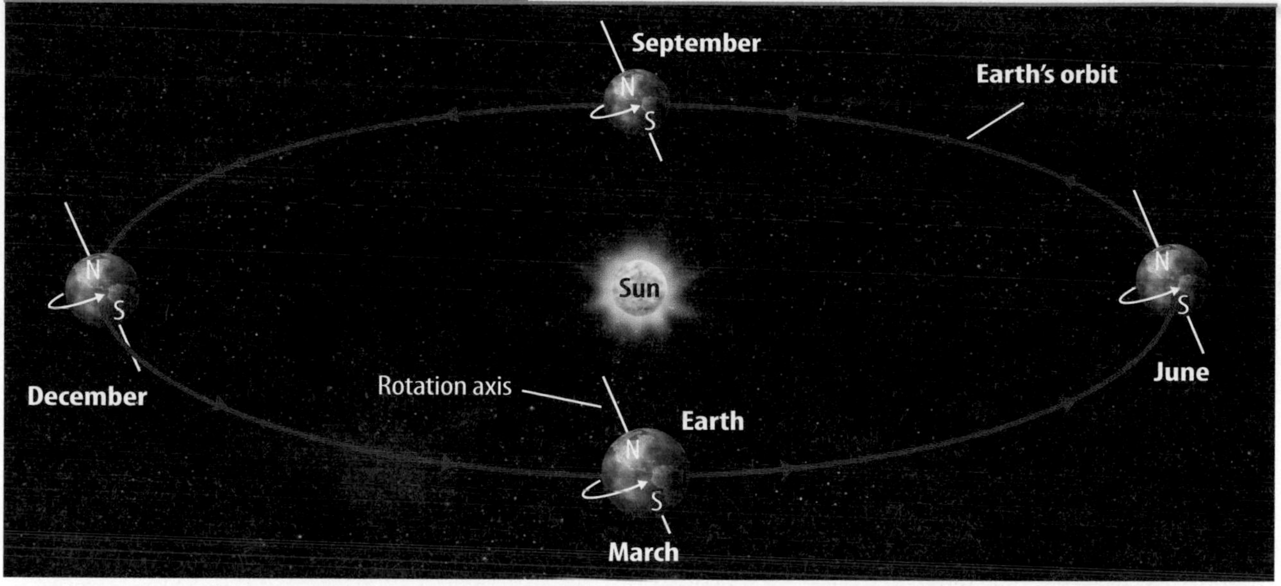

Figure 3 This diagram shows Earth's orbit, which is nearly circular, from an angle. Earth spins on its rotation axis as it revolves around the Sun. Earth's rotation axis always points in the same direction.

 Visual Check Between which months is the north end of Earth's rotation axis away from the Sun?

Earth's Rotation

As Earth revolves around the Sun, it spins. *A spinning motion is called* **rotation.** Some spinning objects rotate on a rod or axle. Earth rotates on an imaginary line through its center. *The line on which an object rotates is the* **rotation axis.**

Suppose you could look down on Earth's North Pole and watch Earth rotate. You would see that Earth rotates on its rotation axis in a counterclockwise direction, from west to east. One complete rotation of Earth takes about 24 hours. This rotation helps produce Earth's cycle of day and night. It is daytime on the half of Earth facing toward the Sun and nighttime on the half of Earth facing away from the Sun.

The Sun's Apparent Motion Each day the Sun appears to move from east to west across the sky. It seems as if the Sun is moving around Earth. However, it is Earth's rotation that causes the Sun's apparent motion.

Earth rotates from west to east. As a result, the Sun appears to move from east to west across the sky. The stars and the Moon also seem to move from east to west across the sky due to Earth's west to east rotation.

To better understand this, imagine riding on a merry-go-round. As you and the ride move, people on the ground appear to be moving in the opposite direction. In the same way, as Earth rotates from west to east, the Sun appears to move from east to west.

✓ **Reading Check** What causes the Sun's apparent motion across the sky?

The Tilt of Earth's Rotation Axis As shown in **Figure 3,** Earth's rotation axis is tilted. The tilt of Earth's rotation axis is always in the same direction by the same amount. This means that during half of Earth's orbit, the north end of the rotation axis is toward the Sun. During the other half of Earth's orbit, the north end of the rotation axis is away from the Sun.

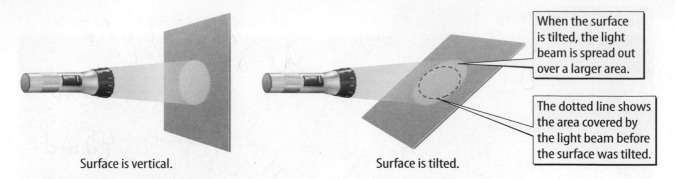

Surface is vertical.

Surface is tilted.

When the surface is tilted, the light beam is spread out over a larger area.

The dotted line shows the area covered by the light beam before the surface was tilted.

Figure 4 The light energy on a surface becomes more spread out as the surface becomes more tilted relative to the light beam.

✔️ **Visual Check** Is the light energy more spread out on the vertical or tilted surface?

Temperature and Latitude

As Earth orbits the Sun, only one half of Earth faces the Sun at a time. A beam of sunlight carries energy. The more sunlight that reaches a part of Earth's surface, the warmer that part becomes. Because Earth's surface is curved, different parts of Earth's surface receive different amounts of the Sun's energy.

Energy Received by a Tilted Surface

Suppose you shine a beam of light on a flat card, as shown in **Figure 4.** As you tilt the card relative to the direction of the light beam, light becomes more spread out on the card's surface. As a result, the energy that the light beam carries also spreads out more over the card's surface. An area on the surface within the light beam receives less energy when the surface is more tilted relative to the light beam.

The Tilt of Earth's Curved Surface

Instead of being flat like a card, Earth's surface is curved. Relative to the direction of a beam of sunlight, Earth's surface becomes more tilted as you move away from the **equator.** As shown in **Figure 5,** the energy in a beam of sunlight tends to become more spread out the farther you travel from the equator. This means that regions near the poles receive less energy than regions near the equator. This makes Earth colder at the poles and warmer at the equator.

 Key Concept Check Why is Earth warmer at the equator and colder at the poles?

ACADEMIC VOCABULARY

equator
(noun) the imaginary line that divides Earth into its northern and southern hemispheres

Figure 5 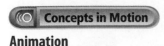 Energy from the Sun becomes more spread out as you move away from the equator.

((◎)) Concepts in Motion

Animation

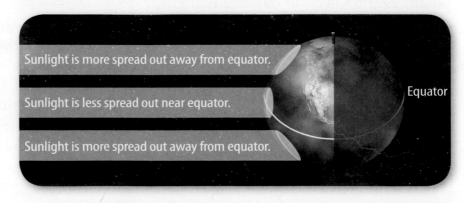

Sunlight is more spread out away from equator.

Sunlight is less spread out near equator.

Sunlight is more spread out away from equator.

Equator

North end of rotation axis is away from the Sun. **North end of rotation axis is toward the Sun.**

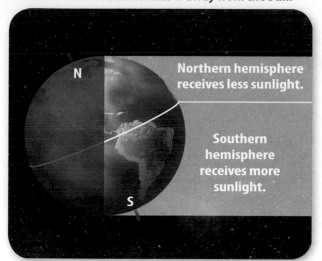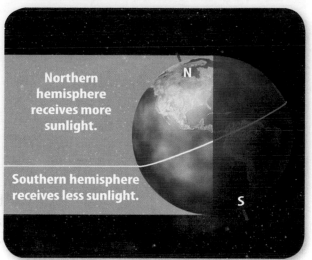

Figure 6 The northern hemisphere receives more sunlight in June, and the southern hemisphere receives more sunlight in December.

Seasons

You might think that summer happens when Earth is closest to the Sun, and winter happens when Earth is farthest from the Sun. However, seasonal changes do not depend on Earth's distance from the Sun. In fact, Earth is closest to the Sun in January! Instead, it is the tilt of Earth's rotation axis, combined with Earth's motion around the Sun, that causes the seasons to change.

Spring and Summer in the Northern Hemisphere

During one half of Earth's orbit, the north end of the rotation axis is toward the Sun. Then, the northern hemisphere receives more energy from the Sun than the southern hemisphere, as shown in **Figure 6.** Temperatures increase in the northern hemisphere and decrease in the southern hemisphere. Daylight hours last longer in the northern hemisphere, and nights last longer in the southern hemisphere. This is when spring and summer happen in the northern hemisphere, and fall and winter happen in the southern hemisphere.

Fall and Winter in the Northern Hemisphere

During the other half of Earth's orbit, the north end of the rotation axis is away from the Sun. Then, the northern hemisphere receives less solar energy than the southern hemisphere, as shown in **Figure 6.** Temperatures decrease in the northern hemisphere and increase in the southern hemisphere. This is when fall and winter happen in the northern hemisphere, and spring and summer happen in the southern hemisphere.

 Key Concept Check How does the tilt of Earth's rotation axis affect Earth's weather?

Math Skills

Convert Units

When Earth is 147,000,000 km from the Sun, how far is Earth from the Sun in miles? To calculate the distance in miles, multiply the distance in km by the conversion factor

$$147{,}000{,}000 \text{ km} \times \frac{0.62 \text{ miles}}{1 \text{ km}}$$
$$= 91{,}100{,}000 \text{ miles}$$

Practice

When Earth is 152,000,000 km from the Sun, how far is Earth from the Sun in miles?

 Review

- **Math Practice**
- **Personal Tutor**

Review **Personal Tutor**

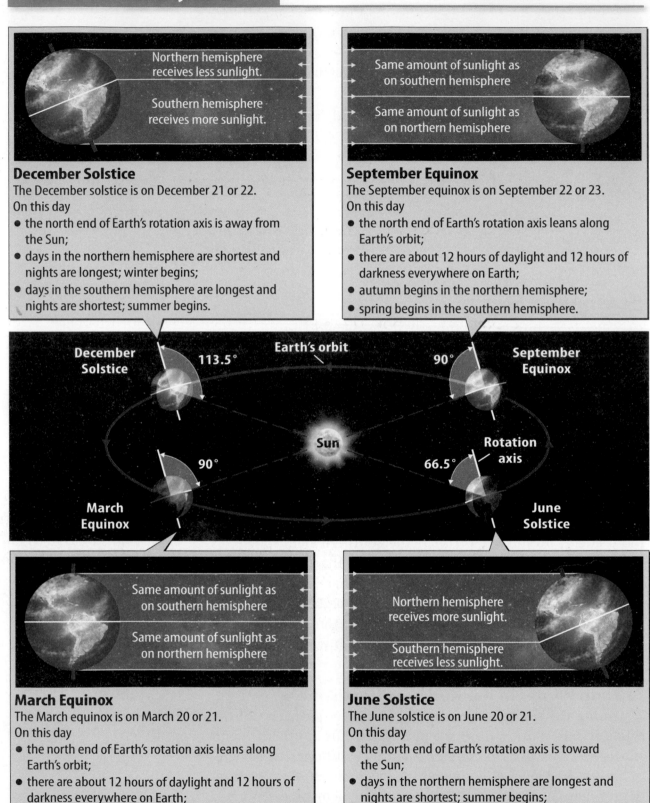

December Solstice

The December solstice is on December 21 or 22.
On this day

- the north end of Earth's rotation axis is away from the Sun;
- days in the northern hemisphere are shortest and nights are longest; winter begins;
- days in the southern hemisphere are longest and nights are shortest; summer begins.

September Equinox

The September equinox is on September 22 or 23.
On this day

- the north end of Earth's rotation axis leans along Earth's orbit;
- there are about 12 hours of daylight and 12 hours of darkness everywhere on Earth;
- autumn begins in the northern hemisphere;
- spring begins in the southern hemisphere.

March Equinox

The March equinox is on March 20 or 21.
On this day

- the north end of Earth's rotation axis leans along Earth's orbit;
- there are about 12 hours of daylight and 12 hours of darkness everywhere on Earth;
- spring begins in the northern hemisphere;
- autumn begins in the southern hemisphere.

June Solstice

The June solstice is on June 20 or 21.
On this day

- the north end of Earth's rotation axis is toward the Sun;
- days in the northern hemisphere are longest and nights are shortest; summer begins;
- days in the southern hemisphere are shortest and nights are longest; winter begins.

Figure 7 The seasons change as Earth moves around the Sun. Earth's motion around the Sun causes Earth's tilted rotation axis to be leaning toward the Sun and away from the Sun.

Solstices, Equinoxes, and the Seasonal Cycle

Figure 7 shows that as Earth travels around the Sun, its rotation axis always points in the same direction in space. However, the amount that Earth's rotation axis is toward or away from the Sun changes. This causes the seasons to change in a yearly cycle.

There are four days each year when the direction of Earth's rotation axis is special relative to the Sun. *A **solstice** is a day when Earth's rotation axis is the most toward or away from the Sun. An **equinox** is a day when Earth's rotation axis is leaning along Earth's orbit, neither toward nor away from the Sun.*

March Equinox to June Solstice When the north end of the rotation axis gradually points more and more toward the Sun, the northern hemisphere gradually receives more solar energy. This is spring in the northern hemisphere.

June Solstice to September Equinox The north end of the rotation axis continues to point toward the Sun but does so less and less. The northern hemisphere starts to receive less solar energy. This is summer in the northern hemisphere.

September Equinox to December Solstice The north end of the rotation axis now points more and more away from the Sun. The northern hemisphere receives less and less solar energy. This is fall in the northern hemisphere.

December Solstice to March Equinox The north end of the rotation axis continues to point away from the Sun but does so less and less. The northern hemisphere starts to receive more solar energy. This is winter in the northern hemisphere.

Changes in the Sun's Apparent Path Across the Sky

Figure 8 shows how the Sun's apparent path through the sky changes from season to season in the northern hemisphere. The Sun's apparent path through the sky in the northern hemisphere is lowest on the December solstice and highest on the June solstice.

Figure 8 As the seasons change, the path of the Sun across the sky changes. In the northern hemisphere, the Sun's path is lowest on the December solstice and highest on the June solstice.

✓ **Visual Check** When is the Sun highest in the sky in the northern hemisphere?

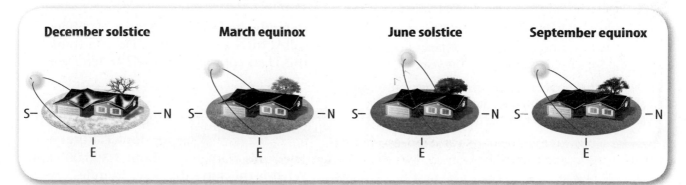

December solstice   March equinox   June solstice   September equinox

S— —N   S— —N   S— —N   S— —N

E   E   E   E

Lesson 1 Review

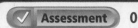

Visual Summary

The gravitational pull of the Sun causes Earth to revolve around the Sun in a near-circular orbit.

Earth's rotation axis is tilted and always points in the same direction in space.

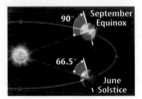

Equinoxes and solstices are days when the direction of Earth's rotation axis relative to the Sun is special.

FOLDABLES

Use your lesson Foldable to review the lesson. Save your Foldable for the project at the end of the chapter.

What do you think NOW?

You first read the statements below at the beginning of the chapter.

1. Earth's movement around the Sun causes sunrises and sunsets.

2. Earth has seasons because its distance from the Sun changes throughout the year.

Did you change your mind about whether you agree or disagree with the statements? Rewrite any false statements to make them true.

Use Vocabulary

1 **Distinguish** between Earth's rotation and Earth's revolution.

2 The path Earth follows around the Sun is Earth's _____.

3 When a(n) _____ occurs, the northern hemisphere and the southern hemisphere receive the same amount of sunlight.

Understand Key Concepts

4 What is caused by the tilt of Earth's rotational axis?
   A. Earth's orbit   C. Earth's revolution
   B. Earth's seasons   D. Earth's rotation

5 **Contrast** the amount of sunlight received by an area near the equator and a same-sized area near the South Pole.

6 **Contrast** the Sun's gravitational pull on Earth when Earth is closest to the Sun and when Earth is farthest from the Sun.

Interpret Graphics

7 **Summarize** Copy and fill in the table below for the seasons in the northern hemisphere.

Season	Starts on Solstice or Equinox?	How Rotation Axis Leans
Summer		
Fall		
Winter		
Spring		

Critical Thinking

8 **Defend** The December solstice is often called the winter solstice. Do you think this is an appropriate label? Defend your answer.

Math Skills
— Math Practice —

9 The Sun's diameter is about 1,390,000 km. What is the Sun's diameter in miles?

Materials

large foam ball

wooden skewer

foam cup

masking tape

flashlight

marker

Safety

How does Earth's tilted rotation axis affect the seasons?

The seasons change as Earth revolves around the Sun. How does Earth's tilted rotation axis change how sunlight spreads out over different parts of Earth's surface?

Learn It

Using a flashlight as the Sun and a foam ball as Earth, you can model how solar energy spreads out over Earth's surface at different times during the year. This will help you **draw conclusions** about Earth's seasons.

Try It

1. Read and complete a lab safety form.

2. Insert a wooden skewer through the center of a foam ball. Draw a line on the ball to represent Earth's equator. Insert one end of the skewer into an upside-down foam cup so the skewer tilts.

3. Prop a flashlight on a stack of books about 0.5 m from the ball. Turn on the flashlight and position the ball so the skewer points toward the flashlight, representing the June solstice.

4. In your Science Journal, draw how the ball's surface is tilted relative to the light beam.

5. Under your diagram, state whether the upper (northern) or lower (southern) hemisphere receives more light energy.

6. With the skewer always pointing in the same direction, move the ball around the flashlight. Turn the flashlight to keep the light on the ball. At the three positions corresponding to the equinoxes and other solstice, make drawings like those in step 4 and statements like those in step 5.

Apply It

7. How did the tilt of the surfaces change relative to the light beam as the ball circled the flashlight?

8. How did the amount of light energy on each hemisphere change as the ball moved around the flashlight?

9. 🔑 **Key Concept** Draw conclusions about how Earth's tilt affects the seasons.

Earth's Moon

Reading Guide

Key Concepts
ESSENTIAL QUESTIONS

- How does the Moon move around Earth?

- Why does the Moon's appearance change?

Vocabulary
maria p. 82

phase p. 84

waxing phase p. 84

waning phase p. 84

g Multilingual eGlossary

Academic Standards for Science

6.2.1 Describe and model how the position, size and relative motions of the earth, moon, and sun cause day and night, solar and lunar eclipses and phases of the moon.

Also covers: 6.NS.4, 6.NS.6, 6.NS.7, 6.NS.10

Inquiry Two Planets?

The smaller body is Earth's Moon, not a planet. Just as Earth moves around the Sun, the Moon moves around Earth. The Moon's motion around Earth causes what kinds of changes to occur?

Why does the Moon appear to change shape?

The Sun is always shining on Earth and the Moon. However, the Moon's shape seems to change from night to night and day to day. What could cause the Moon's appearance to change?

1 Read and complete a lab safety form.

2 Place a **ball** on a level surface.

3 Position a **flashlight** so that the light beam shines fully on one side of the ball. Stand behind the flashlight.

4 Make a drawing of the ball's appearance in your Science Journal.

5 Stand behind the ball, facing the flashlight, and repeat step 4.

6 Stand to the left of the ball and repeat step 4.

Think About This

1. What caused the ball's appearance to change?

2. ⚷ **Key Concept** What do you think produces the Moon's changing appearance in the sky?

Seeing the Moon

Imagine what people thousands of years ago thought when they looked up at the Moon. They might have wondered why the Moon shines and why it seems to change shape. They probably would have been surprised to learn that the Moon does not emit light at all. Unlike the Sun, the Moon is a solid object that does not emit its own light. You only see the Moon because light from the Sun reflects off the Moon and into your eyes. Some facts about the Moon, such as its mass, size, and distance from Earth, are shown in **Table 1**.

FOLDABLES

Use two sheets of paper to make a bound book. Use it to organize information about the lunar cycle. Each page of your book should represent one week of the lunar cycle.

First Week
First Quarter

Table 1 Moon Data				
Mass	Diameter	Average distance from Earth	Time for one rotation	Time for one revolution
1.2% of Earth's mass	27% of Earth's diameter	384,000 km	27.3 days	27.3 days

Figure 9 The Moon probably formed when a large object collided with Earth 4.5 billion years ago. Material ejected from the collision eventually clumped together and became the Moon.

Concepts in Motion Animation

An object the size of Mars crashes into the semi-molten Earth about 4.5 billion years ago.

The impact ejects vaporized rock into space. As the rock cools, it forms a ring of particles around Earth.

The particles gradually clump together and form the Moon.

WORD ORIGIN
maria
from Latin *mare*, means "sea"

The Moon's Formation

The most widely accepted idea for the Moon's formation is the giant impact hypothesis, shown in **Figure 9.** According to this hypothesis, shortly after Earth formed about 4.6 billion years ago, an object about the size of the planet Mars collided with Earth. The impact ejected vaporized rock that formed a ring around Earth. Eventually, the material in the ring cooled and clumped together and formed the Moon.

The Moon's Surface

The surface of the Moon was shaped early in its history. Examples of common features on the Moon's surface are shown in **Figure 10.**

Craters The Moon's craters were formed when objects from space crashed into the Moon. Light-colored streaks called rays extend outward from some craters.

Most of the impacts that formed the Moon's craters occurred more than 3.5 billion years ago, long before dinosaurs lived on Earth. Earth was also heavily bombarded by objects from space during this time. However, on Earth, wind, water, and plate tectonics erased the craters. The Moon has no atmosphere, water, or plate tectonics, so craters formed billions of years ago on the Moon have hardly changed.

Maria *The large, dark, flat areas on the Moon are called* **maria** (MAR ee uh). The maria formed after most impacts on the Moon's surface had stopped. Maria formed when lava flowed up through the Moon's crust and solidified. The lava covered many of the Moon's craters and other features. When this lava solidified, it was dark and flat.

 Reading Check How were maria produced?

Highlands The light-colored highlands are too high for the lava that formed the maria to reach. The highlands are older than the maria and are covered with craters.

The Moon's Surface Features

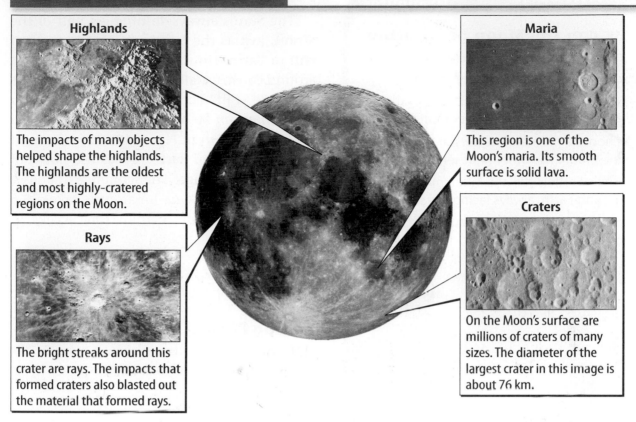

Highlands

The impacts of many objects helped shape the highlands. The highlands are the oldest and most highly-cratered regions on the Moon.

Rays

The bright streaks around this crater are rays. The impacts that formed craters also blasted out the material that formed rays.

Maria

This region is one of the Moon's maria. Its smooth surface is solid lava.

Craters

On the Moon's surface are millions of craters of many sizes. The diameter of the largest crater in this image is about 76 km.

▲ **Figure 10** The Moon's surface features include craters, rays, maria, and highlands.

The Moon's Motion

While Earth is revolving around the Sun, the Moon is revolving around Earth. The gravitational pull of Earth on the Moon causes the Moon to move in an orbit around Earth. The Moon makes one revolution around Earth every 27.3 days.

 Key Concept Check What produces the Moon's revolution around Earth?

The Moon also rotates as it revolves around Earth. One complete rotation of the Moon also takes 27.3 days. This means the Moon makes one rotation in the same amount of time that it makes one revolution around Earth. **Figure 11** shows that, because the Moon makes one rotation for each revolution of Earth, the same side of the Moon always faces Earth. This side of the Moon is called the near side. The side of the Moon that cannot be seen from Earth is called the far side of the Moon.

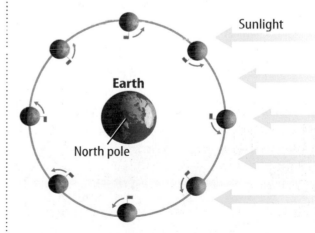

▲ **Figure 11** The Moon rotates once on its axis and revolves around Earth in the same amount of time. As a result, the same side of the Moon always faces Earth.

How can the Moon be rotating if the same side of the Moon is always facing Earth?

The Moon revolves around Earth. Does the Moon also rotate as it revolves around Earth?

1 Choose a partner. One person represents the Moon. The other represents Earth.

2 While Earth is still, the Moon moves slowly around Earth, always facing the same wall.

3 Next, the Moon moves around Earth always facing Earth.

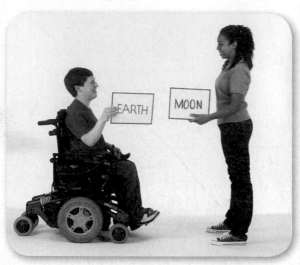

Analyze and Conclude

1. For which motion was the Moon rotating?

2. For each type of motion, how many times did the Moon rotate during one revolution around Earth?

3. 🔑 **Key Concept** How is the Moon actually rotating if the same side of the Moon is always facing Earth?

SCIENCE USE V. COMMON USE · · · · · · · · · · · · · · ·

phase
Science Use how the Moon or a planet is lit as seen from Earth

Common Use a part of something or a stage of development

Phases of the Moon

The Sun is always shining on half of the Moon, just as the Sun is always shining on half of Earth. However, as the Moon moves around Earth, usually only part of the Moon's near side is lit. *The lit part of the Moon or a planet that can be seen from Earth is called a* **phase.** As shown in **Figure 12,** the motion of the Moon around Earth causes the phase of the Moon to change. The sequence of phases is the lunar cycle. One lunar cycle takes 29.5 days or slightly more than four weeks to complete.

 Key Concept Check What produces the phases of the Moon?

Waxing Phases

During the **waxing phases,** *more of the Moon's near side is lit each night.*

Week 1—First Quarter As the lunar cycle begins, a sliver of light can be seen on the Moon's western edge. Gradually the lit part becomes larger. By the end of the first week, the Moon is at its first quarter phase. In this phase, the Moon's entire western half is lit.

Week 2—Full Moon During the second week, more and more of the near side becomes lit. When the Moon's near side is completely lit, it is at the full moon phase.

Waning Phases

During the **waning phases,** *less of the Moon's near side is lit each night.* As seen from Earth, the lit part is now on the Moon's eastern side.

Week 3—Third Quarter During this week, the lit part of the Moon becomes smaller until only the eastern half of the Moon is lit. This is the third quarter phase.

Week 4—New Moon During this week, less and less of the near side is lit. When the Moon's near side is completely dark, it is at the new moon phase.

Figure 12 As the Moon revolves around Earth, the part of the Moon's near side that is lit changes. The figure below shows how the Moon would look at different places in its orbit.

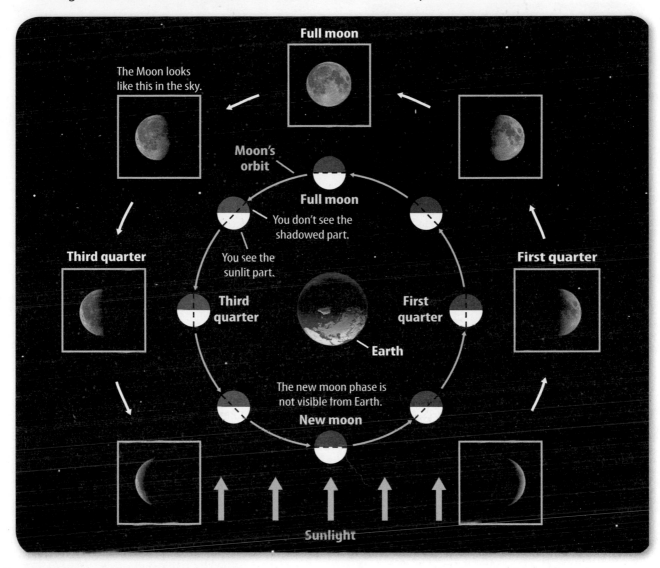

The Moon at Midnight

The Moon's motion around Earth causes the Moon to rise, on average, about 50 minutes later each day. The figure below shows how the Moon looks at midnight during three phases of the lunar cycle.

First quarter

East   West

Full moon

East   West

Third Quarter

East   West

At midnight, the first-quarter moon is setting. It rises during the day at about noon.

The full moon is highest in the sky at about midnight. It rises at sunset and sets at sunrise.

The third-quarter Moon rises at about midnight, about six hours later than the full moon rises.

Lesson 2 Review

Visual Summary

According to the giant impact hypothesis, a large object collided with Earth about 4.5 billion years ago to form the Moon.

Features like maria, craters, and highlands formed on the Moon's surface early in its history.

The Moon's phases change in a regular pattern during the Moon's lunar cycle.

FOLDABLES®

Use your lesson Foldable to review the lesson. Save your Foldable for the project at the end of the chapter.

What do you think NOW?

You first read the statements below at the beginning of the chapter.

3. The Moon was once a planet that orbited the Sun between Earth and Mars.

4. Earth's shadow causes the changing appearance of the Moon.

Did you change your mind about whether you agree or disagree with the statements? Rewrite any false statements to make them true.

Use Vocabulary

1 The lit part of the Moon as viewed from Earth is a(n) _____.

2 For the first half of the lunar cycle, the lit part of the Moon's near side is _____.

3 For the second half of the lunar cycle, the lit part of the Moon's near side is _____.

Understand Key Concepts

4 Which phase occurs when the Moon is between the Sun and Earth?
   A. first quarter   C. new moon
   B. full moon   D. third quarter

5 **Reason** Why does the Moon have phases?

Interpret Graphics

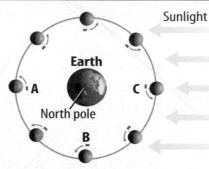

6 **Draw** how the Moon looks from Earth when it is at positions A, B, and C in the diagram above.

7 **Organize Information** Copy and fill in the table below with details about the lunar surface.

Crater	
Ray	
Maria	
Highland	

Critical Thinking

8 **Reflect** Imagine the Moon rotates twice in the same amount of time the Moon orbits Earth once. Would you be able to see the Moon's far side from Earth?

Return to the Moon

Astronauts prepare to live and work on the Moon and learn more about our solar system.

"That's one small step for a man; one giant leap for mankind," announced Neil Armstrong upon setting foot on the Moon in 1969. Forty years later, NASA is preparing to send humans back to the Moon.

The United States undertook a series of human spaceflight missions from 1961–1975 called the Apollo program. The goal of the program was to land humans on the Moon and bring them safely back to Earth. Six of the missions reached this goal. The Apollo program was a huge success, but it was just the beginning.

NASA has launched a space program that has a new goal—to return astronauts to the Moon to live and work. However, before that can happen, scientists need to know more about conditions on the Moon and what materials are available there.

Collecting data is the first step. In 2009, NASA plans to launch the Lunar Reconnaissance Orbiter (LRO) spacecraft. The LRO will spend a year orbiting the Moon's two poles. It will collect detailed data that scientists will use to make maps of the Moon's features and resources. These maps will help scientists design a lunar outpost.

One of LRO's jobs will be to look for water. While astronauts can bring some water with them to the Moon, they cannot bring enough for long periods of time. Billions of years ago, deep craters formed on the Moon when comets and asteroids slammed into it. Some scientists predict that these deep craters contain frozen water. The water has remained frozen because it has not been exposed to the Sun's light and heat. This mission will test these predictions.

NASA plans to have humans on the Moon again by the year 2020. That means one day you could help build and operate a lunar base!

Apollo
SPACE PROGRAM

The Apollo Space Program included 17 missions. Here are some milestones:

January 27 1967
Apollo 1 Fire killed all three astronauts on board during a launch simulation for the first piloted flight to the Moon.

December 21–27 1968
Apollo 8 First manned spacecraft orbits the Moon.

July 16–24 1969
Apollo 11 First humans, Neil Armstrong and Buzz Aldrin, walk on the Moon.

July 1971
Apollo 15 Astronauts drive the first rover on the Moon.

December 7–19 1972
Apollo 17 The first phase of human exploration of the Moon ended with this last lunar landing mission.

It's Your Turn

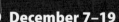

BRAINSTORM As a group, brainstorm all the different occupations that will be needed to successfully operate a base on the Moon. Discuss the tasks that a person would perform in each occupation.

Reading Guide

Key Concepts
ESSENTIAL QUESTIONS

- What is a solar eclipse?
- What is a lunar eclipse?
- How do the Moon and the Sun affect Earth's oceans?

Vocabulary

umbra p. 89

penumbra p. 89

solar eclipse p. 90

lunar eclipse p. 92

tide p. 93

 Multilingual eGlossary

Video

- BrainPOP®
- Science Video

Academic Standards for Science

6.2.1 Describe and model how the position, size and relative motions of the earth, moon, and sun cause day and night, solar and lunar eclipses and phases of the moon.

6.2.2 Recognize that gravity is a force that keeps celestial bodies in regular and predictable motion, holds objects to earth's surface, and is responsible for ocean tides.

Also covers: 6.NS.7, 6.NS.10, 6.NS.11

Eclipses and Tides

Inquiry What is this dark spot?

Cosmonauts took this photo from aboard the *Mir* orbiting space station. An eclipse caused the shadow that you see. Do you know what kind of eclipse?

How do shadows change?

You can see a shadow when an object blocks a light source. What happens to an object's shadow when the object moves?

1 Read and complete a lab safety form.

2 Select an **object** provided by your teacher.

3 Shine a **flashlight** on the object, projecting its shadow on the wall.

4 While holding the flashlight in the same position, move the object closer to the wall—away from the light. Then, move the object toward the light. Record your observations in your Science Journal.

Think About This

1. Compare and contrast the shadows created in each situation. Did the shadows have dark parts and light parts? Did these parts change?

2. 🔑 **Key Concept** Imagine you look at the flashlight from behind your object, looking from the darkest and lightest parts of the object's shadow. How much of the flashlight could you see from each location?

Shadows—the Umbra and the Penumbra

A shadow results when one object blocks the light that another object emits or reflects. When a tree blocks light from the Sun, it casts a shadow. If you want to stand in the shadow of a tree, the tree must be in a line between you and the Sun.

If you go outside on a sunny day and look carefully at a shadow on the ground, you might notice that the edges of the shadow are not as dark as the rest of the shadow. Light from the Sun and other wide sources casts shadows with two distinct parts, as shown in **Figure 13**. *The **umbra** is the central, darker part of a shadow where light is totally blocked. The **penumbra** is the lighter part of a shadow where light is partially blocked.* If you stood within an object's penumbra, you would be able to see only part of the light source. If you stood within an object's umbra, you would not see the light source at all.

WORD ORIGIN ···········

penumbra
from Latin *paene*, means "almost"; and *umbra*, means "shade, shadow"

Figure 13 The shadow that a wide light source produces has two parts—the umbra and the penumbra. The light source cannot be seen from within the umbra. The light source can be partially seen from within the penumbra.

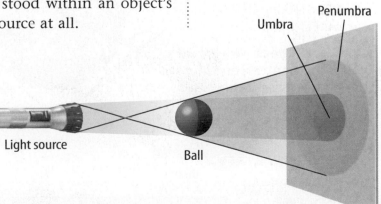

What does the Moon's shadow look like?

Like every shadow cast by a wide light source, the Moon's shadow has two parts.

1 Read and complete a lab safety form.

2 Working with a partner, use a **pencil** to connect two **foam balls**. One ball should be one-fourth the size of the other.

3 While one person holds the balls, the other should stand 1 m away and shine a **flashlight** or **desk lamp** on the balls. The balls and light should be in a direct line, with the smallest ball closest to the light.

4 Sketch and describe your observations in your Science Journal.

Analyze and Conclude

1. 🔑 **Key Concept** Explain the relationship between the two types of shadows and solar eclipses?

Solar Eclipses

As the Sun shines on the Moon, the Moon casts a shadow that extends out into space. Sometimes the Moon passes between Earth and the Sun. This can only happen during the new moon phase. When Earth, the Moon, and the Sun are lined up, the Moon casts a shadow on Earth's surface, as shown in **Figure 14.** You can see the Moon's shadow in the photo at the beginning of this lesson. *When the Moon's shadow appears on Earth's surface, a* **solar eclipse** *is occurring.*

🔑 **Key Concept Check** Why does a solar eclipse occur only during a new moon?

As Earth rotates, the Moon's shadow moves along Earth's surface, as shown in **Figure 14.** The type of eclipse you see depends on whether you are in the path of the umbra or the penumbra. If you are outside the umbra and penumbra, you cannot see a solar eclipse at all.

Total Solar Eclipses

You can only see a total solar eclipse from within the Moon's umbra. During a total solar eclipse, the Moon appears to cover the Sun completely, as shown in **Figure 15** on the next page. Then, the sky becomes dark enough that you can see stars. A total solar eclipse lasts no longer than about 7 minutes.

Solar Eclipse 🔑

Figure 14 A solar eclipse occurs only when the Moon moves directly between Earth and the Sun. The Moon's shadow moves across Earth's surface.

✔ **Visual Check** Why would a person in North America not see the solar eclipse shown here?

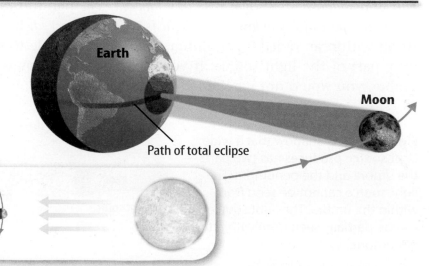

Earth

Moon

Path of total eclipse

Penumbra

Umbra

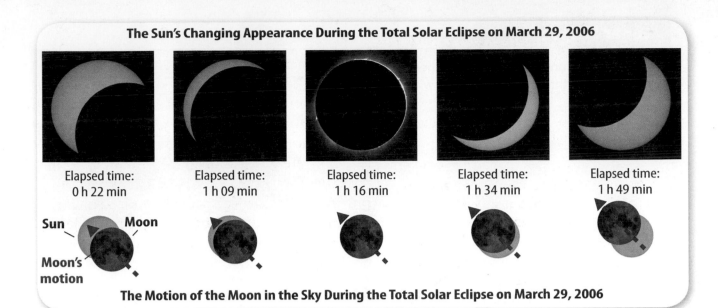

The Sun's Changing Appearance During the Total Solar Eclipse on March 29, 2006

| Elapsed time: 0 h 22 min | Elapsed time: 1 h 09 min | Elapsed time: 1 h 16 min | Elapsed time: 1 h 34 min | Elapsed time: 1 h 49 min |

Sun Moon

Moon's motion

The Motion of the Moon in the Sky During the Total Solar Eclipse on March 29, 2006

Partial Solar Eclipses

You can only see a total solar eclipse from within the Moon's umbra, but you can see a partial solar eclipse from within the Moon's much larger penumbra. The stages of a partial solar eclipse are similar to the stages of a total solar eclipse, except that the Moon never completely covers the Sun.

Why don't solar eclipses occur every month?

Solar eclipses only can occur during a new moon, when Earth and the Sun are on opposite sides of the Moon. However, solar eclipses do not occur during every new-moon phase. **Figure 16** shows why. The Moon's orbit is tilted slightly compared to Earth's orbit. As a result, during most new moons, Earth is either above or below the Moon's shadow. However, every so often the Moon is in a line between the Sun and Earth. Then the Moon's shadow passes over Earth and a solar eclipse occurs.

Figure 15 This sequence of photographs shows how the Sun's appearance changed during a total solar eclipse in 2006.

✓ **Visual Check** How much time elapsed from the start to the finish of this sequence?

Figure 16 A solar eclipse occurs only when the Moon crosses Earth's orbit and is in a direct line between Earth and the Sun.

The Moon's Tilted Orbit

Concepts in Motion Animation

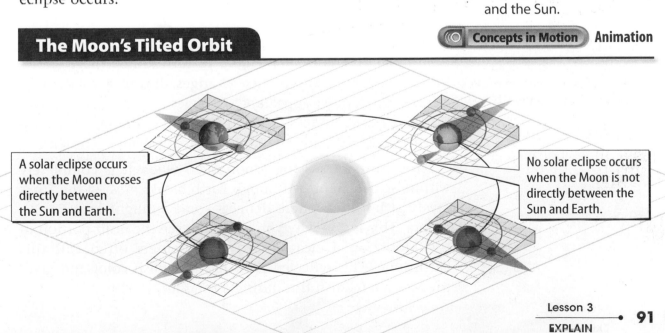

A solar eclipse occurs when the Moon crosses directly between the Sun and Earth.

No solar eclipse occurs when the Moon is not directly between the Sun and Earth.

Figure 17 A lunar eclipse occurs when the Moon moves through Earth's shadow.

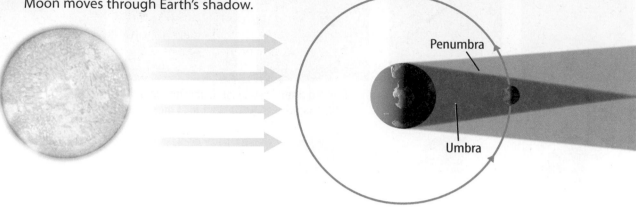

Penumbra

Umbra

✓ **Visual Check** Why would more people be able to see a lunar eclipse than a solar eclipse?

Lunar Eclipses

Just like the Moon, Earth casts a shadow into space. As the Moon revolves around Earth, it sometimes moves into Earth's shadow, as shown in **Figure 17.** *A lunar eclipse occurs when the Moon moves into Earth's shadow.* Then Earth is in a line between the Sun and the Moon. This means that a lunar eclipse can occur only during the full moon phase.

Like the Moon's shadow, Earth's shadow has an umbra and a penumbra. Different types of lunar eclipses occur depending on which part of Earth's shadow the Moon moves through. Unlike solar eclipses, you can see any lunar eclipse from any location on the side of Earth facing the Moon.

 Key Concept Check When can a lunar eclipse occur?

Total Lunar Eclipses

When the entire Moon moves through Earth's umbra, a total lunar eclipse occurs. **Figure 18** on the next page shows how the Moon's appearance changes during a total lunar eclipse. The Moon's appearance changes as it gradually moves into Earth's penumbra, then into Earth's umbra, back into Earth's penumbra, and then out of Earth's shadow entirely.

You can still see the Moon even when it is completely within Earth's umbra. Although Earth blocks most of the Sun's rays, Earth's atmosphere deflects some sunlight into Earth's umbra. This is also why you can often see the unlit portion of the Moon on a clear night. Astronomers often call this Earthshine. This reflected light has a reddish color and gives the Moon a reddish tint during a total lunar eclipse.

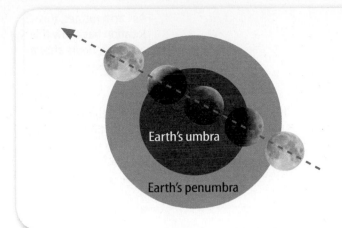

Figure 18 If the entire Moon passes through Earth's umbra, the Moon gradually darkens until a dark shadow covers it completely.

Earth's umbra

Earth's penumbra

✔ **Visual Check** How would a total lunar eclipse look different from a total solar eclipse?

Partial Lunar Eclipses

When only part of the Moon passes through Earth's umbra, a partial lunar eclipse occurs. The stages of a partial lunar eclipse are similar to those of a total lunar eclipse, shown in **Figure 18,** except the Moon is never completely covered by Earth's umbra. The part of the Moon in Earth's penumbra appears only slightly darker, while the part of the Moon in Earth's umbra appears much darker.

Why don't lunar eclipses occur every month?

Lunar eclipses can only occur during a full moon phase, when the Moon and the Sun are on opposite sides of Earth. However, lunar eclipses do not occur during every full moon because of the tilt of the Moon's orbit with respect to Earth's orbit. During most full moons, the Moon is slightly above or slightly below Earth's penumbra.

Tides

The positions of the Moon and the Sun also affect Earth's oceans. If you have spent time near an ocean, you might have seen how the ocean's height, or sea level, rises and falls twice each day. *A* **tide** *is the daily rise and fall of sea level.* Examples of tides are shown in **Figure 19.** It is primarily the Moon's gravity that causes Earth's oceans to rise and fall twice each day.

Figure 19 In the Bay of Fundy, high tides can be more than 10 m higher than low tides.

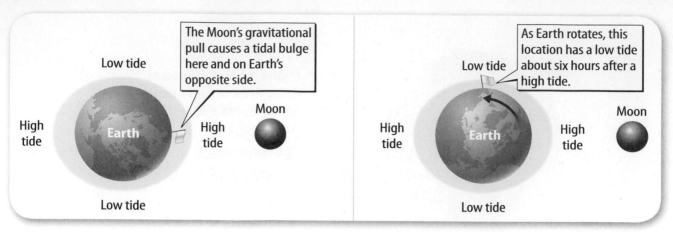

Figure 20 🔑 In this view down on Earth's North Pole, the flag moves into a tidal bulge as Earth rotates. A coastal area has a high tide about once every 12 hours.

The Moon's Effect on Earth's Tides

The difference in the strength of the Moon's gravity on opposite sides of the Earth causes Earth's tides. The Moon's gravity is slightly stronger on the side of Earth closer to the Moon and slightly weaker on the side of Earth opposite the Moon. These differences cause tidal bulges in the oceans on opposite sides of Earth, shown in **Figure 20**. High tides occur at the tidal bulges, and low tides occur between them.

The Sun's Effect on Earth's Tides

Because the Sun is so far away from Earth, its effect on tides is about half that of the Moon. **Figure 21** shows how the positions of the Sun and the Moon affect Earth's tides.

Spring Tides During the full moon and new moon phases, spring tides occur. This is when the Sun's and the Moon's gravitational effects combine and produce higher high tides and lower low tides.

Neap Tides A week after a spring tide, a neap tide occurs. Then the Sun, Earth, and the Moon form a right angle. When this happens, the Sun's effect on tides reduces the Moon's effect. High tides are lower and low tides are higher at neap tides.

🔑 **Key Concept Check** Why is the Sun's effect on tides less than the Moon's effect?

Figure 21 A spring tide occurs when the Sun, Earth, and the Moon are in a line. A neap tide occurs when the Sun and the Moon form a right angle with Earth.

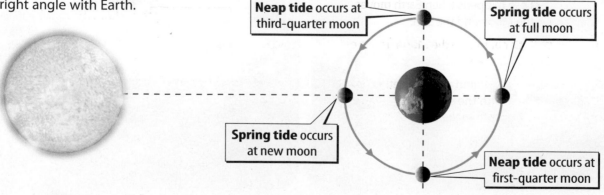

Visual Summary

Shadows from a wide light source have two distinct parts.

The Moon's shadow produces solar eclipses. Earth's shadow produces lunar eclipses.

The positions of the Moon and the Sun in relation to Earth cause gravitational differences that produce tides.

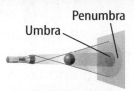

Use your lesson Foldable to review the lesson. Save your Foldable for the project at the end of the chapter.

What do you think NOW?

You first read the statements below at the beginning of the chapter.

5. A solar eclipse happens when Earth moves between the Moon and the Sun.

6. The gravitational pull of the Moon and the Sun on Earth's oceans causes tides.

Did you change your mind about whether you agree or disagree with the statements? Rewrite any false statements to make them true.

Use Vocabulary

❶ **Distinguish** between an umbra and a penumbra.

❷ **Use the term** *tide* in a sentence.

❸ The Moon turns a reddish color during a total _____ eclipse.

Understand Key Concepts

❹ **Summarize** the effect of the Sun on Earth's tides.

❺ **Illustrate** the positions of the Sun, Earth, and the Moon during a solar eclipse and during a lunar eclipse.

❻ **Contrast** a total lunar eclipse with a partial lunar eclipse.

❼ Which could occur during a total solar eclipse?
  A. first quarter moon   C. neap tide
  B. full moon   D. spring tide

Interpret Graphics

❽ **Conclude** What type of eclipse does the figure above illustrate?

❾ **Categorize Information** Copy and fill in the graphic organizer below to identify two bodies that affect Earth's tides.

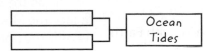

Critical Thinking

❿ **Compose** a short story about a person long ago viewing a total solar eclipse.

⓫ **Research** ways to view a solar eclipse safely. Summarize your findings here.

Materials

foam ball

pencil

lamp

stool

Safety

Phases of the Moon

The Moon appears slightly different every night of its 29.5-day lunar cycle. The Moon's appearance changes as Earth and the Moon move. Depending on where the Moon is in relation to Earth and the Sun, observers on Earth see only part of the light the Moon reflects from the Sun.

Question

How do the positions of the Sun, the Moon, and Earth cause the phases of the Moon?

Procedure

1. Read and complete a lab safety form.

2. Hold a foam ball that represents the Moon. Make a handle for the ball by inserting a pencil about two inches into the ball. Your partner will represent an observer on Earth. Have your partner sit on a stool and record observations during the activity.

3. Place a lamp on a desk or other flat surface. Remove the shade from the lamp. The lamp represents the Sun.

4. Turn on the lamp and darken the lights in the room.
   ⚠ *Do not touch the bulb or look directly at it after the lamp is turned on.*

5. Position the Earth observer's stool about 1 m from the Sun. Position the Moon 0.5–1 m from the observer so that the Sun, Earth, and the Moon are in a line. The student holding the Moon holds the Moon so it is completely illuminated on one half. The observer records the phase and what the phase looks like in a data table.

6. Move the Moon clockwise about one-eighth of the way around its "orbit" of Earth. The observer swivels on the stool to face the Moon and records the phase.

7. Continue the Moon's orbit until the Earth observer has recorded all the Moon's phases.

8 Return to your positions as the Moon and Earth observer. Choose a part in the Moon's orbit that you did not model. Predict what the Moon would look like in that position, and check if your prediction is correct.

Analyze and Conclude

9 **Explain** Use your observations to explain how the positions of the Sun, the Moon, and Earth produce the different phases of the Moon.

10 **The Big Idea** Why is half of the Moon always lit? Why do you usually see only part of the Moon's lit half?

11 **Draw Conclusions** Based on your observations, why is the Moon not visible from Earth during the new-moon phase?

12 **Summarize** Which parts of your model were waxing phases? Which parts were waning phases?

13 **Think Critically** During which phases of the Moon can eclipses occur? Explain.

Communicate Your Results

Create a poster of the results from your lab. Illustrate various positions of the Sun, the Moon, and Earth and draw the phase of the Moon for each. Include a statement of your hypothesis on the poster.

Inquiry **Extension**

The Moon is not the only object in the sky that has phases when viewed from Earth. The planets Venus and Mercury also have phases. Research the phases of these planets and create a calendar that shows when the various phases of Venus and Mercury occur.

Lab Tips

☑ Make sure the observer's head does not cast a shadow on the Moon.

☑ The student holding the Moon should hold the pencil so that he or she always stands on the unlit side of the Moon.

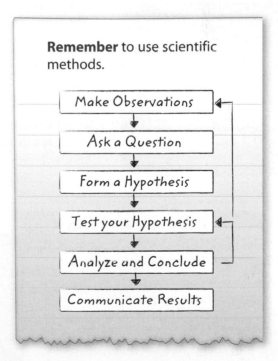

Remember to use scientific methods.

Make Observations

↓

Ask a Question

↓

Form a Hypothesis

↓

Test your Hypothesis

↓

Analyze and Conclude

↓

Communicate Results

Chapter 3 Study Guide

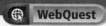

 THE BIG IDEA

Earth's motion around the Sun causes seasons. The Moon's motion around Earth causes phases of the Moon. Earth and the Moon's motions together cause eclipses and ocean tides.

Key Concepts Summary 🔑	Vocabulary

Lesson 1: Earth's Motion

- The gravitational pull of the Sun on Earth causes Earth to revolve around the Sun in a nearly circular **orbit.**

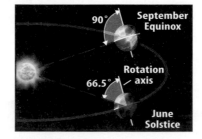

- Areas on Earth's curved surface become more tilted with respect to the direction of sunlight the farther you travel from the equator. This causes sunlight to spread out closer to the poles, making Earth colder at the poles and warmer at the equator.

- As Earth revolves around the Sun, the tilt of Earth's **rotation axis** produces changes in how sunlight spreads out over Earth's surface. These changes in the concentration of sunlight cause the seasons.

Vocabulary:
orbit p. 72
revolution p. 72
rotation p. 73
rotation axis p. 73
solstice p. 77
equinox p. 77

Lesson 2: Earth's Moon

- The gravitational pull of Earth on the Moon makes the Moon revolve around Earth. The Moon rotates once as it makes one complete orbit around Earth.

- The lit part of the Moon that you can see from Earth—the Moon's **phase**—changes during the lunar cycle as the Moon revolves around Earth.

Vocabulary:
maria p. 82
phase p. 84
waxing phase p. 84
waning phase p. 84

Lesson 3: Eclipses and Tides

- When the Moon's shadow appears on Earth's surface, a **solar eclipse** occurs.

- When the Moon moves into Earth's shadow, a **lunar eclipse** occurs.

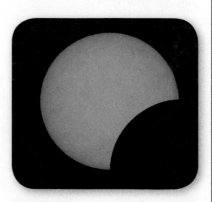

- The gravitational pull of the Moon and the Sun on Earth produces **tides**, the rise and fall of sea level that occurs twice each day.

Vocabulary:
umbra p. 89
penumbra p. 89
solar eclipse p. 90
lunar eclipse p. 92
tide p. 93

FOLDABLES® Chapter Project

Assemble your Lesson Foldables as shown to make a Chapter Project. Use the project to review what you have learned in this chapter.

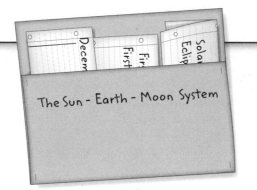

The Sun - Earth - Moon System

Use Vocabulary

Distinguish between the terms in the each of the following pairs.

1 revolution, orbit

2 rotation, rotation axis

3 solstice, equinox

4 waxing phases, waning phases

5 umbra, penumbra

6 solar eclipse, lunar eclipse

7 tide, phase

Link Vocabulary and Key Concepts

 **Concepts in Motion** Interactive Concept Map

Copy this concept map, and then use vocabulary terms from the previous page to complete the concept map.

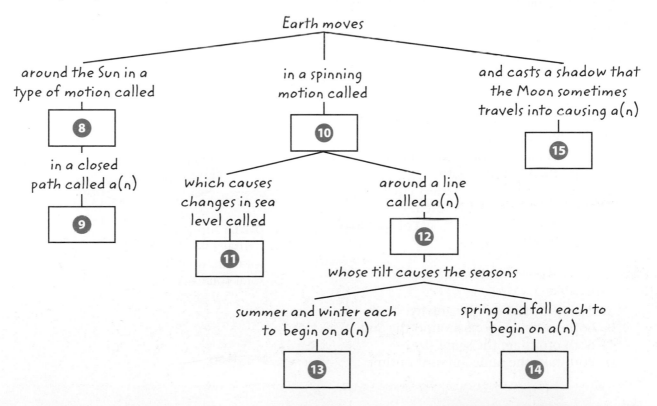

Chapter 3 Review

Understand Key Concepts

1 Which property of the Sun most affects the strength of gravitational attraction between the Sun and Earth?
  A. mass
  B. radius
  C. shape
  D. temperature

2 Which would be different if Earth rotated from east to west but at the same rate?
  A. the amount of energy striking Earth
  B. the days on which solstices occur
  C. the direction of the Sun's apparent motion across the sky
  D. the number of hours in a day

3 In the image below, which season is the northern hemisphere experiencing?

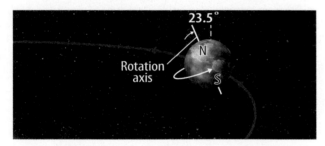

  A. fall
  B. spring
  C. summer
  D. winter

4 Which best explains why Earth is colder at the poles than at the equator?
  A. Earth is farther from the Sun at the poles than at the equator.
  B. Earth's orbit is not a perfect circle.
  C. Earth's rotation axis is tilted.
  D. Earth's surface is more tilted at the poles than at the equator.

5 How are the revolutions of the Moon and Earth alike?
  A. Both are produced by gravity.
  B. Both are revolutions around the Sun.
  C. Both orbits are the same size.
  D. Both take the same amount of time.

6 Which moon phase occurs about one week after a new moon?
  A. another new moon
  B. first quarter moon
  C. full moon
  D. third quarter moon

7 Why is the same side of the Moon always visible from Earth?
  A. The Moon does not revolve around Earth.
  B. The Moon does not rotate.
  C. The Moon makes exactly one rotation for each revolution around Earth.
  D. The Moon's rotation axis is not tilted.

8 About how often do spring tides occur?
  A. once each month
  B. once each year
  C. twice each month
  D. twice each year

9 If a coastal area has a high tide at 7:00 A.M., at about what time will the next low tide occur?
  A. 11:00 A.M.
  B. 1:00 P.M.
  C. 3:00 P.M.
  D. 7:00 P.M.

10 Which type of eclipse would a person standing at point X in the diagram below see?

  A. partial lunar eclipse
  B. partial solar eclipse
  C. total lunar eclipse
  D. total solar eclipse

Critical Thinking

11 **Outline** the ways Earth moves and how each affects Earth.

12 **Create** a poster that illustrates and describes the relationship between Earth's tilt and the seasons.

13 **Contrast** Why can you see phases of the Moon but not phases of the Sun?

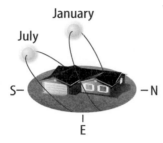

January

July

S— —N

E

14 **Interpret Graphics** The figure above shows the Sun's position in the sky at noon in January and July. Is the house located in the northern hemisphere or the southern hemisphere? Explain.

15 **Illustrate** Make a diagram of the Moon's orbit and phases. Include labels and explanations with your drawing.

16 **Differentiate** between a total solar eclipse and a partial solar eclipse.

17 **Generalize** the reason that solar and lunar eclipses do not occur every month.

18 **Role Play** Write and present a play with several classmates that explains the causes and types of tides.

Writing in Science

19 **Survey** a group of at least ten people to determine how many know the cause of Earth's seasons. Write a summary of your results, including a main idea, supporting details, and a concluding sentence.

REVIEW THE BIG IDEA

20 At the South Pole, the Sun does not appear in the sky for six months out of the year. When does this happen? What is happening at the North Pole during these months? Explain why Earth's poles receive so little solar energy.

21 A solar eclipse, shown in the time-lapse photo below, is one phenomenon that the motions of Earth and the Moon produce. What other phenomena do the motions of Earth and the Moon produce?

Math Skills ×÷+

Review
— Math Practice —

Convert Units

22 When the Moon is 384,000 km from Earth, how far is the Moon from Earth in miles?

23 If you travel 205 mi on a train from Washington D.C. to New York City, how many kilometers do you travel on the train?

24 The nearest star other than the Sun is about 40 trillion km away. About how many miles away is the nearest star other than the Sun?

Record your answers on the answer sheet provided by your teacher or on a sheet of paper.

Multiple Choice

1 Which is the movement of one object around another object in space?

  A axis

  B orbit

  C revolution

  D rotation

Use the diagram below to answer question 2.

Time 1

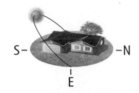

S— —N
E

Time 2

S— —N
E

2 What happens between times *1* and *2* in the diagram above?

  A Days grow shorter and shorter.

  B The season changes from fall to winter.

  C The region begins to point away from the Sun.

  D The region gradually receives more solar energy.

3 How many times larger is the Sun's diameter than Earth's diameter?

  A about 10 times larger

  B about 100 times larger

  C about 1,000 times larger

  D about 10,000 times larger

4 Which diagram illustrates the Moon's third quarter phase?

  A

  B

  C

  D

5 Which accurately describes Earth's position and orientation during summer in the northern hemisphere?

  A Earth is at its closest point to the Sun.

  B Earth's hemispheres receive equal amounts of solar energy.

  C The north end of Earth's rotational axis leans toward the Sun.

  D The Sun emits a greater amount of light and heat energy.

6 Which are large, dark lunar areas formed by cooled lava?

  A craters

  B highlands

  C maria

  D rays

7 During one lunar cycle, the Moon

  A completes its east-to-west path across the sky exactly once.

  B completes its entire sequence of phases.

  C progresses only from the new-moon phase to the full-moon phase.

  D revolves around Earth twice.

Use the diagram below to answer question 8.

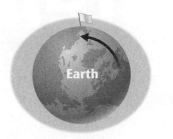

8 What does the flag in the diagram above represent?

A high tide

B low tide

C neap tide

D spring tide

9 During which lunar phase might a solar eclipse occur?

A first quarter moon

B full moon

C new moon

D third quarter moon

10 Which does the entire Moon pass through during a partial lunar eclipse?

A Earth's penumbra

B Earth's umbra

C the Moon's penumbra

D the Moon's umbra

Constructed Response

Use the diagram below to answer questions 11 and 12.

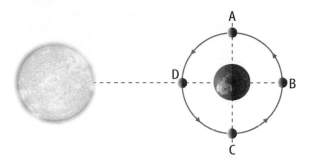

11 Where are neap tides indicated in the above diagram? What causes neap tides? What happens during a neap tide?

12 Where are spring tides indicated in the above diagram? What causes spring tides? What happens during a spring tide?

13 How would Earth's climate be different if its rotational axis were not tilted?

14 Why can we see only one side of the Moon from Earth? What is the name given to this side of the Moon?

15 What is a lunar phase? How do waxing and waning phases differ?

16 Why don't solar eclipses occur monthly?

NEED EXTRA HELP?																
If You Missed Question...	1	2	3	4	5	6	7	8	9	10	11	12	13	14	15	16
Go to Lesson...	1	1	1	2	1	2	2	3	3	3	3	3	1	2	2	3

The Solar System

THE BIG IDEA What kinds of objects are in the solar system?

 Inquiry **One, Two, or Three Planets?**

This photo, taken by the Cassini spacecraft, shows part of Saturn's rings and two of its moons. Saturn is a planet that orbits the Sun. The moons, tiny Epimetheus and much larger Titan, orbit Saturn. Besides planets and moons, many other objects are in the solar system.

- How would you describe a planet such as Saturn?

- How do astronomers classify the objects they discover?

- What types of objects do you think make up the solar system?

Get Ready to Read

What do you think?

Before you read, decide if you agree or disagree with each of these statements. As you read this chapter, see if you change your mind about any of the statements.

1 Astronomers measure distances between space objects using astronomical units.

2 Gravitational force keeps planets in orbit around the Sun.

3 Earth is the only inner planet that has a moon.

4 Venus is the hottest planet in the solar system.

5 The outer planets also are called the gas giants.

6 The atmospheres of Saturn and Jupiter are mainly water vapor.

7 Asteroids and comets are mainly rock and ice.

8 A meteoroid is a meteor that strikes Earth.

ConnectED Your one-stop online resource

connectED.mcgraw-hill.com

- Video
- WebQuest
- Audio
- Assessment
- Review
- Concepts in Motion
- Inquiry
- Multilingual eGlossary

The Structure of the Solar System

Reading Guide

Key Concepts
ESSENTIAL QUESTIONS

- How are the inner planets different from the outer planets?
- What is an astronomical unit and why is it used?
- What is the shape of a planet's orbit?

Vocabulary

asteroid p. 109

comet p. 109

astronomical unit p. 110

period of revolution p. 110

period of rotation p. 110

 Multilingual eGlossary

Video

- **BrainPOP®**
- **Science Video**

Academic Standards for Science

6.2.2 Recognize that gravity is a force that keeps celestial bodies in regular and predictable motion, holds objects to earth's surface, and is responsible for ocean tides.

Also covers: 6.2.3, 6.2.4, 6.NS.3, 6.NS.5, 6.NS.7

Inquiry Are these stars?

Did you know that shooting stars are not actually stars? The bright streaks are small, rocky particles burning up as they enter Earth's atmosphere. These particles are part of the solar system and are often associated with comets.

How do you know which distance unit to use?

You can use different units to measure distance. For example, millimeters might be used to measure the length of a bolt, and kilometers might be used to measure the distance between cities. In this lab, you will investigate why some units are easier to use than others for certain measurements.

1 Read and complete a lab safety form.

2 Use a **centimeter ruler** to measure the length of a **pencil** and the thickness of this **book.** Record the distances in your Science Journal.

3 Use the centimeter ruler to measure the width of your classroom. Then measure the width of the room using a **meterstick.** Record the distances in your Science Journal.

Think About This

1. Why are meters easier to use than centimeters for measuring the classroom?

2. 🔑 **Key Concept** Why do you think astronomers might need a unit larger than a kilometer to measure distances in the solar system?

What is the solar system?

Have you ever made a wish on a star? If so, you might have wished on a planet instead of a star. Sometimes, as shown in **Figure 1,** the first starlike object you see at night is not a star at all. It's Venus, the planet closest to Earth.

It's hard to tell the difference between planets and stars in the night sky because they all appear as tiny lights. Thousands of years ago, observers noticed that a few of these tiny lights moved, but others did not. The ancient Greeks called these objects planets, which means "wanderers." Astronomers now know that the planets do not wander about the sky; the planets move around the Sun. The Sun and the group of objects that move around it make up the solar system.

When you look at the night sky, a few of the tiny lights that you can see are part of our solar system. Almost all of the other specks of light are stars. They are much farther away than any objects in our solar system. Astronomers have discovered that some of those stars also have planets moving around them.

✔ **Reading Check** What object do the planets in the solar system move around?

Figure 1 When looking at the night sky, you will likely see stars and planets. In the photo below, the planet Venus is the bright object seen above the Moon.

Objects in the Solar System

Ancient observers looking at the night sky saw many stars but only five planets—Mercury, Venus, Mars, Jupiter, and Saturn. The invention of the telescope in the 1600s led to the discovery of additional planets and many other space objects.

The Sun

The largest object in the solar system is the Sun, a **star**. Its diameter is about 1.4 million km—ten times the diameter of the largest planet, Jupiter. The Sun is made mostly of hydrogen gas. Its mass makes up about 99 percent of the entire solar system's mass.

Inside the Sun, a process called nuclear fusion produces an enormous amount of energy. The Sun emits some of this energy as light. The light from the Sun shines on all of the planets every day. The Sun also applies gravitational forces to objects in the solar system. Gravitational forces cause the planets and other objects to move around, or **orbit**, the Sun.

Objects That Orbit the Sun

Different types of objects orbit the Sun. These objects include planets, dwarf planets, asteroids, and comets. Unlike the Sun, these objects don't emit light but only reflect the Sun's light.

Planets Astronomers classify some objects that orbit the Sun as planets, as shown in **Figure 2**. An object is a planet only if it orbits the Sun and has a nearly spherical shape. Also, the mass of a planet must be much larger than the total mass of all other objects whose orbits are close by. The solar system has eight objects classified as planets.

✓ **Reading Check** What is a planet?

SCIENCE USE V. COMMON USE

star

Science Use an object in space made of gases in which nuclear fusion reactions occur that emit energy

Common Use a shape that usually has five or six points around a common center

REVIEW VOCABULARY

orbit

(noun) the path an object follows as it moves around another object
(verb) to move around another object

Figure 2 🔑 The orbits of the inner and outer planets are shown to scale. The Sun and the planets are not to scale. The outer planets are much larger than the inner planets.

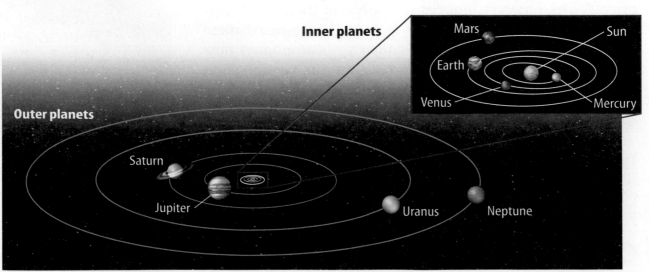

Inner planets
Mars
Sun
Earth
Venus
Mercury

Outer planets
Saturn
Jupiter
Uranus
Neptune

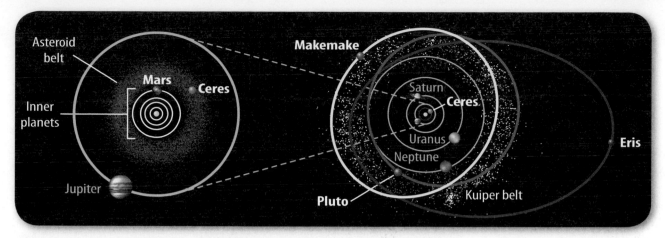

Inner Planets and Outer Planets As shown in **Figure 2,** the four planets closest to the Sun are the inner planets. The inner planets are Mercury, Venus, Earth, and Mars. These planets are made mainly of solid rocky materials. The four planets farthest from the Sun are the outer planets. The outer planets are Jupiter, Saturn, Uranus (YOOR uh nus), and Neptune. These planets are made mainly of ice and gases such as hydrogen and helium. The outer planets are much larger than Earth and are sometimes called gas giants.

 Key Concept Check Describe how the inner planets differ from the outer planets.

Dwarf Planets Scientists classify some objects in the solar system as dwarf planets. A dwarf planet is a spherical object that orbits the Sun. It is not a moon of another planet and is in a region of the solar system where there are many objects orbiting near it. But, unlike a planet, a dwarf planet does not have more mass than objects in nearby orbits. **Figure 3** shows the locations of the dwarf planets Ceres (SIHR eez), Eris (IHR is), Pluto, and Makemake (MAH kay MAH kay). Dwarf planets are made of rock and ice and are much smaller than Earth.

Asteroids *Millions of small, rocky objects called* **asteroids** *orbit the Sun in the asteroid belt between the orbits of Mars and Jupiter.* The asteroid belt is shown in **Figure 3.** Asteroids range in size from less than a meter to several hundred kilometers in length. Unlike planets and dwarf planets, asteroids, such as the one shown in **Figure 4,** usually are not spherical.

Comets You might have seen a picture of a comet with a long, glowing tail. *A* **comet** *is made of gas, dust, and ice and moves around the Sun in an oval-shaped orbit.* Comets come from the outer parts of the solar system. There might be 1 trillion comets orbiting the Sun. You will read more about comets, asteroids, and dwarf planets in Lesson 4.

▲ **Figure 3** Ceres, a dwarf planet, orbits the Sun as planets do. The orbit of Ceres is in the asteroid belt between Mars and Jupiter.

Visual Check Which dwarf planet is farthest from the Sun?

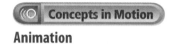
Concepts in Motion
Animation

WORD ORIGIN · · · · · · · · · · ·
asteroid
from Greek *asteroeides,* means "resembling a star"

Figure 4 The asteroid Gaspra orbits the Sun in the asteroid belt. Its odd shape is about 19 km long and 11 km wide. ▼

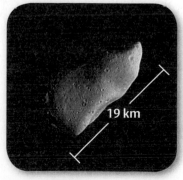
19 km

The Astronomical Unit

On Earth, distances are often measured in meters (m) or kilometers (km). Objects in the solar system, however, are so far apart that astronomers use a larger distance unit. *An* **astronomical unit** *(AU) is the average distance from Earth to the Sun—about 150 million km.* **Table 1** lists each planet's average distance from the Sun in km and AU.

 Key Concept Check Define what an astronomical unit is and explain why it is used.

Table 1 Because the distances of the planets from the Sun are so large, it is easier to express these distances using astronomical units rather than kilometers.

Concepts in Motion

Interactive Table

Table 1 Average Distance of the Planets from the Sun		
Planet	**Average Distance (km)**	**Average Distance (AU)**
Mercury	57,910,000	0.39
Venus	108,210,000	0.72
Earth	149,600,000	1.00
Mars	227,920,000	1.52
Jupiter	778,570,000	5.20
Saturn	1,433,530,000	9.58
Uranus	2,872,460,000	19.20
Neptune	4,495,060,000	30.05

The Motion of the Planets

Have you ever swung a ball on the end of a string in a circle over your head? In some ways, the motion of a planet around the Sun is like the motion of that ball. As shown in **Figure 5** on the next page, the Sun's gravitational force pulls each planet toward the Sun. This force is similar to the pull of the string that keeps the ball moving in a circle. The Sun's gravitational force pulls on each planet and keeps it moving along a curved path around the Sun.

Reading Check What causes planets to orbit the Sun?

Revolution and Rotation

Objects in the solar system move in two ways. They orbit, or revolve, around the Sun. *The time it takes an object to travel once around the Sun is its* **period of revolution.** Earth's period of revolution is one year. The objects also spin, or rotate, as they orbit the Sun. *The time it takes an object to complete one rotation is its* **period of rotation.** Earth has a period of rotation of one day.

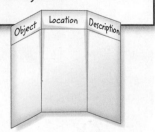

FOLDABLES

Make a tri-fold book from a sheet of paper and label it as shown. Use it to summarize information about the types of objects that make up the solar system.

Object | Location | Description

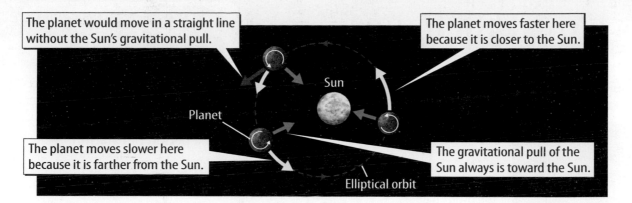

The planet would move in a straight line without the Sun's gravitational pull.

The planet moves faster here because it is closer to the Sun.

Sun

Planet

The planet moves slower here because it is farther from the Sun.

The gravitational pull of the Sun always is toward the Sun.

Elliptical orbit

Planetary Orbits and Speeds

Unlike a ball swinging on the end of a string, planets do not move in circles. Instead, a planet's orbit is an ellipse—a stretched-out circle. Inside an ellipse are two special points, each called a focus. These focus points, or foci, determine the shape of the ellipse. The foci are equal distances from the center of the ellipse. As shown in **Figure 5,** the Sun is at one of the foci; the other foci is empty space. As a result, the distance between the planet and the Sun changes as the planet moves.

A planet's speed also changes as it orbits the Sun. The closer the planet is to the Sun, the faster it moves. This also means that planets farther from the Sun have longer periods of revolution. For example, Jupiter is more than five times farther from the Sun than Earth. Not surprisingly, Jupiter takes 12 times longer than Earth to revolve around the Sun.

Figure 5 Planets and other objects in the solar system revolve around the Sun because of its gravitational pull on them.

Review
Personal Tutor

Key Concept Check Describe the shape of a planet's orbit.

Inquiry MiniLab

20 minutes

How can you model an elliptical orbit?

In this lab you will explore how the locations of foci affect the shape of an ellipse.

1. Read and complete a lab safety form.
2. Place a sheet of **paper** on a **corkboard.** Insert two **push pins** 8 cm apart in the center of the paper.
3. Use **scissors** to cut a 24-cm piece of **string.** Tie the ends of the string together.
4. Place the loop of string around the pins. Use a pencil to draw an ellipse as shown.
5. Measure the maximum width and length of the ellipse. Record the data in your Science Journal.

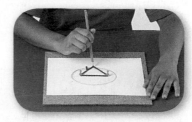

6. Move one of the push pins so that the pins are 5 cm apart. Repeat steps 4 and 5.

Analysis

1. **Compare and contrast** the two ellipses.
2. **Key Concept** How are the shapes of the ellipses you drew similar to the orbits of the inner and outer planets?

Lesson 1 Review

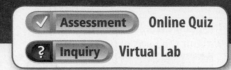
Visual Summary

The solar system contains the Sun, the inner planets, the outer planets, the dwarf planets, asteroids, and comets.

5 AU
Sun
Jupiter

An astronomical unit (AU) is a unit of distance equal to about 150 million km.

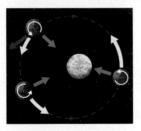

The speeds of the planets change as they move around the Sun in elliptical orbits.

FOLDABLES®

Use your lesson Foldable to review the lesson. Save your Foldable for the project at the end of the chapter.

What do you think NOW?

You first read the statements below at the beginning of the chapter.

1. Astronomers measure distances between space objects using astronomical units.

2. Gravitational force keeps planets in orbit around the Sun.

Did you change your mind about whether you agree or disagree with the statements? Rewrite any false statements to make them true.

Use Vocabulary

1. **Compare and contrast** a period of revolution and a period of rotation.

2. **Define** *dwarf planet* in your own words.

3. **Distinguish** between an asteroid and a comet.

Understand Key Concepts

4. **Summarize** how and why planets orbit the Sun and how and why a planet's speed changes in orbit.

5. **Infer** why an astronomical unit is not used to measure distances on Earth.

6. Which distinguishes a dwarf planet from a planet?
   A. mass
   B. the object it revolves around
   C. shape
   D. type of orbit

Interpret Graphics

7. **Explain** what each arrow in the diagram represents.

8. **Take Notes** Copy the table below. List information about each object or group of objects in the solar system mentioned in the lesson. Add additional lines as needed.

Object	Description
Sun	
Planets	

Critical Thinking

9. **Evaluate** How would the speed of a planet be different if its orbit were a circle instead of an ellipse?

Meteors are pieces of a comet or an asteroid that heat up as they fall through Earth's atmosphere. Meteors that strike Earth are called meteorites. ▶

AMERICAN MUSEUM of NATURAL HISTORY

History from Space

Meteorites give a peek back in time.

About 4.6 billion years ago, Earth and the other planets did not exist. In fact, there was no solar system. Instead, a large disk of gas and dust, known as the solar nebula, swirled around a forming Sun, as shown in the top picture to the right. How did the planets and other objects in the solar system form?

▲ Denton Ebel holds a meteorite that broke off the Vesta asteroid.

Denton Ebel is looking for the answer. He is a geologist at the American Museum of Natural History in New York City. Ebel explores the hypothesis that over millions of years, tiny particles in the solar nebula clumped together and formed the asteroids, comets, and planets that make up our solar system.

The solar nebula contained tiny particles called chondrules (KON drewls). They formed when the hot gas of the nebula condensed and solidified. Chondrules and other tiny particles collided and then accreted (uh KREET ed) or clumped together. This process eventually formed asteroids, comets, and planets. Some of the asteroids and comets have not changed much in over 4 billion years. Chondrite meteorites are pieces of asteroids and comets that fell to Earth. The chondrules within the meteorites are the oldest solid material in our solar system.

For Ebel, chondrite meteorites contain information about the formation of the solar system. Did the materials in the meteorite form throughout the solar system and then accrete? Or did asteroids and comets form and accrete near the Sun, drift outward to where they are today, and then grow larger by accreting ice and dust? Ebel's research is helping to solve the mystery of how our solar system formed.

Accretion Hypothesis

According to the accretion hypothesis, the solar system formed in stages.

First there was a solar nebula. The Sun formed when gravity caused the nebula to collapse.

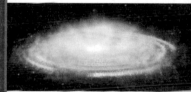

The rocky inner planets formed from accreted particles.

The gaseous outer planets formed as gas, ice, and dust condensed and accreted.

It's Your Turn

TIME LINE Work in groups. Learn more about the history of Earth from its formation until life began to appear. Create a time line showing major events. Present your time line to the class.

The Inner Planets

Reading Guide

Key Concepts
ESSENTIAL QUESTIONS

- How are the inner planets similar?
- Why is Venus hotter than Mercury?
- What kind of atmospheres do the inner planets have?

Vocabulary

terrestrial planet p. 115

greenhouse effect p. 117

 Multilingual eGlossary

 Video

What's Science Got to do With It?

Academic Standards for Science

6.2.4 Compare and contrast the planets of the solar system with one another and with asteroids and comets with regard to their size, composition, distance from sun, surface features and ability to support life.

Also covers: 6.NS.3, 6.NS.5, 6.NS.7, 6.NS.8

Inquiry Where is this?

This spectacular landscape is the surface of Mars, one of the inner planets. Other inner planets have similar rocky surfaces. It might surprise you to learn that there are planets in the solar system that have no solid surface on which to stand.

What affects the temperature on the inner planets?

Mercury and Venus are closer to the Sun than Earth. What determines the temperature on these planets? Let's find out.

1. Read and complete a lab safety form.

2. Insert a **thermometer** into a **clear 2-L plastic bottle.** Wrap **modeling clay** around the lid to hold the thermometer in the center of the bottle. Form an airtight seal with the clay.

3. Rest the bottle against the side of a **shoe box** in direct sunlight. Lay a second **thermometer** on top of the box next to the bottle so that the bulbs are at about the same height. The thermometer bulb should not touch the box. Secure the thermometer in place using **tape.**

4. Read the thermometers and record the temperatures in your Science Journal.

5. Wait 15 minutes and then read and record the temperature on each thermometer.

Think About This

1. How did the temperature of the two thermometers compare?

2. 🔑 **Key Concept** What do you think caused the difference in temperature?

Planets Made of Rock

Imagine that you are walking outside. How would you describe the ground? You might say it is dusty or grassy. If you live near a lake or an ocean, you might say sandy or wet. But beneath the ground or lake or ocean is a layer of solid rock.

The inner planets—Mercury, Venus, Earth, and Mars—are the planets closest to the Sun, as shown in **Figure 6.** *Earth and the other inner planets are also called the* **terrestrial planets.** Like Earth, the other inner planets also are made of rock and metallic materials and have a solid outer layer. Inner planets, however, have different sizes, atmospheres, and surfaces.

WORD ORIGIN
terrestrial
from Latin *terrestris*, means "earthly"

Figure 6 The inner planets are roughly similar in size. Earth is about two and half times larger than Mercury. All inner planets have a solid outer layer.

INNER PLANETS 🔑

Mercury   Venus   Earth   Mars

✓ **Visual Check** Which is the smallest inner planet?

Figure 7 🔑 The *Messenger* space probe recorded these images of Mercury as it flew by the planet in 2008.

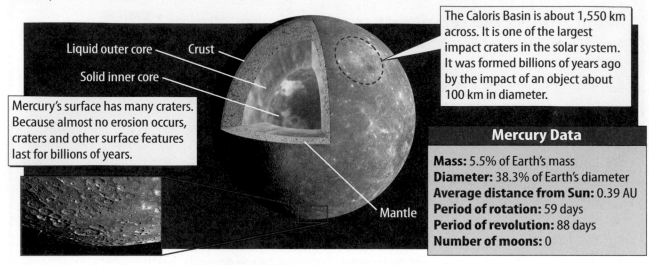

Liquid outer core — Crust

Solid inner core

The Caloris Basin is about 1,550 km across. It is one of the largest impact craters in the solar system. It was formed billions of years ago by the impact of an object about 100 km in diameter.

Mercury's surface has many craters. Because almost no erosion occurs, craters and other surface features last for billions of years.

Mantle

Mercury Data

Mass: 5.5% of Earth's mass
Diameter: 38.3% of Earth's diameter
Average distance from Sun: 0.39 AU
Period of rotation: 59 days
Period of revolution: 88 days
Number of moons: 0

FOLDABLES®

Make a four-door book. Label each door with the name of an inner planet. Use the book to organize your notes on the inner planets.

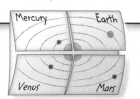

Mercury

The smallest planet and the planet closest to the Sun is Mercury, shown in **Figure 7.** Mercury has no atmosphere. A planet has an atmosphere when its gravity is strong enough to hold gases close to its surface. The strength of a planet's gravity depends on the planet's mass. Because Mercury's mass is so small, its gravity is not strong enough to hold onto an atmosphere. Without an atmosphere there is no wind that moves energy from place to place across the planet's surface. This results in temperatures as high as 450°C on the side of Mercury facing the Sun and as cold as −170°C on the side facing away from the Sun.

Mercury's Surface

Impact craters cover the surface of Mercury. There are also smooth plains of solidified lava from long-ago eruptions. Long, high cliffs occur also. These might have formed when the planet cooled quickly, causing the surface to wrinkle and crack. Without an atmosphere, almost no erosion occurs on the surface. As a result, features that formed billions of years ago have changed very little.

Mercury's Structure

The structures of the inner planets are similar. Like all inner planets, Mercury has a core made of iron and nickel. Surrounding the core is a layer called the mantle. It is mainly made of silicon and oxygen. The crust is a thin, rocky layer above the mantle. Mercury's large core might have been formed by a collision with a large object during Mercury's formation.

🔑 **Key Concept Check** How are the inner planets similar?

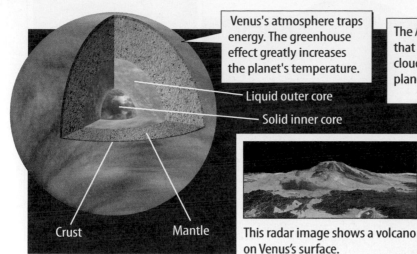

Venus's atmosphere traps energy. The greenhouse effect greatly increases the planet's temperature.

The *Magellan* orbiter used radar that can see through Venus's clouds to make images of the planet's surface.

Liquid outer core

Solid inner core

Crust

Mantle

This radar image shows a volcano on Venus's surface.

Venus Data

Mass: 81.5% of Earth's mass
Diameter: 95% of Earth's diameter
Average distance from Sun: 0.72 AU
Period of rotation: 244 days
Period of revolution: 225 days
Number of moons: 0

Venus

The second planet from the Sun is Venus, as shown in **Figure 8.** It is about the same size as Earth. Venus spins so slowly that its period of rotation is longer than its period of revolution. This means that a day on Venus is longer than a year. Unlike most planets, Venus rotates from east to west. Several space probes have flown by or landed on Venus.

Venus's Atmosphere

The atmosphere of Venus is about 97 percent carbon dioxide. It is so dense that the atmospheric pressure on Venus is about 90 times greater than on Earth. Even though Venus has almost no water in its atmosphere or on its surface, a thick layer of clouds covers the planet. Unlike the clouds of water vapor on Earth, the clouds on Venus are made of acid.

The Greenhouse Effect on Venus

With an average temperature of about 460°C, Venus is the hottest planet in the solar system. The high temperatures are caused by the greenhouse effect. *The* **greenhouse effect** *occurs when a planet's atmosphere traps solar energy and causes the surface temperature to increase.* Carbon dioxide in Venus's atmosphere traps some of the solar energy that is absorbed and then emitted by the planet. This heats up the planet. Without the greenhouse effect, Venus would be almost 450°C cooler.

 Key Concept Check Why is Venus hotter than Mercury?

Venus's Structure and Surface

Venus's internal structure, as shown in **Figure 8,** is similar to Earth's. Radar images show that more than 80 percent of Venus's surface is covered by solidified lava. Much of this lava might have been produced by volcanic eruptions that occurred about half a billion years ago.

Figure 8 Because a thick layer of clouds covers Venus, its surface has not been seen. Between 1990 and 1994, the *Magellan* space probe mapped the surface using radar.

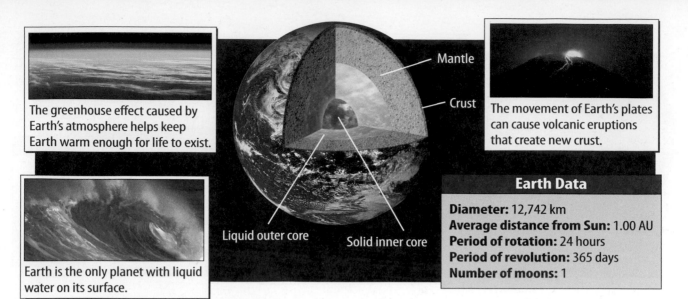

The greenhouse effect caused by Earth's atmosphere helps keep Earth warm enough for life to exist.

Earth is the only planet with liquid water on its surface.

Mantle

Crust

Liquid outer core

Solid inner core

The movement of Earth's plates can cause volcanic eruptions that create new crust.

Earth Data

Diameter: 12,742 km
Average distance from Sun: 1.00 AU
Period of rotation: 24 hours
Period of revolution: 365 days
Number of moons: 1

Figure 9 Earth has more water in its atmosphere and on its surface than the other inner planets. Earth's surface is younger than the surfaces of the other inner planets because new crust is constantly forming.

Inquiry MiniLab
20 minutes

How can you model the inner planets?

In this lab, you will use modeling clay to make scale models of the inner planets.

Planet	Actual Diameter (km)	Model Diameter (cm)
Mercury	4,879	
Venus	12,103	
Earth	12,756	8.0
Mars	6,792	

1. Use the data above for Earth to calculate in your Science Journal each model's diameter for the other three planets.

2. Use **modeling clay** to make a ball that represents the diameter of each planet. Check the diameter with a **centimeter ruler**.

Analyze Your Results

1. **Explain** how you converted actual diameters (km) to model diameters (cm).

2. **Key Concept** How do the inner planets compare? Which planets have approximately the same diameter?

Earth

Earth, shown in **Figure 9,** is the third planet from the Sun. Unlike Mercury and Venus, Earth has a moon.

Earth's Atmosphere

A mixture of gases and a small amount of water vapor make up most of Earth's atmosphere. They produce a greenhouse effect that increases Earth's average surface temperature. This effect and Earth's distance from the Sun warm Earth enough for large bodies of liquid water to exist. Earth's atmosphere also absorbs much of the Sun's radiation and protects the surface below. Earth's protective atmosphere, the presence of liquid water, and the planet's moderate temperature range support a variety of life.

Earth's Structure

As shown in **Figure 9,** Earth has a solid inner core surrounded by a liquid outer core. The mantle surrounds the liquid outer core. Above the mantle is Earth's crust. It is broken into large pieces, called plates, that constantly slide past, away from, or into each other. The crust is made mostly of oxygen and silicon and is constantly created and destroyed.

Reading Check Why is there life on Earth?

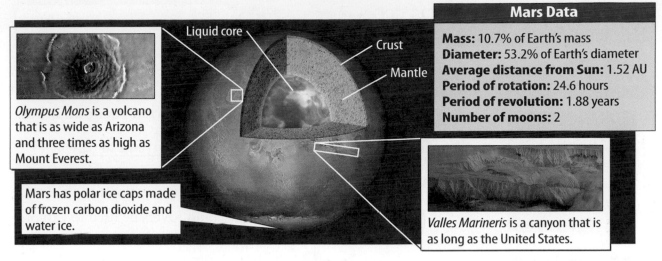

Liquid core

Crust

Mantle

Olympus Mons is a volcano that is as wide as Arizona and three times as high as Mount Everest.

Mars has polar ice caps made of frozen carbon dioxide and water ice.

Valles Marineris is a canyon that is as long as the United States.

Mars Data

Mass: 10.7% of Earth's mass
Diameter: 53.2% of Earth's diameter
Average distance from Sun: 1.52 AU
Period of rotation: 24.6 hours
Period of revolution: 1.88 years
Number of moons: 2

▲ **Figure 10** 🗝 Mars is a small, rocky planet with deep canyons and tall mountains.

Mars

The fourth planet from the Sun is Mars, shown in **Figure 10.** Mars is about half the size of Earth. It has two very small and irregularly shaped moons. These moons might be asteroids that were captured by Mars's gravity.

Many space probes have visited Mars. Most of them have searched for signs of water that might indicate the presence of living organisms. Images of Mars show features that might have been made by water, such as the gullies in **Figure 11.** So far no evidence of liquid water or life has been found.

Mars's Atmosphere

The atmosphere of Mars is about 95 percent carbon dioxide. It is thin and much less dense than Earth's atmosphere. Temperatures range from about −125°C at the poles to about 20°C at the equator during a martian summer. Winds on Mars sometimes produce great dust storms that last for months.

Mars's Surface

The reddish color of Mars is because its soil contains iron oxide, a compound in rust. Some of Mars's major surface features are shown in **Figure 10.** The enormous canyon Valles Marineris is about 4,000 km long. The Martian volcano Olympus Mons is the largest known mountain in the solar system. Mars also has polar ice caps made of frozen carbon dioxide and ice.

The southern hemisphere of Mars is covered with craters. The northern hemisphere is smoother and appears to be covered by lava flows. Some scientists have proposed that the lava flows were caused by the impact of an object about 2,000 km in diameter.

 Key Concept Check Describe the atmosphere of each inner planet.

Figure 11 Gullies such as these might have been formed by the flow of liquid water. ▼

Lesson 2 Review

Visual Summary

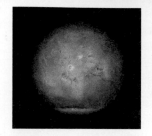

The terrestrial planets include Mercury, Venus, Earth, and Mars.

The inner planets all are made of rocks and minerals, but they have different characteristics. Earth is the only planet with liquid water.

The greenhouse effect greatly increases the surface temperature of Venus.

FOLDABLES

Use your lesson Foldable to review the lesson. Save your Foldable for the project at the end of the chapter.

What do you think NOW?

You first read the statements below at the beginning of the chapter.

3. Earth is the only inner planet that has a moon.

4. Venus is the hottest planet in the solar system.

Did you change your mind about whether you agree or disagree with the statements? Rewrite any false statements to make them true.

Use Vocabulary

1 **Define** *greenhouse effect* in your own words.

Understand Key Concepts

2 **Explain** why Venus is hotter than Mercury, even though Mercury is closer to the Sun.

3 **Infer** Why could rovers be used to explore Mars but not Venus?

4 Which of the inner planets has the greatest mass?
   A. Mercury   C. Earth
   B. Venus   D. Mars

5 **Relate** Describe the relationship between an inner planet's distance from the Sun and its period of revolution.

Interpret Graphics

6 **Infer** Which planet shown below is most likely able to support life now or was able to in the past? Explain your reasoning.

Mercury   Venus   Mars

7 **Compare and Contrast** Copy and fill in the table below to compare and contrast properties of Venus and Earth.

Planet	Similarities	Differences
Venus		
Earth		

Critical Thinking

8 **Imagine** How might the temperatures on Mercury be different if it had the same mass as Earth? Explain.

9 **Judge** Do you think the inner planets should be explored or should the money be spent on other things? Justify your opinion.

What can we learn about planets by graphing their characteristics?

Scientists collect and analyze data, and draw conclusions based on data. They are particularly interested in finding trends and relationships in data. One commonly used method of finding relationships is by graphing data. Graphing allows different types of data be to seen in relation to one another.

Learn It

Scientists know that some properties of the planets are related. **Graphing data** makes the relationships easy to identify. The graphs can show mathematical relationships such as direct and inverse relationships. Often, however, the graphs show that there is no relationship in the data.

Try It

1. You will plot two graphs that explore the relationships in data. The first graph compares a planet's distance from the Sun and its orbital period. The second graph compares a planet's distance from the Sun and its radius. Make a prediction about how these two sets of data are related, if at all. The data is shown in the table below.

Planet	Average Distance From the Sun (AU)	Orbital Period (yr)	Planet Radius (km)
Mercury	0.39	0.24	2440
Venus	0.72	0.62	6051
Earth	1.00	1.0	6378
Mars	1.52	1.9	3397
Jupiter	5.20	11.9	71,492
Saturn	9.58	29.4	60,268
Uranus	19.2	84.0	25,559
Neptune	30.1	164	24,764

2. Use the data in the table to plot a line graph showing orbital period versus average distance from the Sun. On the x-axis, plot the planet's distance from the Sun. On the y-axis, plot the planet's orbital period. Make sure the range of each axis is suitable for the data to be plotted, and clearly label each planet's data point.

3. Use the data in the table to plot a line graph showing planet radius versus average distance from the Sun. On the y-axis, plot the planet's radius. Make sure the range of each axis is suitable for the data to be plotted, and clearly label each planet's data point.

Apply It

4. Examine the *Orbital Period v. Distance from the Sun* graph. Does the graph show a relationship? If so, describe the relationship between a planet's distance from the Sun and its orbital period in your Science Journal.

5. Examine the *Planet Radius v. Distance from the Sun* graph. Does the graph show a relationship? If so, describe the relationship between a planet's distance from the Sun and its radius.

6. **Key Concept** Identify one or two characteristics the inner planets share that you learned from your graphs.

The Outer Planets

Reading Guide

Key Concepts
ESSENTIAL QUESTIONS

- How are the outer planets similar?
- What are the outer planets made of?

Vocabulary
Galilean moons p. 125

 Multilingual eGlossary

Academic Standards for Science

6.2.4 Compare and contrast the planets of the solar system with one another and with asteroids and comets with regard to their size, composition, distance from sun, surface features and ability to support life.

Also covers: 6.NS.4, 6.NS.6, 6.NS.7

Inquiry What's below?

Clouds often prevent airplane pilots from seeing the ground below. Similarly, clouds block the view of Jupiter's surface. What do you think is below Jupiter's colorful cloud layer? The answer might surprise you—Jupiter is not at all like Earth.

How do we see distant objects in the solar system?

Some of the outer planets were discovered hundreds of years ago. Why weren't all planets discovered?

1. Read and complete a lab safety form.
2. Use a **meterstick, masking tape,** and the **data table** to mark and label the position of each object on the tape on the floor along a straight line.
3. Shine a **flashlight** from "the Sun" horizontally along the tape.
4. Have a partner hold a page of this **book** in the flashlight beam at each planet location. Record your observations in your Science Journal.

Object	Distance from Sun (cm)
Sun	0
Jupiter	39
Saturn	71
Uranus	143
Neptune	295

Think About This

1. What happens to the image of the page as you move away from the flashlight?

2. **Key Concept** Why do you think it is more difficult to observe the outer planets than the inner planets?

The Gas Giants

Have you ever seen water drops on the outside of a glass of ice? They form because water vapor in the air changes to a liquid on the cold glass. Gases also change to liquids at high pressures. These properties of gases affect the outer planets.

The outer planets, shown in **Figure 12,** are called the gas giants because they are primarily made of hydrogen and helium. These elements are usually gases on Earth.

The outer planets have strong gravitational forces because of their huge sizes. These forces apply tremendous pressure to the atmosphere of each planet and changes gases to liquids. Thus, the outer planets mainly have liquid interiors. In general, an outer planet has a thick gas and liquid layer covering a small solid core.

Key Concept Check How are the outer planets similar?

Figure 12 The outer planets are primarily made of gases and liquids.

Visual Check Which outer planet is the largest?

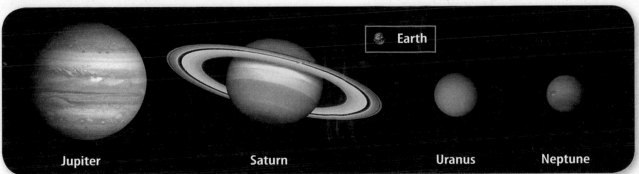

Jupiter   Saturn   Earth   Uranus   Neptune

Make a four-door book. Label each door with the name of an outer planet. Use the book to organize your notes on the outer planets.

Jupiter

The largest planet in the solar system, Jupiter, is shown in **Figure 13.** Its diameter is more than 11 times larger than the diameter of Earth. Its mass is more than twice the mass of all the other planets combined. One way to understand just how big Jupiter is is to realize that more than 1,000 Earths would fit within this gaseous planet's volume.

Jupiter takes almost 12 Earth years to complete one orbit. Yet, it spins faster than any other planet. Its period of rotation is less than 10 hours. Like all the outer planets, Jupiter has a ring system.

Jupiter's Atmosphere

The atmosphere on Jupiter is about 90 percent hydrogen and 10 percent helium and is about 1,000 km deep. Within the atmosphere are layers of dense, colorful clouds. Because Jupiter rotates so quickly, these clouds stretch into colorful, swirling bands. The Great Red Spot on the planet's surface is a storm of swirling gases.

Jupiter's Structure

Overall, Jupiter is about 80 percent hydrogen and 20 percent helium with small amounts of other materials. The planet is a ball of gas swirling around a thick liquid layer that conceals a solid core. About 1,000 km below the outer edge of the cloud layer, the pressure is so great that the hydrogen gas changes to liquid. This thick layer of liquid hydrogen covers Jupiter's core. Scientists do not know for sure what makes up the core. They suspect that the core is made of rock and iron. The core might be as large as Earth and could have 10 times more mass.

Key Concept Check Describe what makes up each of Jupiter's three distinct layers.

Figure 13 Jupiter is mainly hydrogen and helium. Throughout most of the planet, the pressure is high enough to change the hydrogen gas into a liquid.

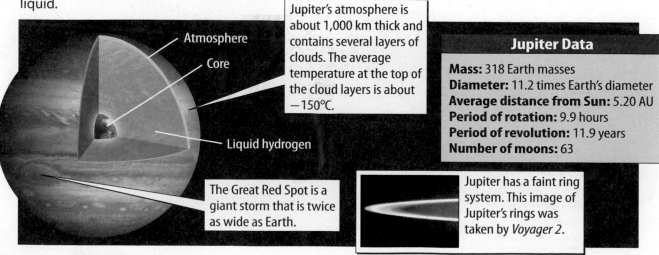

Atmosphere
Core
Liquid hydrogen

Jupiter's atmosphere is about 1,000 km thick and contains several layers of clouds. The average temperature at the top of the cloud layers is about −150°C.

The Great Red Spot is a giant storm that is twice as wide as Earth.

Jupiter Data

Mass: 318 Earth masses
Diameter: 11.2 times Earth's diameter
Average distance from Sun: 5.20 AU
Period of rotation: 9.9 hours
Period of revolution: 11.9 years
Number of moons: 63

Jupiter has a faint ring system. This image of Jupiter's rings was taken by *Voyager 2*.

The Moons of Jupiter

Jupiter has at least 63 moons, more than any other planet. Jupiter's four largest moons were first spotted by Galileo Galilei in 1610. *The four largest moons of Jupiter—Io, Europa, Ganymede, and Callisto—are known as the* **Galilean moons.** The Galilean moons all are made of rock and ice. The moons Ganymede, Callisto, and Io are larger than Earth's Moon. Collisions between Jupiter's moons and meteorites likely resulted in the particles that make up the planet's faint rings.

Saturn

Saturn is the sixth planet from the Sun. Like Jupiter, Saturn rotates rapidly and has horizontal bands of clouds. Saturn is about 90 percent hydrogen and 10 percent helium. It is the least dense planet. Its density is less than that of water.

Saturn's Structure

Saturn is made mostly of hydrogen and helium with small amounts of other materials. As shown in **Figure 14,** Saturn's structure is similar to Jupiter's structure—an outer gas layer, a thick layer of liquid hydrogen, and a solid core.

The ring system around the planet is the largest and most complex in the solar system. Saturn has seven bands of rings, each containing thousands of narrower ringlets. The main ring system is over 70,000 km wide, but it is likely less than 30 m thick. The ice particles in the rings are possibly from a moon that was shattered in a collision with another icy object.

 Key Concept Check Describe what makes up Saturn and its ring system.

Figure 14  Like Jupiter, Saturn is mainly hydrogen and helium. Saturn's rings are one of the most noticeable features of the solar system.

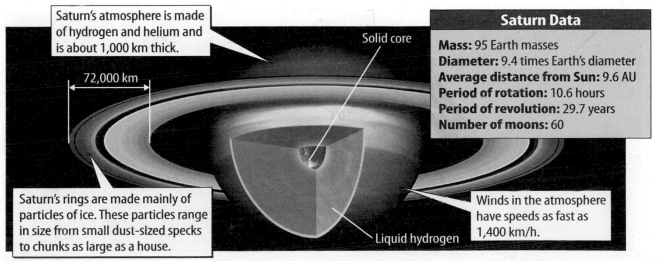

Saturn's atmosphere is made of hydrogen and helium and is about 1,000 km thick.

72,000 km

Solid core

Saturn's rings are made mainly of particles of ice. These particles range in size from small dust-sized specks to chunks as large as a house.

Liquid hydrogen

Winds in the atmosphere have speeds as fast as 1,400 km/h.

Saturn Data

Mass: 95 Earth masses
Diameter: 9.4 times Earth's diameter
Average distance from Sun: 9.6 AU
Period of rotation: 10.6 hours
Period of revolution: 29.7 years
Number of moons: 60

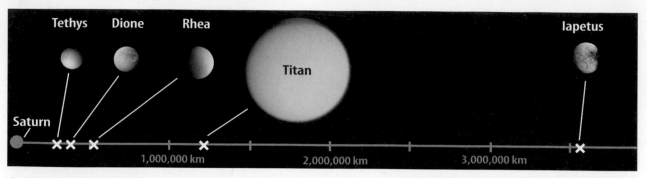

▲ **Figure 15** The five largest moons of Saturn are shown above drawn to scale. Titan is Saturn's largest moon.

(Labels in figure: Tethys, Dione, Rhea, Titan, Iapetus, Saturn; scale: 1,000,000 km, 2,000,000 km, 3,000,000 km)

WORD ORIGIN ·············

probe
from Medieval Latin *proba*,
means "examination"

Saturn's Moons

Saturn has at least 60 moons. The five largest moons, Titan, Rhea, Dione, Iapetus, and Tethys, are shown in **Figure 15.** Most of Saturn's moons are chunks of ice less than 10 km in diameter. However, Titan is larger than the planet Mercury. Titan is the only moon in the solar system with a dense atmosphere. In 2005, the *Cassini* orbiter released the *Huygens* (HOY guns) **probe** that landed on Titan's surface.

Uranus

Uranus, shown in **Figure 16,** is the seventh planet from the Sun. It has a system of narrow, dark rings and a diameter about four times that of Earth. *Voyager 2* is the only space probe to explore Uranus. The probe flew by the planet in 1986.

Uranus has a deep atmosphere composed mostly of hydrogen and helium. The atmosphere also contains a small amount of methane. Beneath the atmosphere is a thick, slushy layer of water, ammonia, and other materials. Uranus might also have a solid, rocky core.

Key Concept Check Identify the substances that make up the atmosphere and the thick slushy layer on Uranus.

Figure 16 Uranus is mainly gas and liquid, with a small solid core. Methane gas in the atmosphere gives Uranus a bluish color. ▼

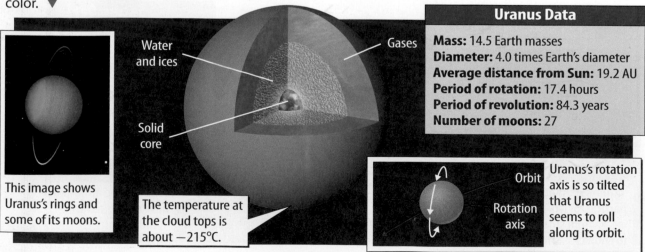

This image shows Uranus's rings and some of its moons.

Water and ices

Solid core

Gases

The temperature at the cloud tops is about −215°C.

Uranus Data
Mass: 14.5 Earth masses
Diameter: 4.0 times Earth's diameter
Average distance from Sun: 19.2 AU
Period of rotation: 17.4 hours
Period of revolution: 84.3 years
Number of moons: 27

Orbit

Rotation axis

Uranus's rotation axis is so tilted that Uranus seems to roll along its orbit.

Uranus's Axis and Moons

Figure 16 shows that Uranus has a tilted axis of rotation. In fact, it is so tilted that the planet moves around the Sun like a rolling ball. This sideways tilt might have been caused by a collision with an Earth-sized object.

Uranus has at least 27 moons. The two largest moons, Titania and Oberon, are considerably smaller than Earth's moon. Titania has an icy cracked surface that once might have been covered by an ocean.

Neptune

Neptune, shown in **Figure 17,** was discovered in 1846. Like Uranus, Neptune's atmosphere is mostly hydrogen and helium, with a trace of methane. Its interior also is similar to the interior of Uranus. Neptune's interior is partially frozen water and ammonia with a rock and iron core.

Neptune has at least 13 moons and a faint, dark ring system. Its largest moon, Triton, is made of rock with an icy outer layer. It has a surface of frozen nitrogen and geysers that erupt nitrogen gas.

 Key Concept Check How does the atmosphere and interior of Neptune compare with that of Uranus?

 **MiniLab**   **15 minutes**

How do Saturn's moons affect its rings?

In this lab, sugar models Saturn's rings. How might Saturn's moons affect its rings?

1. Read and complete a lab safety form.

2. Hold two **sharpened pencils** with their points even and then **tape** them together.

3. Insert a third pencil into the hole in a **record.** Hold the pencil so the record is in a horizontal position.

4. Have your partner sprinkle **sugar** evenly over the surface of the record. Hold the taped pencils vertically over the record so that the tips rest in the record's grooves.

5. Slowly turn the record. In your Science Journal, record what happens to the sugar.

Analyze and Conclude

1. **Compare and Contrast** What feature of Saturn's rings do the pencils model?

2. **Infer** What do you think causes the spaces between the rings of Saturn?

3. 🔑 **Key Concept** What would have to be true for a moon to interact in this way with Saturn's rings?

Figure 17 🔑 The atmosphere of Neptune is similar to that of Uranus—mainly hydrogen and helium with a trace of methane. The dark circular areas on Neptune are swirling storms. Winds on Neptune sometimes exceed 1,000 km/h.

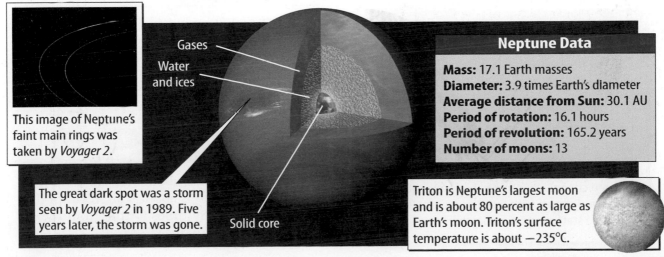

This image of Neptune's faint main rings was taken by *Voyager 2.*

Gases

Water and ices

The great dark spot was a storm seen by *Voyager 2* in 1989. Five years later, the storm was gone.

Solid core

Neptune Data

Mass: 17.1 Earth masses
Diameter: 3.9 times Earth's diameter
Average distance from Sun: 30.1 AU
Period of rotation: 16.1 hours
Period of revolution: 165.2 years
Number of moons: 13

Triton is Neptune's largest moon and is about 80 percent as large as Earth's moon. Triton's surface temperature is about −235°C.

Lesson 3 Review

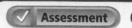
Visual Summary

All of the outer planets are primarily made of materials that are gases on Earth. Colorful clouds of gas cover Saturn and Jupiter.

Jupiter is the largest outer planet. Its four largest moons are known as the Galilean moons.

Uranus has an unusual tilt, possibly due to a collision with a large object.

FOLDABLES

Use your lesson Foldable to review the lesson. Save your Foldable for the project at the end of the chapter.

What do you think NOW?

You first read the statements below at the beginning of the chapter.

5. The outer planets also are called the gas giants.

6. The atmospheres of Saturn and Jupiter are mainly water vapor.

Did you change your mind about whether you agree or disagree with the statements? Rewrite any false statements to make them true.

Use Vocabulary

1. **Identify** What are the four Galilean moons of Jupiter?

Understand Key Concepts

2. **Contrast** How are the rings of Saturn different from the rings of Jupiter?

3. Which planet's rings probably formed from a collision between an icy moon and another icy object?
   A. Jupiter   C. Saturn
   B. Neptune   D. Uranus

4. **List** the outer planets by increasing mass.

Interpret Graphics

5. **Infer** from the diagram below how Uranus's tilted axis affects its seasons.

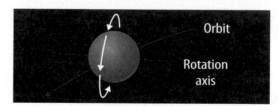

Orbit

Rotation axis

6. **Organize Information** Copy the organizer below and use it to list the outer planets.

Outer Planets

Critical Thinking

7. **Predict** what would happen to Jupiter's atmosphere if its gravitational force suddenly decreased. Explain.

8. **Evaluate** Is life more likely on a dry and rocky moon or on an icy moon? Explain.

Math Skills   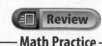 Review
————————————————— Math Practice ———

9. **Calculate** Mars is about 1.52 AU from the Sun, and Saturn is about 9.58 AU from the Sun. How many times farther from the Sun is Saturn than Mars?

Pluto

What in the world is it?

Since Pluto's discovery in 1930, students have learned that the solar system has nine planets. But in 2006, the number of planets was changed to eight. What happened?

Neil deGrasse Tyson is an astrophysicist at the American Museum of Natural History in New York City. He and his fellow Museum scientists were among the first to question Pluto's classification as a planet. One reason was that Pluto is smaller than six moons in our solar system, including Earth's moon. Another reason was that Pluto's orbit is more oval-shaped, or elliptical, than the orbits of other planets. Also, Pluto has the most tilted orbit of all planets—17 degrees out of the plane of the solar system. Finally, unlike other planets, Pluto is mostly ice.

Tyson also questioned the definition of a planet—an object that orbits the Sun. Then shouldn't comets be planets? In addition, he noted that when Ceres, an object orbiting the Sun between Jupiter and Mars, was discovered in 1801, it was classified as a planet. But, as astronomers discovered more objects like Ceres, it was reclassified as an asteroid. Then, during the 1990s, many space objects similar to Pluto were discovered. They orbit the Sun beyond Neptune's orbit in a region called the Kuiper belt.

These new discoveries led Tyson and others to conclude that Pluto should be reclassified. In 2006, the International Astronomical Union agreed. Pluto was reclassified as a dwarf planet—an object that is spherical in shape and orbits the Sun in a zone with other objects. Pluto lost its rank as smallest planet, but became "king of the Kuiper belt."

Pluto TIME LINE

1930
Astronomer Clyde Tombaugh discovers a ninth planet, Pluto.

1992
The first object is discovered in the Kuiper belt.

July 2005
Eris—a Pluto-sized object—is discovered in the Kuiper belt.

January 2006
NASA launches *New Horizons* spacecraft, expected to reach Pluto in 2015.

August 2006
Pluto is reclassified as a dwarf planet.

Neil deGrasse Tyson is director of the Hayden Planetarium at the American Museum of Natural History. ▶

This illustration shows what Pluto might look like if you were standing on one of its moons.

It's Your Turn

RESEARCH With a group, identify the different types of objects in our solar system. Consider size, composition, location, and whether the objects have moons. Propose at least two different ways to group the objects.

Reading Guide

Key Concepts 🔑
ESSENTIAL QUESTIONS

- What is a dwarf planet?
- What are the characteristics of comets and asteroids?
- How does an impact crater form?

Vocabulary

meteoroid p. 134

meteor p. 134

meteorite p. 134

impact crater p. 134

g Multilingual eGlossary

Academic Standards for Science

6.2.4 Compare and contrast the planets of the solar system with one another and with asteroids and comets with regard to their size, composition, distance from sun, surface features and ability to support life.

Also covers: 6.NS.5, 6.NS.7, 6.NS.9, 6.NS.11

Dwarf Planets and Other Objects

Inquiry Will it return?

You would probably remember a sight like this. This image of comet C/2006 P1 was taken in 2007. The comet is no longer visible from Earth. Believe it or not, many comets appear then reappear hundreds to millions of years later.

How might asteroids and moons form?

In this activity, you will explore one way moons and asteroids might have formed.

1. Read and complete a lab safety form.

2. Form a small ball from **modeling clay** and roll it in **sand.**

3. Press a thin layer of modeling clay around a **marble.**

4. Tie equal lengths of **string** to each ball. Hold the strings so the balls are above a **sheet of paper.**

5. Have someone pull back the marble so that its string is parallel to the tabletop and then release it. Record the results in your Science Journal.

Think About This

1. If the collision you modeled occurred in space, what would happen to the sand?

2. **Key Concept** Infer one way scientists propose moons and asteroids formed.

Dwarf Planets

Ceres was discovered in 1801 and was called a planet until similar objects were discovered near it. Then it was called an asteroid. For decades after Pluto's discovery in 1930, it was called a planet. Then, similar objects were discovered, and Pluto lost its planet classification. What type of object is Pluto?

In 2006, the International Astronomical Union (IAU) adopted a new category—dwarf planets. The IAU defines a dwarf planet as an object that orbits a star. When a dwarf planet formed, there was enough mass and gravity that it made a sphere. A dwarf planet has objects similar in mass orbiting near it or crossing its orbital path. Astronomers classify Pluto, Ceres, Eris, Makemake, and Haumea (how May ah) as dwarf planets. **Figure 18** shows four dwarf planets.

Key Concept Check Describe the characteristics of a dwarf planet.

Figure 18 Four dwarf planets are shown to scale. All dwarf planets are smaller than the Moon.

Dwarf Planets

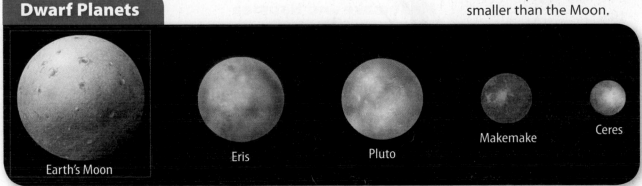

Earth's Moon

Eris

Pluto

Makemake

Ceres

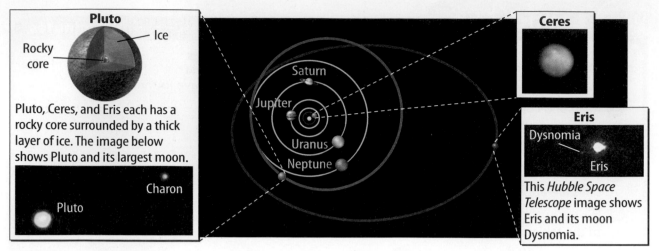

Pluto

Rocky core — Ice

Pluto, Ceres, and Eris each has a rocky core surrounded by a thick layer of ice. The image below shows Pluto and its largest moon.

Charon

Pluto

Ceres

Eris

Dysnomia

Eris

This *Hubble Space Telescope* image shows Eris and its moon Dysnomia.

Figure 19 Because most dwarf planets are so far from Earth, astronomers do not have detailed images of them.

✓**Visual Check** Which dwarf planet orbits closest to Earth?

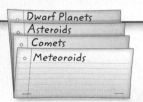

FOLDABLES

Make a layered book from two sheets of paper. Label it as shown. Use it to organize your notes on other objects in the solar system.

○ Dwarf Planets
○ Asteroids
○ Comets
○ Meteoroids

Ceres

Ceres, shown in **Figure 19,** orbits the Sun in the asteroid belt. With a diameter of about 950 km, Ceres is about one-fourth the size of the Moon. It is the smallest dwarf planet. Ceres might have a rocky core surrounded by a layer of water ice and a thin, dusty crust.

Pluto

Pluto is about two-thirds the size of the Moon. Pluto is so far from the Sun that its period of revolution is about 248 years. Like Ceres, Pluto has a rocky core surrounded by ice. With an average surface temperature of about −230°C, Pluto is so cold that it is covered with frozen nitrogen.

Pluto has three known moons. The largest moon, Charon, has a diameter that is about half the diameter of Pluto. Pluto also has two smaller moons, Hydra and Nix.

Eris

The largest dwarf planet, Eris, was discovered in 2003. Its orbit lasts about 557 years. Currently, Eris is three times farther from the Sun than Pluto is. The structure of Eris is probably similar to Pluto. Dysnomia (dis NOH mee uh) is the only known moon of Eris.

Makemake and Haumea

In 2008, the IAU designated two new objects as dwarf planets: Makemake and Haumea. Though smaller than Pluto, Makemake is one of the largest objects in a region of the solar system called the Kuiper (KI puhr) belt. The Kuiper belt extends from about the orbit of Neptune to about 50 AU from the Sun. Haumea is also in the Kuiper belt and is smaller than Pluto.

✓ **Reading Check** Which dwarf planet is the largest? Which dwarf planet is the smallest?

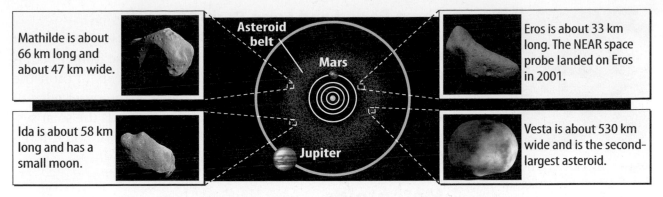

Mathilde is about 66 km long and about 47 km wide.

Ida is about 58 km long and has a small moon.

Asteroid belt

Mars

Jupiter

Eros is about 33 km long. The NEAR space probe landed on Eros in 2001.

Vesta is about 530 km wide and is the second-largest asteroid.

Figure 20 The asteroids that orbit the Sun in the asteroid belt are many sizes and shapes.

Asteroids

Recall from Lesson 1 that asteroids are pieces of rock and ice. Most asteroids orbit the Sun in the asteroid belt. The asteroid belt is between the orbits of Mars and Jupiter, as shown in **Figure 20.** Hundreds of thousands of asteroids have been discovered. The largest asteroid, Pallas, is over 500 km in diameter.

Asteroids are chunks of rock and ice that never clumped together like the rocks and ice that formed the inner planets. Some astronomers suggest that the strength of Jupiter's gravitational field might have caused the chunks to collide so violently, and they broke apart instead of sticking together. This means that asteroids are objects left over from the formation of the solar system.

Key Concept Check Where do the orbits of most asteroids occur?

Comets

Recall that comets are mixtures of rock, ice, and dust. The particles in a comet are loosely held together by the gravitational attractions among the particles. As shown in **Figure 21,** comets orbit the Sun in long elliptical orbits.

The Structure of Comets

The solid, inner part of a comet is its nucleus, as shown in **Figure 21.** As a comet moves closer to the Sun, it heats and can develop a bright tail. Heating changes the ice in the comet into a gas. Energy from the Sun pushes some of the gas and dust away from the nucleus and makes it glow. This produces the comet's bright tail and glowing nucleus, called a coma.

Key Concept Check Describe the characteristics of a comet.

Figure 21 When energy from the Sun strikes the gas and dust in the comet's nucleus, it can create a two-part tail. The gas tail always points away from the Sun.

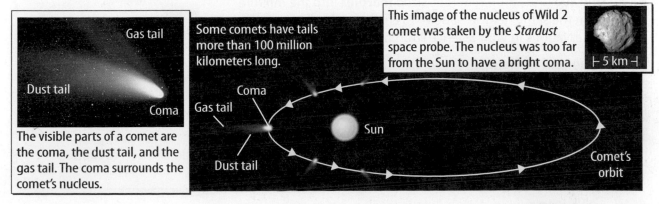

Gas tail

Dust tail

Coma

The visible parts of a comet are the coma, the dust tail, and the gas tail. The coma surrounds the comet's nucleus.

Some comets have tails more than 100 million kilometers long.

Coma

Gas tail

Dust tail

Sun

Comet's orbit

This image of the nucleus of Wild 2 comet was taken by the *Stardust* space probe. The nucleus was too far from the Sun to have a bright coma.

⊢ 5 km ⊣

Figure 22 🔑 When a large meteorite strikes, it can form a giant impact crater like this 1.2-km wide crater in Arizona.

WORD ORIGIN ·············

meteor
from Greek *meteoros*, means "high up"

Short-Period and Long-Period Comets

A short-period comet takes less than 200 Earth years to orbit the Sun. Most short-period comets come from the Kuiper belt. A long-period comet takes more than 200 Earth years to orbit the Sun. Long-period comets come from a area at the outer edge of the solar system, called the Oort cloud. It surrounds the solar system and extends about 100,000 AU from the Sun. Some long-period comets take millions of years to orbit the Sun.

Meteoroids

Every day, many millions of particles called meteoroids enter Earth's atmosphere. *A* **meteoroid** *is a small, rocky particle that moves through space.* Most meteoroids are only about as big as a grain of sand. As a meteoroid passes through Earth's atmosphere, friction makes the meteoroid and the air around it hot enough to glow. *A* **meteor** *is a streak of light in Earth's atmosphere made by a glowing meteoroid.* Most meteoroids burn up in the atmosphere. However, some meteoroids are large enough that they reach Earth's surface before they burn up completely. When this happens, it is called a meteorite. *A* **meteorite** *is a meteoroid that strikes a planet or a moon.*

When a large meteoroite strikes a moon or planet, it often forms a bowl-shaped depression such as the one shown in **Figure 22.** *An* **impact crater** *is a round depression formed on the surface of a planet, moon, or other space object by the impact of a meteorite.* There are more than 170 impact craters on Earth.

🔑 **Key Concept Check** What causes an impact crater to form?

Inquiry MiniLab
20 minutes

How do impact craters form?

In this lab, you will model the formation of an impact crater.

1. Pour a layer of **flour** about 3 cm deep in a **cake pan.**
2. Pour a layer of **cornmeal** about 1 cm deep on top of the flour.
3. One at a time, drop different-sized **marbles** into the mixture from the same height—about 15 cm. Record your observations in your Science Journal.

Analyze and Conclude

1. **Describe** the mixture's surface after you dropped the marbles.

2. **Recognize Cause and Effect** Based on your results, explain why impact craters on moons and planets differ.

3. 🔑 **Key Concept** Explain how the marbles used in the activity could be used to model meteoroids, meteors, and meteorites.

Lesson 4 Review

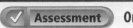

Visual Summary

An asteroid, such as Ida, is a chunk of rock and ice that orbits the Sun.

Comets, which are mixture of rock, ice, and dust, orbit the Sun. A comet's tail is caused by its interaction with the Sun.

When a large meteorite strikes a planet or moon, it often makes an impact crater.

FOLDABLES

Use your lesson Foldable to review the lesson. Save your Foldable for the project at the end of the chapter.

What do you think NOW?

You first read the statements below at the beginning of the chapter.

7. Asteroids and comets are mainly rock and ice.

8. A meteoroid is a meteor that strikes Earth.

Did you change your mind about whether you agree or disagree with the statements? Rewrite any false statements to make them true.

Use Vocabulary

1 **Define** *impact crater* in your own words.

2 **Distinguish** between a meteorite and a meteoroid.

3 **Use the term** *meteor* in a complete sentence.

Understand Key Concepts

4 Which produces an impact crater?
   A. comet   C. meteorite
   B. meteor   D. planet

5 **Reason** Are you more likely to see a meteor or a meteoroid? Explain.

6 **Differentiate** between objects located in the asteroid belt and objects located in the Kuiper belt.

Interpret Graphics

7 **Explain** why some comets have a two-part tail during portions of their orbit.

8 **Organize Information** Copy the table below and list the major characteristics of a dwarf planet.

Object	Defining Characteristic
Dwarf Plant	

Critical Thinking

9 **Compose** a paragraph describing what early sky observers might have thought when they saw a comet.

10 **Evaluate** Do you agree with the decision to reclassify Pluto as a dwarf planet? Defend your opinion.

Scaling down the Solar System

Materials

2.25 in–wide register tape (several rolls)

meterstick

masking tape

colored markers

Safety

A scale model is a physical representation of something that is much smaller or much larger. Reduced-size scale models are made of very large things, such as the solar system. The scale used must reduce the actual size to a size reasonable for the model.

Question

What scale can you use to represent the distances between solar system objects?

Procedure

1 First, decide how big your solar system will be. Use the data given in the table to figure out how far apart the Sun and Neptune would be if a scale of 1 meter = 1 AU is used. Would a solar system based on that scale fit in the space you have available?

2 With your group determine the scale that results in a model that fits the available space. Larger models are usually more accurate, so choose a scale that produces the largest model that fits in the available space.

3 Once you have decided on a scale, copy the table in your Science Journal. Replace the word (Scale) in the third column of the table with the unit you have chosen. Then fill in the scaled distance for each planet.

Planet	Distance from the Sun (AU)	Distance from the Sun (Scale)
Mercury	0.39	
Venus	0.72	
Earth	1.00	
Mars	1.52	
Jupiter	5.20	
Saturn	9.54	
Uranus	19.18	
Neptune	30.06	

④ On register tape, mark the positions of objects in the solar system based on your chosen scale. Use a length of register tape that is slightly longer than the scaled distance between the Sun and Neptune.

⑤ Tape the ends of the register tape to a table or the floor. Mark a dot at one end of the paper to represent the Sun. Measure along the tape from the center of the dot to the location of Mercury. Mark a dot at this position and label it *Mercury*. Repeat this process for the remaining planets.

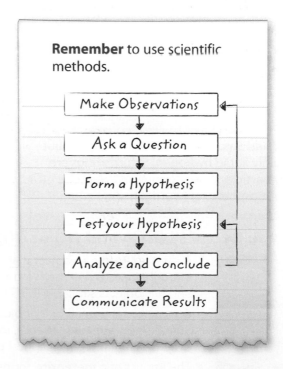

Analyze and Conclude

⑥ **Critique** There are many objects in the solar system. These objects have different sizes, structures, and orbits. Examine your scale model of the solar system. How accurate is the model? How could the model be changed to be more accurate?

⑦ 🅑 **The Big Idea** Pluto is a dwarf planet located beyond Neptune. Based on the pattern of distance data for the planets shown in the table, approximately how far from the Sun would you expect to find Pluto? Explain you reasoning.

⑧ **Calculate** What length of register tape is needed if a scale of 30 cm = 1 AU is used for the solar system model?

Communicate Your Results

Compare your model with other groups in your class by taping them all side-by-side. Discuss any major differences in your models. Discuss the difficulties in making the scale models much smaller.

 **Extension**

How can you build a scale model of the solar system that accurately shows both planetary diameters and distances? Describe how you would go about figuring this out.

Lab Tips

☑ A scale is the ratio between the actual size of something and a representation of it.

☑ The distances between the planets and the Sun are average distances because planetary orbits are not perfect circles.

Remember to use scientific methods.

Make Observations
↓
Ask a Question
↓
Form a Hypothesis
↓
Test your Hypothesis
↓
Analyze and Conclude
↓
Communicate Results

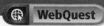
WebQuest

THE BIG IDEA

The solar system contains planets, dwarf planets, comets, asteroids, and other small solar system bodies.

Key Concepts Summary	Vocabulary

Lesson 1: The Structure of the Solar System

- The inner planets are made mainly of solid materials. The outer planets, which are larger than the inner planets, have thick gas and liquid layers covering a small solid core.
- Astronomers measure vast distances in space in **astronomical units;** an astronomical unit is about 150 million km.
- The speed of each planet changes as it moves along its elliptical orbit around the Sun.

asteroid p. 109
comet p. 109
astronomical unit p. 110
period of revolution p. 110
period of rotation p. 110

Lesson 2: The Inner Planets

- The inner planets—Mercury, Venus, Earth, and Mars—are made of rock and metallic materials.
- The **greenhouse effect** makes Venus the hottest planet.
- Mercury has no atmosphere. The atmospheres of Venus and Mars are almost entirely carbon dioxide. Earth's atmosphere is a mixture of gases and a small amount of water vapor.

terrestrial planet p. 115
greenhouse effect p. 117

Lesson 3: The Outer Planets

- The outer planets—Jupiter, Saturn, Uranus, and Neptune—are primarily made of hydrogen and helium.
- Jupiter and Saturn have thick cloud layers, but are mainly liquid hydrogen. Saturn's rings are largely particles of ice. Uranus and Neptune have thick atmospheres of hydrogen and helium.

Galilean moons p. 125

Lesson 4: Dwarf Planets and Other Objects

- A dwarf planet is an object that orbits a star, has enough mass to pull itself into a spherical shape, and has objects similar in mass orbiting near it.
- An asteroid is a small rocky object that orbits the Sun. Comets are made of rock, ice, and dust and orbit the Sun in highly elliptical paths.
- The impact of a **meteorite** forms an **impact crater.**

meteoroid p. 134
meteor p. 134
meteorite p. 134
impact crater p. 134

FOLDABLES® Chapter Project

Assemble your lesson Foldables as shown to make a Chapter Project. Use the project to review what you have learned in this chapter.

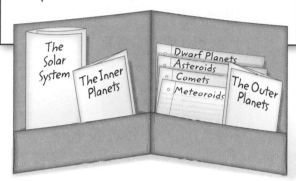

The Solar System
The Inner Planets
Dwarf Planets
Asteroids
Comets
Meteoroids
The Outer Planets

Use Vocabulary

Match each phrase with the correct vocabulary term from the Study Guide.

1. the time it takes an object to complete one rotation on its axis

2. the average distance from Earth to the Sun

3. the time it takes an object to travel once around the Sun

4. an increase in temperature caused by energy trapped by a planet's atmosphere

5. an inner planet

6. the four largest moons of Jupiter

7. a streak of light in Earth's atmosphere made by a glowing meteoroid

Link Vocabulary and Key Concepts

Concepts in Motion **Interactive Concept Map**

Copy this concept map, and then use vocabulary terms to complete the concept map.

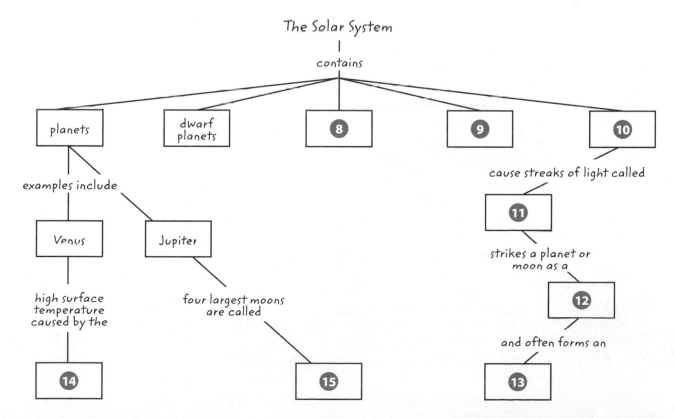

The Solar System
|
contains

planets   dwarf planets   8   9   10

examples include

cause streaks of light called

Venus   Jupiter   11

high surface temperature caused by the

strikes a planet or moon as a

four largest moons are called   12

and often forms an

14   15   13

Chapter 4 Review

Understand Key Concepts

1. Which solar system object is the largest?
   A. Jupiter
   B. Neptune
   C. the Sun
   D. Saturn

2. Which best describes the asteroid belt?
   A. another name for the Oort cloud
   B. the region where comets originate
   C. large chunks of gas, dust, and ice
   D. millions of small rocky objects

3. Which describes a planet's speed as it orbits the Sun?
   A. It constantly decreases.
   B. It constantly increases.
   C. It does not change.
   D. It increases then decreases.

4. The diagram below shows a planet's orbit around the Sun. What does the blue arrow represent?
   A. the gravitational pull of the Sun
   B. the planet's orbital path
   C. the planet's path if Sun did not exist
   D. the planet's speed

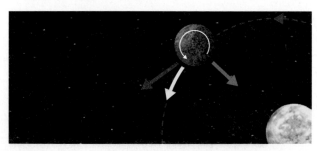

5. Which describes the greenhouse effect?
   A. effect of gravity on temperature
   B. energy emitted by the Sun
   C. energy trapped by atmosphere
   D. reflection of light from a planet

6. How are the terrestrial planets similar?
   A. similar densities
   B. similar diameters
   C. similar periods of rotation
   D. similar rocky surfaces

7. Which inner planet is the hottest?
   A. Earth
   B. Mars
   C. Mercury
   D. Venus

8. The photograph below shows how Earth appears from space. How does Earth differ from other inner planets?

   A. Its atmosphere contains large amounts of methane.
   B. Its period of revolution is much greater.
   C. Its surface is covered by large amounts of liquid water.
   D. Its surface temperature is higher.

9. Which two gases make up most of the outer planets?
   A. ammonia and helium
   B. ammonia and hydrogen
   C. hydrogen and helium
   D. methane and hydrogen

10. Which is true of the dwarf planets?
    A. more massive than nearby objects
    B. never have moons
    C. orbit near the Sun
    D. spherically shaped

11. Which is a bright streak of light in Earth's atmosphere?
    A. a comet
    B. a meteor
    C. a meteorite
    D. a meteoroid

12. Which best describes an asteroid?
    A. icy
    B. rocky
    C. round
    D. wet

Critical Thinking

13 **Relate** changes in speed during a planet's orbit to the shape of the orbit and the gravitational pull of the Sun.

14 **Compare** In what ways are planets and dwarf planets similar?

15 **Apply** Like Venus, Earth's atmosphere contains carbon dioxide. What might happen on Earth if the amount of carbon dioxide in the atmosphere increases? Explain.

16 **Defend** A classmate states that life will someday be found on Mars. Defend the statement and offer a reason why life might exist on Mars.

17 **Infer** whether a planet with active volcanoes would have more or fewer craters than a planet without active volcanoes. Explain.

18 **Support** Use the diagram of the asteroid belt to support the explanation of how the belt formed.

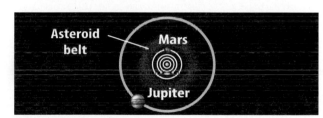

19 **Evaluate** The *Huygens* probe transmitted data about Titan for only 90 min. In your opinion, was this worth the effort of sending the probe?

20 **Explain** why Jupiter's moon Ganymede is not considered a dwarf planet, even though it is bigger than Mercury.

Writing in Science

21 **Compose** a pamphlet that describes how the International Astronomical Union classifies planets, dwarf planets, and small solar system objects.

REVIEW **THE BIG IDEA**

22 What kinds of objects are in the solar system? Summarize the types of space objects that make up the solar system and give at least one example of each.

23 The photo below shows part of Saturn's rings and two of its moons. Describe what Saturn and its rings are made of and explain why the other two objects are moons.

Math Skills

Review — **Math Practice** —

Use Ratios

Inner Planet Data			
Planet	Diameter (% of Earth's diameter)	Mass (% of Earth's mass)	Average Distance from Sun (AU)
Mercury	38.3	5.5	0.39
Venus	95	81.5	0.72
Earth	100	100	1.00
Mars	53.2	10.7	1.52

24 Use the table above to calculate how many times farther from the Sun Mars is compared to Mercury.

25 Calculate how much greater Venus's mass is compared to Mercury's mass.

Record your answers on the answer sheet provided by your teacher or on a sheet of paper.

Multiple Choice

1 Which is a terrestrial planet?

A Ceres

B Neptune

C Pluto

D Venus

2 An astronomical unit (AU) is the average distance

A between Earth and the Moon.

B from Earth to the Sun.

C to the nearest star in the galaxy.

D to the edge of the solar system.

3 Which is NOT a characteristic of ALL planets?

A exceed the total mass of nearby objects

B have a nearly spherical shape

C have one or more moons

D make an elliptical orbit around the Sun

Use the diagram below to answer question 4.

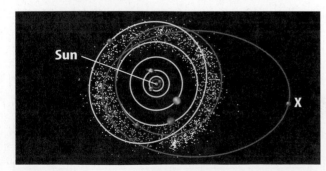

4 Which object in the solar system is marked by an *X* in the diagram?

A asteroid

B meteoroid

C dwarf planet

D outer planet

Use the diagram of Saturn below to answer questions 5 and 6.

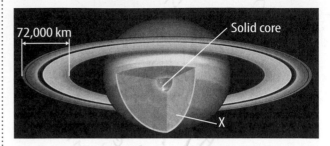

5 The thick inner layer marked *X* in the diagram above is made of which material?

A carbon dioxide

B gaseous helium

C liquid hydrogen

D molten rock

6 In the diagram, Saturn's rings are shown to be 72,000 km in width. Approximately how thick are Saturn's rings?

A 30 m

B 1,000 km

C 14,000 km

D 1 AU

7 Which are NOT found on Mercury's surface?

A high cliffs

B impact craters

C lava flows

D sand dunes

8 What is the primary cause of the extremely high temperatures on the surface of Venus?

A heat rising from the mantle

B lack of an atmosphere

C proximity to the Sun

D the greenhouse effect

Use the diagram below to answer question 9.

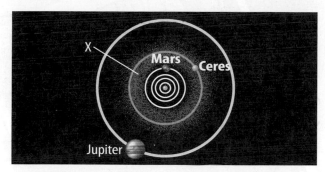

9 In the diagram above, which region of the solar system is marked by an *X*?

   A the asteroid belt

   B the dwarf planets

   C the Kuiper belt

   D the Oort cloud

10 What is a meteorite?

   A a surface depression formed by collision with a rock from space

   B a fragment of rock that strikes a planet or a moon

   C a mixture of ice, dust, and gas with a glowing tail

   D a small rocky particle that moves through space

11 What gives Mars its reddish color?

   A ice caps of frozen carbon dioxide

   B lava from Olympus Mons

   C liquid water in gullies

   D soil rich in iron oxide

Constructed Response

Use the table below to answer questions 12 and 13.

	Inner Planets	Outer Planets
Also called		
Relative size		
Main materials		
General structure		
Number of moons		

12 Copy the table and complete the first five rows to compare the features of the inner planets and outer planets.

13 In the blank row of the table, add another feature of the inner planets and outer planets. Then, describe the feature you have chosen.

14 What features of Earth make it suitable for supporting life as we know it?

15 How are planets, dwarf planets, and asteroids both similar and different?

NEED EXTRA HELP?															
If You Missed Question...	1	2	3	4	5	6	7	8	9	10	11	12	13	14	15
Go to Lesson...	2	1	1	1	3	3	2	2	1, 4	4	2	2, 3	2, 3	2	1, 4

Patterns

Have you ever caught a snowflake in your hand or seen one close-up in a book or on TV? You might have heard someone say that no two snowflakes are alike. While this is true, it is also true that all snowflakes have similar patterns. A **pattern** is a consistent plan or model used as a guide for understanding or predicting things. Patterns can be created or occur naturally. The formation of snowflakes is an example of a repeating pattern. They form piece by piece, as water drops in the air freeze into a six-sided crystal.

How Scientists Use Patterns

Studying and using patterns is useful to scientists because it can help explain the natural world or predict future events. A biologist might study patterns in DNA to predict what organisms will look like. A meteorologist might study cloud formation patterns to predict the weather. When doing research, scientists also try to match patterns found in their data with patterns that occur in nature. This helps to determine whether data are accurate and helps to predict outcomes.

Types of Patterns

Cyclic Patterns

A cycle, or repeated series of events, is a form of pattern. An organism's life cycle typically follows the pattern of birth, growth, and death. Scientists study an organism's life cycle to predict the life of its offspring.

Adult

Eggs

Late tadpole

Early tadpole

Physical Patterns

Physical patterns have an artistic or decorative design. Physical patterns can occur naturally, such as the patterns in the colors on butterfly wings or flower petals, or they can be created intentionally, such as a design in a brick wall.

Patterns in Life Science

Why do police detectives or forensic scientists take fingerprints at a crime scene? Forensic scientists know that every fingerprint is unique. Fingerprints contain patterns that can help detectives narrow a list of suspects. The patterns on the fingerprints can then be examined more closely to identify an exact individual. This is because no two humans have the same fingerprint, just as no two zebras have the same stripe pattern.

Patterns are an important key to understanding life science. They are found across all classifications of life and are studied by scientists. Patterns help scientists understand the genetic makeup, lifestyle, and similarities of various species of plants and animals. Zoologists might study the migration patterns of animals to determine the effects climate has on different species. Botanists might study patterns in the leaves of flowering plants to classify the species of the plant and predict the characteristics of the offspring.

Mathematical Patterns

Patterns are applied in mathematics all the time. Whenever you read a number, perform a mathematical operation, or describe a shape or graph, you are using patterns.

2, 5, 8, 11, ___, ___, ___

What numbers come next in this number pattern?

What will the next shape look like according to the pattern?

MiniLab

15 minutes

Leaf Patterns

Each species of flowering plant has leaves with unique patterns.

Leaf Venation

Pinnate
one main vein with smaller branching veins

Palmate
several main veins that branch from one point

Parallel
veins that do not branch

① Obtain a collection of leaves.

② Use the leaves above to identify the venation, or vein patterns, of each leaf.

Analyze and Conclude

1. **Describe** the physical pattern you see in each leaf.

2. **Choose** Besides venation, what other patterns can you use to group the leaves?

3. **Identify** What types of patterns can be used to classify other organisms?

Chapter 5

Life's Classification and Structure

THE BIG IDEA

How is the classification of living things related to the structure of their cells?

Inquiry Why All the Hooks?

This color-enhanced scanning electron micrograph shows the hooked fruit of the goosegrass plant. The hooks attach to the fur of passing animals. This enables the plant's seeds, which are in the fruit, to spread.

- What characteristics would you use to classify this plant?

- How is the classification of living things related to the structure of their cells?

Get Ready to Read

What do you think?

Before you read, decide if you agree or disagree with each of these statements. As you read this chapter, see if you change your mind about any of the statements.

1. All living things are made of cells.

2. A group of organs that work together and perform a function is called a tissue.

3. Living things are classified based on similar characteristics.

4. *Cell wall* is a term used to describe the cell membrane.

5. Prokaryotic cells contain a nucleus.

6. Plants use chloroplasts to process energy.

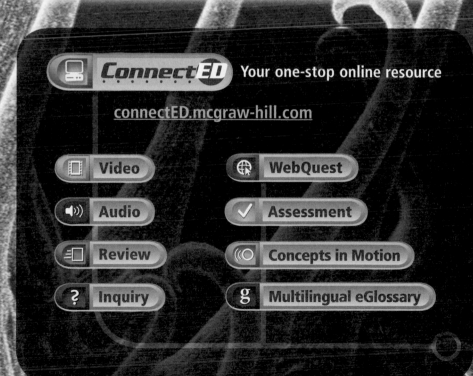

ConnectED Your one-stop online resource

connectED.mcgraw-hill.com

- Video
- Audio
- Review
- Inquiry
- WebQuest
- Assessment
- Concepts in Motion
- Multilingual eGlossary

Lesson 1

Classifying Living Things

Reading Guide

Key Concepts
ESSENTIAL QUESTIONS

- What are living things?
- What do living things need?
- How are living things classified?

Vocabulary

autotroph p. 154

heterotroph p. 154

habitat p. 155

binomial nomenclature p. 156

taxon p. 157

g Multilingual eGlossary

Academic Standards for Science

6.3.6 Recognize that food provides the energy for the work that cells do and is a source of the molecular building blocks that can be incorporated into a cell's structure or stored for later use.

Also covers: 6.NS.7, 6.NS.11

Inquiry Living or Not?

This tide pool contains sea anemones, barnacles, and sea stars that are living and rocks that are not living. How can you tell whether something is alive? Do all living things move? All living things have certain characteristics that you will read about in this lesson.

Launch Lab

How can you tell whether it is alive?

Living things share several basic characteristics. Think about what you have in common with other living things such as a bug or a tree. Do other things have some of those same characteristics?

1 Read and complete a lab safety form.

2 Observe a **lit candle** for 1–2 min. Pay attention to both the candle and the flame.

3 Write what you observe in your Science Journal.

4 Write what you think you would observe if you were to observe the candle for several hours.

Think About This

1. What characteristics does the flame have that would lead some people to think the flame is alive?

2. What qualities did you think of earlier (that you share with other living things) that the candle does not possess?

3. **Key Concept** What characteristics do you think something must have to be considered alive?

What are living things?

It might be easy to tell whether a bird, a tree, or a person is alive. But for some organisms, it is harder to tell whether they are living things. Look at the moldy bread shown in **Figure 1**. Is the bread a living thing? What about the green mold and white mold on the bread? All living things have six characteristics in common:

• Living things are made of cells.

• Living things are organized.

• Living things grow and develop.

• Living things respond to their environment.

• Living things reproduce.

• Living things use energy.

The bread shown in **Figure 1** is not living, but the molds growing on the bread are living things. Mold is a type of fungus. If you looked at the mold using a microscope, you would see that it is made of cells. Mold cells respond to their environment by growing and reproducing. The molds obtain energy, which they need to grow, from the bread.

Figure 1 Mold is a living thing.

Key Concept Check What are living things?

Living things are organized.

Marching bands are made up of rows of people playing different instruments. Some rows are made up of people playing flutes, and other rows are filled with drummers. Although marching bands are organized into different rows, all band members work together to play a song. Like marching bands, living things also are organized. Some living things are more complex than others, but all organisms are made of cells. In all cells, **macromolecules** are organized into different structures that help cells function. You might recall that there are four macromolecules in cells—nucleic acids, lipids, proteins, and carbohydrates. Nucleic acids, such as DNA, store information. Lipids are the main component of cell membranes and provide structure. Some proteins are enzymes, and others provide structure. Carbohydrates are used for energy.

 Reading Check Name the four macromolecules in cells.

Unicellular Organisms Some living things are unicellular, which means they are made up of only one cell. In fact, most living things on Earth are unicellular organisms. Unicellular organisms are the earliest forms of life. There are many groups of unicellular organisms, each with **unique** characteristics. Bacteria, amoebas (uh MEE buhz), and paramecia (per uh MEE see ah) are examples of unicellular organisms. Unicellular organisms have everything needed to obtain and use energy, reproduce, and grow inside one cell. Some unicellular organisms are tiny and cannot be seen without a microscope. Other unicellular organisms, such as the plasmodial (plaz MOH dee ul) slime mold shown in **Figure 2,** can be large.

REVIEW VOCABULARY

macromolecule
substance in a cell that forms by joining many small molecules together

ACADEMIC VOCABULARY

unique
(adjective) without an equal, distinctive

Figure 2 A plasmodial slime mold is a huge cell formed by many cells that join together and form one cell.

Multicellular Organisms Soccer teams are made up of many types of players, including goalkeepers, forwards, and fullbacks. Each team member has a specific job, but they all work together when playing a game. Many living things are made of more than one cell and are called multicellular organisms. Like the different types of players on a soccer team, multicellular organisms have different types of cells that carry out specialized functions. The ladybug shown in **Figure 3** has cells that form wings and other cells that form eyes.

Multicellular organisms have different levels of organization. Groups of cells that work together and perform a specific function are called tissues. Tissues that work together and carry out a specific function are called organs. Organs that work together and perform a specific function are called organ systems. Organ systems work together and perform all the functions an organism needs to survive.

Living things grow, develop, and reproduce.

During their lifetimes, living things grow, or increase in size. For a unicellular organism, the size of its cell increases. For a multicellular organism, the number of its cells increases. Living things also develop, or change, during their lifetimes. For some organisms, it is easy to see the changes that happen as they grow and develop. As shown in **Figure 4,** ladybug larva grow into pupae (PYEW pec; singular, pupa), an intermediate stage, before developing into adults.

Once an organism is an adult, it can reproduce either asexually or sexually and form new organisms. Unicellular organisms, such as bacteria, reproduce asexually when one cell divides and forms two new organisms. Some multicellular organisms also can reproduce asexually; one parent organism produces offspring when body cells replicate and divide. Sexual reproduction occurs when the reproductive cells of one or two parent organisms join and form a new organism. Multicellular organisms such as humans and other mammals reproduce sexually. Some organisms such as yeast can reproduce both asexually and sexually.

▲ **Figure 3** 🔑
Multicellular organisms, such as this ladybug, contain groups of cells that carry out special functions.

✅ **Visual Check** What structures can you identify in the ladybug?

Larva   Pupa

◀ **Figure 4** 🔑
A ladybug grows and develops from a larva to a pupa.

✅ **Visual Check** What differences do you see between the two stages?

▲ **Figure 5** Algae are autotrophic because they use sunlight to produce energy.

Figure 6 An octopus responds to potential harm by secreting ink. The ink hides the octopus while it escapes. ▼

Living things use energy.

All living things need energy to survive. Some organisms are able to convert light energy to chemical energy that is used for many cellular processes. *Organisms that convert energy from light or inorganic substances to usable energy are called* **autotrophs** (AW tuh trohfs).

Many autotrophs use energy from light and convert carbon dioxide and water into carbohydrates, or sugars. Autotrophs use the carbohydrates for energy. Plants and the algae shown growing on the pond in **Figure 5** are autotrophs.

Other autotrophs, called chemoautotrophs (kee moh AW tuh trohfs), grow on energy released by chemical reactions of inorganic substances such as sulfur and ammonia. Many chemoautotrophs are bacteria that live in extreme environments such as deep in the ocean or in hot sulfur springs.

Reading Check How do some autotrophs use energy from sunlight?

Heterotrophs (HE tuh roh trohfs) *are organisms that obtain energy from other organisms.* Heterotrophs eat autotrophs or other heterotrophs to obtain energy. Animals and fungi are examples of heterotrophs.

Living things respond to stimuli.

All living things sense their environments. If an organism detects a change in its external environment, it will respond to that change. A change in an organism's environment is called a stimulus (STIHM yuh lus; plural, stimuli). Responding to a stimulus might help an organism protect itself. For example, the octopus in **Figure 6** responds to predators by releasing ink, a black liquid. In many organisms, nerve cells detect the environment, process the information, and coordinate a response.

What do living things need?

You just read that all living things need energy in order to survive. Some organisms obtain energy from food. What else do living things need to survive? Living things also need water and a place to live. Organisms live in environments that are specific to their needs where they can obtain food and water and can get shelter.

A Place to Live

Living things are everywhere. Organisms live in the soil, in lakes, and in caves. Some living things live on or in other organisms. For example, bacteria live in your intestines and on other body surfaces. *A specific environment where an organism lives is its* **habitat.** Most organisms can survive in only a few habitats. The land iguana shown in **Figure 7** lives in warm, tropical environments and would not survive in cold places such as the Arctic.

Food and Water

Living things also need food and water. Food is used for energy. Water is essential for survival. You will read about how water is in all cells and helps them function in Lesson 2. The type of food that an organism eats depends on the habitat in which it lives. Marine iguanas live near the ocean and eat algae. Land iguanas, such as the one in **Figure 7,** live in hot, dry areas and eat cactus fruits and leaves. The food is processed to obtain energy. Plants and some bacteria use energy from sunlight and produce chemical energy for use in cells.

 Key Concept Check What do living things need?

WORD ORIGIN · · · · · · · · · · ·

habitat
from Latin *habitare*, means "to live or dwell"

FOLDABLES®

Make a vertical three-column chart book. Label it as shown. Use it to organize your notes about living things, their needs, and classification criteria.

Definition of a Living Thing	Survival Requirements	Classification Criteria

Figure 7 This Galápagos land iguana is eating the fruit of a prickly pear cactus.

Needs of Living Things 🔑

Math Skills

Use Ratios

A ratio expresses the relationship between two or more things. Ratios can be written
3 to 5, 3:5, or $\frac{3}{5}$.

Reduce ratios to their simplest form. For example, of about 3 million species in the animal kingdom, about 50,000 are mammals. What is the ratio of mammals to animals?

Write the ratio as a fraction.

$$\frac{50{,}000}{3{,}000{,}000}$$

Reduce the fraction to the simplest form.

$$\frac{50{,}000}{3{,}000{,}000} = \frac{5}{300} = \frac{1}{60}$$

(or 1:60 or 1 to 60)

Practice

Of the 5,000 species of mammals, 250 species are carnivores. What is the ratio of carnivores to mammals? Write the ratio in all three ways.

 **Review**

- **Math Practice**
- **Personal Tutor**

How are living things classified?

You might have a notebook with different sections. Each section might contain notes from a different class. This organizes information and makes it easy to find notes on different subjects. Scientists use a classification system to group organisms with similar traits. Classifying living things makes it easier to organize organisms and to recall how they are similar and how they differ.

Naming Living Things

Scientists name living things using a system called binomial nomenclature (bi NOH mee ul • NOH mun klay chur). **Binomial nomenclature** *is a naming system that gives each living thing a two-word scientific name.*

More than 300 years ago a scientist named Carolus Linnaeus created the binomial nomenclature system. All scientific names are in Latin. *Homo sapiens* is the scientific name for humans. As shown in **Table 1,** the scientific name for an Eastern chipmunk is *Tamias striatus.*

Table 1 Classification of the Eastern Chipmunk — Review Personal Tutor

Taxonomic Group	Number of Species	Examples
Domain Eukarya	about 4–10 million	
Kingdom Animalia	about 2 million	
Phylum Chordata	about 50,000	
Class Mammalia	about 5,000	
Order Rodentia	about 2,300	
Family Sciuridae	299	
Genus *Tamias*	25	
Species *Tamias striatus*	1	

Classification Systems

Linnaeus also classified organisms based on their behavior and appearance. Today, the branch of science that classifies living things is called taxonomy. *A group of organisms is called a* **taxon** (plural, taxa). There are many taxa, as shown in **Table 1.** Recall that all living things share similar traits. However, not all living things are exactly the same.

Taxonomy

Using taxonomy, scientists divide all living things on Earth into three groups called domains. Domains are divided into kingdoms, and then phyla (FI luh; singular, phylum), classes, orders, families, genera (singular, genus), and species. A species is made of all organisms that can mate with one another and produce offspring that can reproduce. The first word in an organism's scientific name is the organism's genus (JEE nus), and the second word might describe a distinguishing characteristic of the organism. For example, dogs belong to the genus *Canis*. The *Canis* genus also includes wolves, coyotes, and jackals.

Recall that Linnaeus used similar physical traits to group organisms. Today, scientists also look for other similarities, such as how an organism reproduces, how it processes energy, and the types of genes it has.

Dichotomous Keys

A dichotomous (di KAH tah mus) **key** is a tool used to identify an organism based on its characteristics. Dichotomous keys contain descriptions of traits that are compared when classifying an organism. Dichotomous keys are organized in steps. Each step might ask a yes or a no question and have two answer choices. Which question is answered next depends on the answer to the previous question. Based on the features, a choice is made that best describes the organism.

> **Key Concept Check** How are living things classified?

Inquiry MiniLab — 20 minutes

Whose shoe is it?

A dichotomous key is a tool to help identify an unknown object or organism.

1. Read and complete a lab safety form.

2. Have each person in your group place one of his or her **shoes** in a pile.

3. Observe the shoes, looking for similarities and differences among them.

4. In your Science Journal, write a question that can be used to separate the shoes into two groups.

5. Divide the shoes into the two groups.

6. Continue asking questions for each subgroup until all of the shoes are identified.

7. Number the questions from the top of the key down, and create your key this way:

> 1. Question 1?
> Yes . . . . go to question _____
> No . . . . go to question _____

Analyze and Conclude

1. **Classify** What characteristics probably should not be used when creating a dichotomous key?

2. **Key Concept** Describe how a doctor and a pest exterminator could use dichotomous keys.

SCIENCE USE V. COMMON USE

key
Science Use an aid to identification

Common Use a device to open a lock

Cells

Key Concepts 🔑
ESSENTIAL QUESTIONS

- What is a cell made of?
- How do the parts of a cell enable it to survive?

Vocabulary

prokaryotic cell p. 162

eukaryotic cell p. 162

cytoplasm p. 164

mitochondrion p. 165

 Multilingual eGlossary

 Video BrainPOP®

Academic Standards for Science

6.3.4 Recognize that plants use energy from the sun to make sugar (glucose) by the process of photosynthesis.

6.3.6 Recognize that food provides the energy for the work that cells do and is a source of the molecular building blocks that can be incorporated into a cell's structure or stored for later use.

Also covers: 6.NS.2, 6.NS.7, 6.NS.11

Inquiry Weird Web?

This isn't a spider's strange web. These are nerve cells shown in a color-enhanced electron micrograph. The yellow parts are the cell bodies. The red threadlike parts carry electrical signals from one nerve cell to another. How do these parts help the cells?

Are all cells alive?

There are many bacteria that live on and in people. These unicellular organisms have all the characteristics of life and are alive. Are human cells, which the bacteria live on and in, also alive?

1 In your Science Journal, draw a circle that takes up half of the page. The circle represents a human cell.

2 Draw and label the following things in your cell:

A power plant to represent the need for and use of energy; label it *energy production.*

A garbage truck to represent waste removal; label it *waste removal.*

A city hall with a mayor to represent the organization and processes of the cell; label it *organization.*

A road system to represent the transportation that occurs in the cell; label it *transportation.*

A cement truck to represent the construction of new structures in the cell; label it *growth.*

A fire truck to represent a cell's ability to respond to changes in its surroundings; label it *response to environment.*

A copy machine in city hall to represent the cell's ability to follow instructions and make more cells; label it *reproduction.*

Think About This

1. Does the human cell you drew have all the characteristics of life? Explain your answer.

2. 🔑 **Key Concept** Do you think each of the trillions of cells that are part of you are either alive or once-living? Why?

What are cells?

What is one thing all living things have in common? All living things have cells, the basic unit of an organism. As you read in Lesson 1, most organisms have only one cell. Other organisms have many cells. Humans have about 100 trillion cells! Most cells are so small that they cannot be seen without a microscope. Microscopes, such as the one shown in **Figure 8,** are used to view details of small objects or to view things that are too small to be seen by the unaided eye.

Scientists first used microscopes to look at cells over 300 years ago. Cells come in different shapes and sizes. Nerve cells are long and slender. Many female reproductive cells, or eggs, are large and round.

✓ **Reading Check** Why is a microscope needed to view most cells?

LM Magnification: 10×

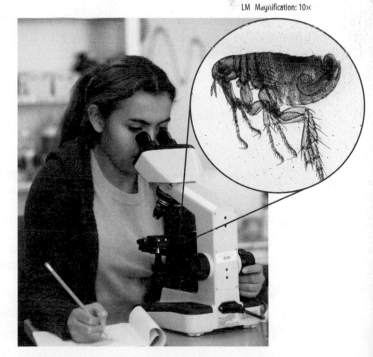

Figure 8 Microscopes increase the size of an image so that a small thing, such as the flea shown here, can be observed.

What are cells made of?

Recall that all cells are made of four macromolecules—nucleic acids, lipids, proteins, and carbohydrates. Cells also have many other characteristics. For example, all cells are surrounded by an outer structure called a cell membrane. The cell membrane keeps substances such as macromolecules inside the cell. It also helps protect cells by keeping harmful substances from entering. About 70 percent of the inside of a cell is water. Because many of the substances inside a cell are dissolved in water, they move easily within the cell.

 Key Concept Check What is a cell made of?

Types of Cells

There are two main types of cells, as shown in **Figure 9.** **Prokaryotic** (pro kayr ee AH tihk) **cells** *do not have a nucleus or other membrane-bound organelles.* Organelles are structures in cells that carry out specific functions. The few organelles in prokaryotic cells are not surrounded by membranes. Organisms with prokaryotic cells are called prokaryotes. Most prokaryotes are unicellular organisms, such as bacteria.

Eukaryotic (yew ker ee AH tihk) **cells** *have a nucleus and other membrane-bound organelles.* Most multicellular organisms and some unicellular organisms are eukaryotes. The eukaryotic cell shown in **Figure 9** contains many structures that are not in a prokaryotic cell. In eukaryotes, membranes surround most of the organelles, including the nucleus.

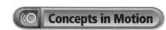 **Concepts in Motion**

Animation

Figure 9 Prokaryotic cells do not have a nucleus. Eukaryotic cells have a nucleus and many other organelles.

Visual Check What structures are in both prokaryotic cells and eukaryotic cells?

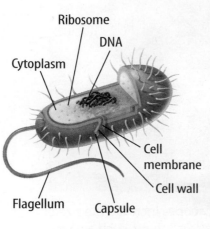

Prokaryotic Cell

Labels: Ribosome, DNA, Cytoplasm, Flagellum, Capsule, Cell membrane, Cell wall

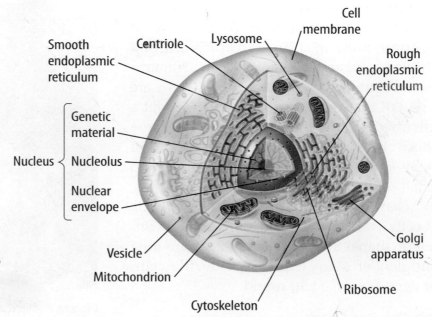

Eukaryotic Cell

Labels: Smooth endoplasmic reticulum, Centriole, Lysosome, Cell membrane, Rough endoplasmic reticulum, Genetic material, Nucleus, Nucleolus, Nuclear envelope, Vesicle, Mitochondrion, Cytoskeleton, Ribosome, Golgi apparatus

The Outside of a Cell

As you have just read, the cell membrane surrounds a cell. Much like a fence surrounds a school, the cell membrane helps keep the substances inside a cell separate from the substances outside a cell. Some cells also are surrounded by a more rigid layer called a cell wall.

Cell Membrane

The cell membrane is made of lipids and proteins. Recall that lipids and proteins are macromolecules that help cells function. Lipids in the cell membrane protect the inside of a cell from the external environment. Proteins in the cell membrane transport substances between a cell's environment and the inside of the cell. Proteins in the cell membrane also communicate with other cells and organisms and sense changes in the cell's environment.

 Reading Check Summarize the major components of cell membranes.

Cell Wall

In addition to a cell membrane, some cells also have a cell wall, as shown in **Figure 10.** The cell wall is a strong, rigid layer outside the cell membrane. Cells in plants, fungi, and many types of bacteria have cell walls. Cell walls provide structure and help protect the cell from the outside environment. Most cell walls are made from different types of carbohydrates.

Animation

Figure 10 This plant cell has a cell membrane and a cell wall.

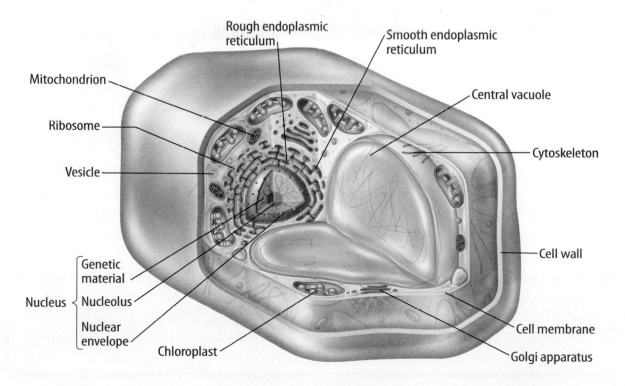

Rough endoplasmic reticulum
Smooth endoplasmic reticulum
Mitochondrion
Ribosome
Vesicle
Central vacuole
Cytoskeleton
Cell wall
Genetic material
Nucleolus
Nuclear envelope
Nucleus
Chloroplast
Cell membrane
Golgi apparatus

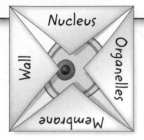

The Inside of a Cell

Recall that the inside of a cell is mainly water. Many substances used for communication, energy, and growth dissolve in water. This makes it easier for the substances to move around inside a cell. Water also gives cells their shapes and helps keep the structures inside a cell organized. The organelles inside a cell perform specific functions. They control cell activities, provide energy, transport materials, and store materials.

Cytoplasm

The liquid part of a cell inside the cell membrane is called the **cytoplasm.** It contains water, macromolecules, and other substances. The organelles in eukaryotic cells are located in the cytoplasm. Proteins in the cytoplasm provide structure and help organelles and other substances move around.

Controlling Cell Activities

The information that controls all of a cell's activities is stored in its genetic material, called DNA. DNA is a type of macromolecule called a nucleic acid. The information in DNA is transferred to another nucleic acid called RNA. RNA gives cells instructions about which proteins need to be made. In prokaryotic cells, DNA is in the cytoplasm. In eukaryotic cells, DNA is stored in an organelle called the nucleus. A membrane, called the nuclear membrane, surrounds the nucleus. Tiny holes in the nuclear membrane let certain substances move between the nucleus and the cytoplasm.

Inquiry MiniLab

20–30 minutes

What can you see in a cell?

When people developed microscopes, they were able to see things that they could not see with their eyes alone.

1. Read and complete a lab safety form.
2. Carefully remove a thin layer of membrane from a piece of **onion.**
3. Place the membrane on the center of a dry **microscope slide.**
4. Add a drop of **iodine** on top of the sample.
5. Place a **cover slip** on top of the sample.
6. Use a **microscope** to focus on the slide using low power. Sketch what you see in your Science Journal.
7. View and sketch the sample on medium and high powers.

Analyze and Conclude

1. **Observe** What structures did you see at low, medium, and high powers?

2. **Infer** How might your view of the cells change if you view them at an even higher power?

3. **Key Concept** How does a microscope help you learn more about the onion plant?

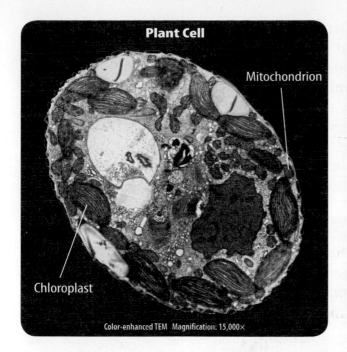

Plant Cell

Chloroplast

Mitochondrion

Color-enhanced TEM Magnification: 15,000×

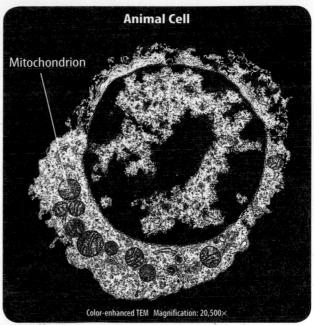

Animal Cell

Mitochondrion

Color-enhanced TEM Magnification: 20,500×

Figure 11 Plant cells have mitochondria and chloroplasts. Animal cells only contain mitochondria.

 Visual Check Where are the mitochondria located in a cell?

Energy for the Cell

You read in Lesson 1 that all living things use energy. Proteins in the cytoplasm process energy in prokaryotes. Eukaryotes have special organelles, the chloroplasts and mitochondria (mi tuh KAHN dree uh; singular, mitochondrion) shown in **Figure 11,** that process energy.

Mitochondria Most eukaryotes contain hundreds of mitochondria. **Mitochondria** *are organelles that break down food and release energy.* This energy is stored in molecules called ATP—adenosine triphosphate (uh DEN uh seen • tri FAHS fayt). ATP provides a cell with energy to perform many functions, such as making proteins, storing information, and communicating with other cells.

✔ **Reading Check** What energy molecule is made in a mitochondrion?

Chloroplasts Energy also can be processed in organelles called chloroplasts, shown in **Figure 11.** Plants and many other autotrophs have chloroplasts and mitochondria. Chloroplasts capture light energy and convert it into chemical energy in a process called photosynthesis. Chloroplasts contain many structures that capture light energy. Like the reactions that occur in mitochondria, ATP molecules are produced during photosynthesis. However, photosynthesis also produces carbohydrates such as glucose that also are used to store energy.

WORD ORIGIN · · · · · · · · ·

mitochondrion
from Greek *mitos*, means "thread"; and *khondrion*, means "little granule"

Protein Production

You just read that cells use protein for many functions. These proteins are made on the surface of ribosomes that are in the cytoplasm of both prokaryotic and eukaryotic cells. In eukaryotic cells, some ribosomes are attached to an organelle called the endoplasmic reticulum (en duh PLAZ mihk • rih TIHK yuh lum), as shown in **Figure 12**. It is made of folded membranes. The proteins can be processed and can move inside the cell through the endoplasmic reticulum.

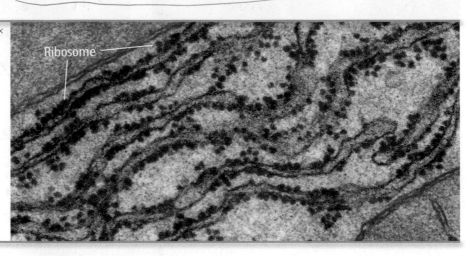

Color-enhanced TEM Magnification: 19,030×

Ribosome

Figure 12 Ribosomes are attached to the rough endoplasmic reticulum. ▶

Cell Storage

What happens to the molecules that are made in a cell? An organelle called the Golgi (GAWL jee) apparatus packages proteins into tiny organelles called vesicles. Vesicles transport proteins around a cell. Other molecules are stored in organelles called vacuoles. A vacuole is usually the largest organelle in a plant cell, as shown in **Figure 13**. In plant cells, vacuoles store water and provide support. In contrast to all plant cells, only some animal and bacterial cells contain vacuoles. The vacuoles in animal and bacterial cells are smaller than the ones in plant cells.

 Key Concept Check How do the parts of a cell enable it to survive?

Figure 13 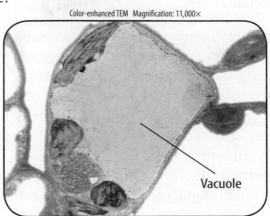 Vacuoles are used by plant cells for storage and to provide structure. ▶

Color-enhanced TEM Magnification: 11,000×

Vacuole

Lesson 2 Review

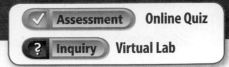
Visual Summary

Prokaryotic cells are surrounded by a cell membrane but have no internal organelles with membranes.

Eukaryotic cells contain a nucleus and many other organelles.

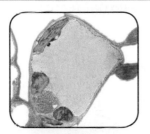

Plant cells have cell walls, chloroplasts, and a large vacuole.

FOLDABLES

Use your lesson Foldable to review the lesson. Save your Foldable for the project at the end of the chapter.

What do you think NOW?

You first read the statements below at the beginning of the chapter.

4. *Cell wall* is a term used to describe the cell membrane.

5. Prokaryotic cells contain a nucleus.

6. Plants use chloroplasts to process energy.

Did you change your mind about whether you agree or disagree with the statements? Rewrite any false statements to make them true.

Use Vocabulary

1 **Distinguish** between prokaryotic cells and eukaryotic cells.

2 Water, proteins, and other substances are found in the _____ of a cell.

3 **Define** *mitochondrion* in your own words.

Understand Key Concepts

4 Which organelles store water, carbohydrates, and wastes in plants?
A. chloroplasts   C. nuclei
B. mitochondria   D. vacuoles

5 **Compare** how energy is processed in animal and plant cells.

6 **Distinguish** between a cell membrane and a cell wall.

Interpret Graphics

7 **Summarize** Use the table below to identify organelles and their functions.

Organelle	Function
Nucleus	
	energy processing
Vacuole	

8 **Compare and contrast** the structures of the two cells shown below.

Critical Thinking

9 **Assess** the role of water in cell function.

10 **Relate** the cell wall to protection in bacteria.

How can living things be classified?

Materials

compound microscope

dissecting microscope

magnifying lens

ruler

Also needed: specimens

Safety

Thousands of new organisms are discovered each year. Today, an organism's DNA can be used to determine how closely a newly discovered organism is related to living things that are already known. A long time ago, taxonomists had to rely on what they could observe with their senses to determine the relationships between organisms. They looked at characteristics such as an organism's parts, behaviors, or the environments in which they lived to help them determine relationships among organisms. The father of taxonomy, Carolus Linnaeus, developed a system in the 1700s by which he classified over 9,000 organisms, primarily based on their external features.

Question

What characteristics can be used to distinguish among different types of organisms?

Procedure

1. Read and complete a lab safety form.

2. Use your background knowledge of the specimens provided and the available tools to identify distinguishing characteristics of the specimens. Be sure to observe each of the specimens thoroughly and completely.

3. In your Science Journal, record as much information as possible about each of the organisms. This information can include your observations and any knowledge you have of the organism.

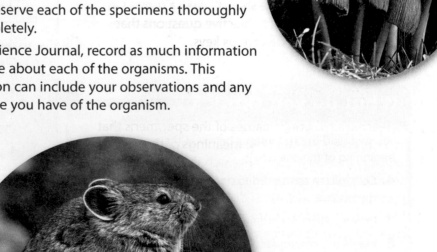

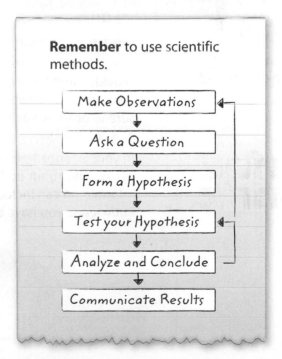

4. Using the information you have recorded, create a dichotomous key that can be used to identify all of the specimens.

5. Trade your key with another student.

6. Verify that the key you received works by trying to identify all ten of the organisms, one at a time.

7. If your key did not work, repeat steps 2–5. If your key did work, move on to the **Analyze and Conclude** section.

Analyze and Conclude

8. **Compare and Contrast** How are the questions in the key you made similar to and different from the questions in the key that you checked?

9. **Classify** How would an elephant, bread mold, and a rose be identified if the key you created were used to identify them? Are these identifications accurate? Why did this happen?

10. **The Big Idea** How would the questions in your key be different if all ten organisms were more closely related, such as ten different plants?

Communicate Your Results

Share your key and questions with a small group of students. After everyone shares, make a group key that combines the most objective questions that were asked among the various keys.

inquiry Extension

Research the scientific names of the specimens that you observed, and find the meanings of the species name of each organism. Research the characteristics by which bacteria are classified. Design a key to be used by younger students to help identify different polygons (triangles, pentagons, octagons, and so on) using correct mathematical terms.

Remember to use scientific methods.

Make Observations
↓
Ask a Question
↓
Form a Hypothesis
↓
Test your Hypothesis
↓
Analyze and Conclude
↓
Communicate Results

Chapter 5 Study Guide

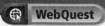

 THE BIG IDEA **Organisms are classified based on similar characteristics, including cell structure and function.**

Key Concepts Summary 🔑	Vocabulary
Lesson 1: Classifying Living Things • Living things are organized, process energy, grow, reproduce, respond to stimuli, and contain cells. • Living things need food, water, and a **habitat.** • Organisms are classified based on similar characteristics. 	**autotroph** p. 154 **heterotroph** p. 154 **habitat** p. 155 **binomial nomenclature** p. 156 **taxon** p. 157
Lesson 2: Cells • Cells are made of water and macromolecules. • Different parts of a cell enable it to perform special functions.	**prokaryotic cell** p. 162 **eukaryotic cell** p. 162 **cytoplasm** p. 164 **mitochondrion** p. 165

FOLDABLES® Chapter Project

Assemble your lesson Foldables as shown to make a Chapter Project. Use the project to review what you have learned in this chapter.

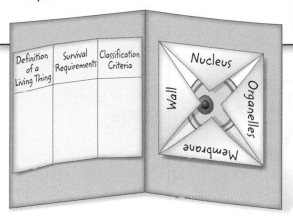

Use Vocabulary

1. The Latin term *Homo sapiens* is an example of _____.
2. Organisms that obtain energy by eating other organisms are called _____.
3. Use the term *habitat* in a sentence.
4. Define the term *cytoplasm* in your own words.
5. Animal cells obtain energy by breaking down food in _____.
6. Use the term *prokaryotic cell* in a sentence.

Link Vocabulary and Key Concepts

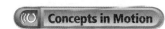 **Concepts in Motion** Interactive Concept Map

Copy this concept map, and then use vocabulary terms from the previous page to complete the concept map.

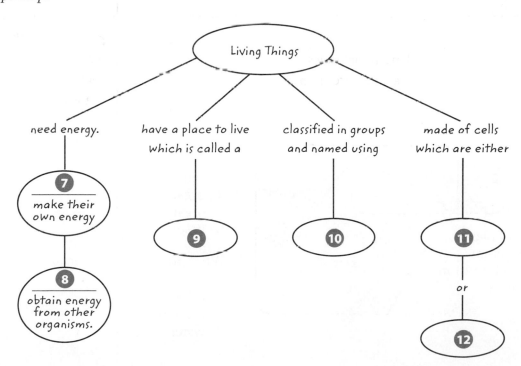

Understand Key Concepts

1 What is a rigid structure that provides support and protection to plants and some types of bacteria?

A. chloroplast
B. nucleus
C. cell membrane
D. cell wall

2 What type of reproduction occurs when a cell divides to form two new cells?

A. autotrophic
B. heterotrophic
C. asexual reproduction
D. sexual reproduction

3 Which is the scientific name for humans?

A. *Canis lupos*
B. *Felis catus*
C. *Homo sapiens*
D. *Tamias striatus*

4 What is a group of organisms called?

A. taxon
B. tissue
C. dichotomous key
D. organ system

5 Which organelle is the arrow pointing to in the picture below?

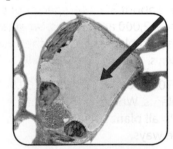

A. chloroplast
B. cytoplasm
C. mitochondrion
D. vacuole

6 Which is NOT a characteristic of all living things?

A. grow
B. reproduce
C. have organelles
D. use energy

7 Which organelle is the arrow pointing to in the picture below?

A. chloroplast
B. cytoplasm
C. mitochondrion
D. nucleus

8 What is the name used to describe the specific place where an organism lives?

A. autotroph
B. habitat
C. heterotroph
D. taxon

9 What is the smallest unit of all living things?

A. cell
B. organ
C. organelle
D. tissue

10 What are cells mostly made of?

A. DNA
B. lipids
C. proteins
D. water

Critical Thinking

11 **Summarize** the characteristics of all living things.

12 **Describe** how the organization of a multicellular organism helps it function. Diagram the relationships.

13 **Assess** how taxonomy relates to the diversity of species.

14 **Explain** why different organisms live in different habitats.

15 **Assess** the role of organelles in the functions of eukaryotic cells.

16 **Relate** the structure in the plant cell shown at the pointer in the picture below to how it obtains energy.

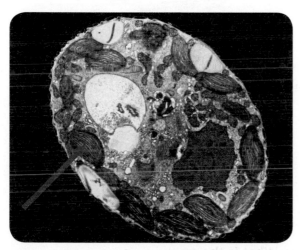

17 **Summarize** the role of nucleic acids in controlling cell functions.

18 **Discuss** how heterotrophs process energy.

Writing in Science

19 **Write** a five-sentence paragraph that describes the characteristics that all living things share.

REVIEW THE B|G IDEA

20 Assess how the classification of prokaryotes and eukaryotes relates to the structure of their cells.

21 How is the classification of living things related to the structure of their cells? Use the plant in the photo below as an example.

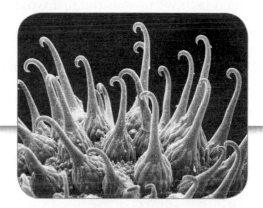

Math Skills ×÷ +

📖 **Review**

— **Math Practice** —

Use Ratios

22 There are about 300,000 species of plants. Of those, 12,000 are mosses. What is the ratio of mosses to plants? Express the answer all three ways.

23 Out of 300,000 plant species, 260,000 are flowering plants. What is the ratio of flowering plants to all plant species? Express the ratio in all three ways.

24 Out of 12,000 species of mosses, only about 400 are club mosses. What is the ratio of club mosses to all mosses? Express the ratio in all three ways.

Standardized Test Practice

Record your answers on the answer sheet provided by your teacher or on a sheet of paper.

Multiple Choice

1 Which would a chemoautotroph use to produce energy?

   A sulfur

   B sunlight

   C carbon dioxide

   D other organisms

2 Which taxon is used as the first word in an organism's scientific name?

   A class

   B genus

   C kingdom

   D order

Use the diagram below to answer question 3.

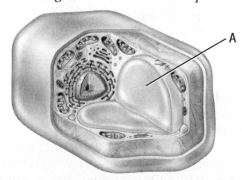

3 The diagram shows the parts of a plant cell. What is the name and function of structure A?

   A chloroplast, making carbohydrates

   B chloroplast, producing energy

   C vacuole, storing water

   D vacuole, transporting proteins

4 Which molecule stores energy for cells?

   A ATP

   B DNA

   C proteins

   D ribosomes

5 What do scientists call the largest taxonomic level of organization for organisms?

   A domains

   B genera

   C kingdoms

   D phyla

Use the image below to answer question 6.

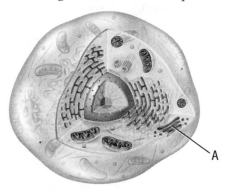

6 In the diagram, the organelle labeled *A* packages proteins into vesicles. What is this organelle called?

   A central vacuole

   B endoplasmic reticulum

   C Golgi apparatus

   D nuclear envelope

7 Which cell structures break down food and release energy?

   A chloroplasts

   B mitochrondria

   C ribosomes

   D vacuoles

Standardized Test Practice

8 Carl Linnaeus grouped organisms into categories based on which characteristic?

   A energy production

   B gene type

   C physical traits

   D reproduction habits

9 Which term defines a group of cells that work together and perform a function?

   A organ

   B taxon

   C tissue

   D phylum

Use the diagram to answer question 10.

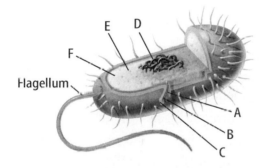

10 In the cell shown, what is the letter for the structure that provides much of the cell's support and helps protect it from the outside environment?

   A A

   B B

   C C

   D D

Constructed Response

Use the figure to answer questions 11 and 12.

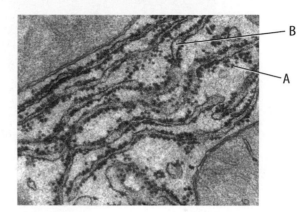

11 Identify the structure labeled *A* in the diagram. What is its function?

12 How are the organelles labeled *A* and *B* related? Are they found in prokaryotic cells, eukaryotic cells, or both?

13 Explain the relationship between cells, tissues, organs, and organ systems in a multicellular organism.

14 Cell membranes are made up mainly of proteins and carbohydrates. How do these molecules function in the cell membrane?

NEED EXTRA HELP?														
If You Missed Question...	1	2	3	4	5	6	7	8	9	10	11	12	13	14
Go to Lesson...	1	1	2	2	1	2	2	1	1	2	2	2	1	2

Plant Processes

THE BIG IDEA What processes enable plants to survive?

Inquiry Holding on for Dear Life?

The tendril of this *Omphalea* (om FAL ee uh) vine grows around a branch in a tropical rain forest.

- How do you think growing around another plant might help the *Omphalea* plant survive?

- Can you think of any other processes that enable plants to survive?

Get Ready to Read

What do you think?

Before you read, decide if you agree or disagree with each of these statements. As you read this chapter, see if you change your mind about any of the statements.

1. Plants do not carry on cellular respiration.

2. Plants are the only organisms that carry on photosynthesis.

3. Plants make food in their underground roots.

4. Plants do not produce hormones.

5. Plants can respond to their environments.

6. All plants flower when nights are 10–12 hours long.

 **ConnectED** Your one-stop online resource

connectED.mcgraw-hill.com

- Video
- WebQuest
- Audio
- Assessment
- Review
- Concepts in Motion
- Inquiry
- Multilingual eGlossary

Energy Processing in Plants

Reading Guide

Key Concepts 🔑
ESSENTIAL QUESTIONS

- How do materials move inside plants?
- How do plants perform photosynthesis?
- What is cellular respiration?
- How are photosynthesis and cellular respiration alike, and how are they different?

Vocabulary
photosynthesis p. 180
cellular respiration p. 182

> **g** Multilingual eGlossary

Academic Standards for Science

6.3.4 Recognize that plants use energy from the sun to make sugar (glucose) by the process of photosynthesis.

6.3.6 Recognize that food provides the energy for the work that cells do and is a source of the molecular building blocks that can be incorporated into a cell's structure or stored for later use.

Also covers: 6.NS.4, 6.NS.7, 6.NS.9

Inquiry All Leaf Cells?

You are looking at a magnified cross section of a leaf. As you can see, the cells in the middle of the leaf are different from the cells on the edges. What do you think this might have to do with the cellular processes a leaf carries out that enable a plant's survival?

How can you show the movement of materials inside a plant?

Most parts of plants need water. They also need a system to move water throughout the plant so cells can use it for plant processes.

1 Read and complete a lab safety form.

2 Gently pull two stalks from the base of a bunch of **celery.** Leave one stalk complete. Use a **paring knife** to carefully cut directly across the bottom of the second stalk.

3 Pour 100 mL of water into each of two **beakers.** Place 3–4 drops of **blue food coloring** into the water. Place one celery stalk in each beaker.

4 After 20 min, observe the celery near the bottom of each stalk. Observe again after 24 h. Record your observations in your Science Journal.

Think About This

1. What happened in each celery stalk?

2. 🔑 **Key Concept** What did the colored water do? Why do you think this occurred?

Materials for Plant Processes

Food, water, and oxygen are three things you need to survive. Some of your organ systems process these materials, and others transport them throughout your body. Like you, plants need food, water, and oxygen to survive. Unlike you, plants do not take in food. Most of them make their own.

Moving Materials Inside Plants

You might recall reading about xylem (ZI lum) and phloem (FLOH em)—the vascular tissue in most plants. These tissues transport materials throughout a plant.

After water enters a plant's roots, it moves into xylem. Water then flows inside xylem to all parts of a plant. Without enough water, plant cells wilt, as shown in **Figure 1.**

Most plants make their own food—a liquid sugar. The liquid sugar moves out of food-making cells, enters phloem, and flows to all plant cells. Cells break down the sugar and release energy. Some plant cells can store food.

Plants require oxygen and carbon dioxide to make food. Like you, plants produce water vapor as a waste product. Carbon dioxide, oxygen, and water vapor pass into and out of a plant through tiny openings in leaves.

🔑 **Key Concept Check** How do materials move through plants?

Figure 1 This plant wilted due to lack of water in the soil.

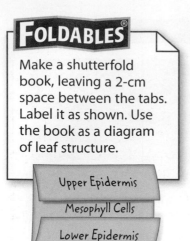
WORD ORIGIN · · · · · · · · · · ·

photosynthesis
from Greek *photo-*, means "light"; and *synthesis*, means "composition"

Photosynthesis

Plants need food, but they cannot eat as people do. They make their own food, and leaves are the major food-producing organs of plants. This means that leaves are the sites of photosynthesis (foh toh SIHN thuh sus). **Photosynthesis** *is a series of chemical reactions that convert light energy, water, and carbon dioxide into the food-energy molecule glucose and give off oxygen.* The structure of a leaf is well-suited to its role in photosynthesis.

Leaves and Photosynthesis

As shown in **Figure 2,** leaves have many types of cells. The cells that make up the top and bottom layers of a leaf are flat, irregularly shaped cells called epidermal (eh puh DUR mul) cells. On the bottom epidermal layer of most leaves are small openings called stomata (STOH muh tuh). Carbon dioxide, water vapor, and oxygen pass through stomata. Epidermal cells can produce a waxy covering called the cuticle.

Most photosynthesis occurs in two types of mesophyll (ME zuh fil) cells inside a leaf. These cells contain chloroplasts, the organelle where photosynthesis occurs. Near the top surface of the leaf are palisade mesophyll cells. They are packed together. This arrangement exposes the most cells to light. Spongy mesophyll cells have open spaces between them. Gases needed for photosynthesis flow through the spaces between the cells.

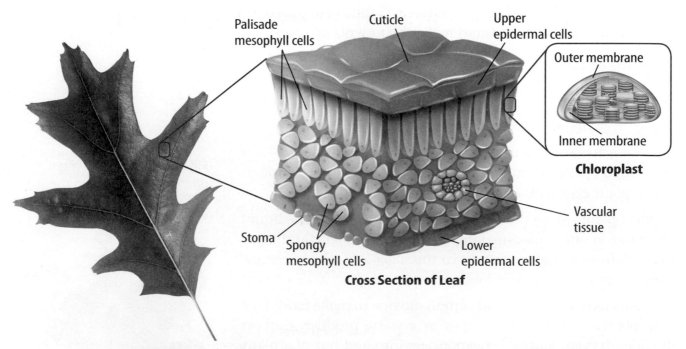

Palisade mesophyll cells · Cuticle · Upper epidermal cells · Outer membrane · Inner membrane · **Chloroplast** · Vascular tissue · Stoma · Spongy mesophyll cells · Lower epidermal cells

Cross Section of Leaf

Figure 2 Photosynthesis occurs inside the chloroplasts of mesophyll cells in most leaves.

✓ **Visual Check** What layer of cells contains vascular tissue?

Capturing Light Energy

As you read about the steps of photosynthesis, refer to **Figure 3** to help you understand the process. In the first step of photosynthesis, plants capture the energy in light. This occurs in chloroplasts. Chloroplasts contain plant pigments. Pigments are chemicals that can absorb and reflect light. Chlorophyll, the most common plant pigment, is necessary for photosynthesis. Most plants appear green because chlorophyll reflects green light. Chlorophyll absorbs other colors of light. This light energy is used during photosynthesis.

Once chlorophyll traps and stores light energy, this energy can be transferred to other molecules. During photosynthesis, water molecules are split apart. This releases oxygen into the atmosphere, as shown in **Figure 3.**

 Reading Check How do plants capture light energy?

Making Sugars

Sugars are made in the second step of photosynthesis. This step can occur without light. In chloroplasts, carbon dioxide from the air is converted into sugars by using the energy stored and trapped by chlorophyll. Carbon dioxide combines with hydrogen atoms from the splitting of water molecules and forms sugar molecules. Plants can use this sugar as an energy source or can store it. Potatoes and carrots are examples of plant structures where excess sugar is stored.

 Key Concept Check What are the two steps of photosynthesis?

Why is photosynthesis important?

Try to imagine a world without plants. How would humans or other animals get the oxygen that they need? Plants help maintain the atmosphere you breathe. Photosynthesis produces most of the oxygen in the atmosphere.

Photosynthesis 🔑

Figure 3 Photosynthesis is a series of complex chemical processes. The first step is capturing light energy. In the second step, that energy is used for making sugar.

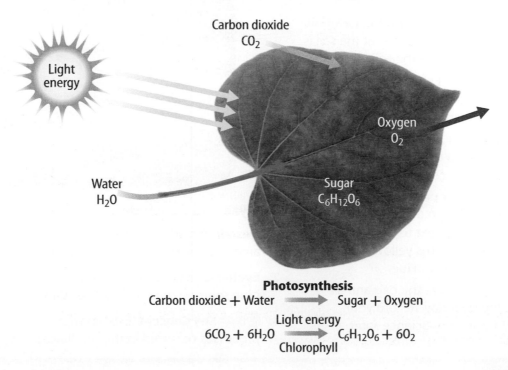

Photosynthesis

Carbon dioxide + Water ⟶ Sugar + Oxygen

$$6CO_2 + 6H_2O \xrightarrow[\text{Chlorophyll}]{\text{Light energy}} C_6H_{12}O_6 + 6O_2$$

Cellular Respiration

ACADEMIC VOCABULARY ·:

energy
(noun) usable power

REVIEW VOCABULARY ·····

molecule
a group of atoms held together
by the energy in chemical
bonds

All organisms require **energy** to survive. Energy is in the chemical bonds in food **molecules.** A process called cellular respiration releases energy. **Cellular respiration** *is a series of chemical reactions that convert the energy in food molecules into a usable form of energy called ATP.*

Releasing Energy from Sugars

Glucose molecules break down during cellular respiration. Much of the energy released during this process is used to make ATP, an energy storage molecule. This process requires oxygen, produces water and carbon dioxide as waste products, and occurs in the cytoplasm and mitochondria of cells.

Why is cellular respiration important?

If your body did not break down the food you eat through cellular respiration, you would not have energy to do anything. Plants produce sugar, but without cellular respiration, plants could not grow, reproduce, or repair tissues.

 Key Concept Check What is cellular respiration?

Inquiry MiniLab   **20 minutes**

Can you observe plant processes?

Plants perform both photosynthesis and cellular respiration. Can you observe both processes in radish seedlings?

1. Read and complete a lab safety form.
2. Put **potting soil** in the bottom of a **small, self-sealing plastic bag** so that the soil is 3–4 cm deep. Dampen the soil.
3. Drop several **radish seeds** into the bag and close the top, but leave a small opening so air can still get into the bag.
4. Place the bag upright in a place that has a **light source.** Each group should use a different light source. Observe for 4–5 days.
5. Carefully place an open container of **bromthymol blue (0.004%) solution** upright in the bag next to the seedlings. Bromthymol blue turns yellow in the presence of carbon dioxide.
6. Seal the bag. Observe the bag and its contents the next day. Record your observations in your Science Journal.

Analyze and Conclude

1. **Describe** the differences in seedling samples among groups. Why are there differences?

2. **Evaluate** What change in the bromthymol blue solution did you observe? Why?

3. **Key Concept** Explain what processes occurred in the seedlings.

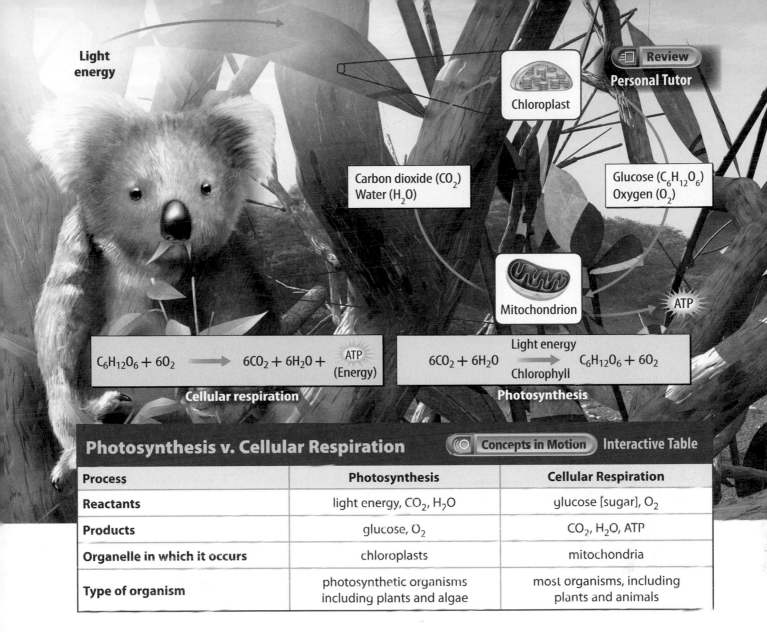

Light energy

Chloroplast

Review
Personal Tutor

Carbon dioxide (CO_2)
Water (H_2O)

Glucose ($C_6H_{12}O_6$)
Oxygen (O_2)

Mitochondrion

ATP

$$C_6H_{12}O_6 + 6O_2 \longrightarrow 6CO_2 + 6H_2O + \text{ATP (Energy)}$$

Cellular respiration

$$6CO_2 + 6H_2O \xrightarrow[\text{Chlorophyll}]{\text{Light energy}} C_6H_{12}O_6 + 6O_2$$

Photosynthesis

Photosynthesis v. Cellular Respiration

Concepts in Motion   Interactive Table

Process	Photosynthesis	Cellular Respiration
Reactants	light energy, CO_2, H_2O	glucose [sugar], O_2
Products	glucose, O_2	CO_2, H_2O, ATP
Organelle in which it occurs	chloroplasts	mitochondria
Type of organism	photosynthetic organisms including plants and algae	most organisms, including plants and animals

Comparing Photosynthesis and Cellular Respiration

Photosynthesis requires light energy and the reactants—substances that react with one another during the process—carbon dioxide and water. Oxygen and the energy-rich molecule glucose are the products, or end substances, of photosynthesis. Most plants, some protists, and some bacteria carry on photosynthesis.

Cellular respiration requires the reactants glucose and oxygen, produces carbon dioxide and water, and releases energy in the form of ATP. Most organisms carry on cellular respiration. Photosynthesis and cellular respiration are interrelated, as shown in **Figure 4.** Life on Earth depends on a balance of these two processes.

Key Concept Check How are photosynthesis and cellular respiration alike, and how are they different?

Figure 4 The relationship between cellular respiration and photosynthesis is important for life.

Visual Check What are the reactants of cellular respiration? What are the products?

Lesson 1 Review

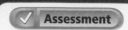

Visual Summary

 Materials that a plant requires to survive move through the plant in the vascular tissue, xylem and phloem.

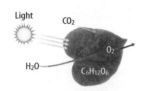 Plants can make their own food by using light energy, water, and carbon dioxide.

 The products of photosynthesis are the reactants for cellular respiration.

FOLDABLES®

Use your lesson Foldable to review the lesson. Save your Foldable for the project at the end of the chapter.

What do you think NOW?

You first read the statements below at the beginning of the chapter.

1. Plants do not carry on cellular respiration.

2. Plants are the only organisms that carry on photosynthesis.

3. Plants make food in their underground roots.

Did you change your mind about whether you agree or disagree with the statements? Rewrite any false statements to make them true.

Use Vocabulary

1 A series of chemical reactions that convert the energy in food molecules into a usable form of energy, called ATP, is called _____.

2 **Define** *photosynthesis* in your own words.

Understand Key Concepts 🔑

3 Which structure moves water through plants?
   A. chloroplast   C. nucleus
   B. mitochondrion   D. xylem

4 **Describe** how plants use chlorophyll for photosynthesis.

5 **Summarize** the process of cellular respiration.

Interpret Graphics

6 **Explain** how the structure shown below is organized for its role in photosynthesis.

7 **Compare and Contrast** Copy and fill in the table below to compare and contrast photosynthesis and cellular respiration.

Process	Similarities	Differences

Critical Thinking

8 **Predict** the effect of a plant disease that destroys all of the chloroplasts in a plant.

9 **Evaluate** why plants perform cellular respiration.

Deforestation and Carbon Dioxide
in the Atmosphere

How does carbon dioxide affect climate?

What do you think when you hear the words *greenhouse gases*? Many people picture pollution from automobiles or factory smokestacks. It might be surprising to learn that cutting down forests affects the amount of one of the greenhouse gases in the atmosphere—carbon dioxide.

Deforestation is the term used to describe the destruction of forests. Deforestation happens because people cut down forests to use the land for other purposes, such as agriculture or building sites, or to use the trees for fuel or building materials.

Trees, like most plants, carry out photosynthesis and make their own food. Carbon dioxide from the atmosphere is one of the raw materials, or reactants, of photosynthesis. When deforestation occurs, trees are unable to remove carbon dioxide from the atmosphere. As a result, the level of carbon dioxide in the atmosphere increases.

Trees affect the amount of atmospheric carbon dioxide in other ways. Large amounts of carbon are stored in the molecules that make up trees. When trees are burned or left to rot, much of this stored carbon is released as carbon dioxide. This increases the amount of carbon dioxide in the atmosphere.

Carbon dioxide in the atmosphere has an impact on climate. Greenhouse gases, such as carbon dioxide, increase the amount of the Sun's energy that is absorbed by the atmosphere. They also reduce the ability of heat to escape back into space. So, when levels of carbon dioxide in the atmosphere increase, more heat is trapped in Earth's atmosphere. This can lead to climate change.

▲ These cattle are grazing on land that once was part of a forest in Brazil.

▲ In a process called slash-and-burn, forest trees are cut down and burned to clear land for agriculture.

It's Your Turn

RESEARCH AND REPORT How can we lower the rate of deforestation? What are some actions you can take that could help slow the rate of deforestation? Research to find out how you can make a difference. Make a poster to share what you learn.

Lesson 2

Reading Guide

Key Concepts
ESSENTIAL QUESTIONS

- How do plants respond to environmental stimuli?
- How do plants respond to chemical stimuli?

Vocabulary

stimulus p. 187

tropism p. 188

photoperiodism p. 190

plant hormone p. 191

 g Multilingual eGlossary

Video BrainPOP®

 Academic Standards for Science

6.3.2 Describe how changes caused by organisms in the habitat where they live can be beneficial or detrimental to themselves or the native plants and animals.

Also covers: 6.NS.1, 6.NS.2, 6.NS.3, 6.NS.4, 6.NS.5, 6.NS.7, 6.NS.9, 6.NS.11, 6.DP.1, 6.DP.2, 6.DP.3, 6.DP.4, 6.DP.5, 6.DP.6, 6.DP.7, 6.DP.8, 6.DP.9, 6.DP.10, 6.DP.11

Plant Responses

Inquiry A Meat-Eating Plant?

Venus flytraps have leaves that look like jaws. The leaves close only when a stimulus, such as a fly, brushes against tiny, sensitive hairs on the surface of the leaves. To what other stimuli do you think plants might respond?

How do plants respond to stimuli?

Plants use light energy and make their own food during photosynthesis. How else do plants respond to light in their environment?

1. Read and complete a lab safety form.

2. Choose a **pot of young radish seedlings.**

3. Place **toothpicks** parallel to a few of the seedlings in the pot in the direction of growth.

4. Place the pot near a **light source**, such as a gooseneck lamp or next to a window. The light source should be to one side of the pot, not directly above the plants.

5. Check the position of the seedlings in relation to the toothpicks after 30 minutes. Record your observations in your Science Journal.

6. Observe the seedlings when you come to class the next day.

Think About This

1. What happened to the position of the seedlings after the first 30 minutes? What is your evidence of change?

2. What happened to the position of the seedlings after a day?

3. 🔑 **Key Concept** Why do you think the position of the seedlings changed?

Stimuli and Plant Responses

Have you ever been in a dark room when someone suddenly turned on the light? You might have reacted by quickly shutting or covering your eyes. **Stimuli** (STIM yuh li; singular, stimulus) *are any changes in an organism's environment that cause a response.*

Often a plant's response to stimuli might be so slow that it is hard to see it happen. The response might occur gradually over a period of hours or days. Light is a stimulus. A plant responds to light by growing toward it, as shown in **Figure 5.** This response occurs over several hours.

In some cases, the response to a stimulus is quick, such as the Venus flytrap's response to touch. When stimulated by an insect's touch, the two sides of the trap snap shut immediately, trapping the insect inside.

✓ **Reading Check** Why is it sometimes hard to see a plant's response to a stimulus?

Figure 5 The light is the stimulus, and the seedlings have responded by growing toward the light.

Environmental Stimuli

When it is cold outside, you probably wear a sweatshirt or a coat. Plants cannot put on warm clothes, but they do respond to their environments in a variety of ways. You might have seen trees flower in the spring or drop their leaves in the fall. Both are plant responses to environmental stimuli.

Growth Responses

Plants respond to a number of different environmental stimuli. These include light, touch, and gravity. *A* **tropism** *(TROH pih zum) is a response that results in plant growth toward or away from a stimulus.* When the growth is toward a stimulus, the tropism is called positive. A plant bending toward light is a positive tropism. Growth away from a stimulus is considered negative. A plant's stem growing upward against gravity is a negative tropism.

Light The growth of a plant toward or away from light is a tropism called phototropism. A plant has a light-sensing chemical that helps it detect light. Leaves and stems tend to grow in the direction of light, as shown in **Figure 6.** This response maximizes the amount of light the plant's leaves receive. Roots generally grow away from light. This usually means that the roots grow down into the soil and help anchor the plant.

 Reading Check How is phototropism beneficial to a plant?

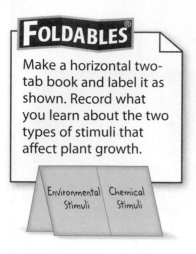

Make a horizontal two-tab book and label it as shown. Record what you learn about the two types of stimuli that affect plant growth.

| Environmental Stimuli | Chemical Stimuli |

WORD ORIGIN ·············

tropism
from Greek *tropos*, means "turn" or "turning"
·················

Response to Light 🔑

Figure 6 As a plant's leaves turn toward the light, the amount of light that the leaves can absorb increases.

Touch The response of a plant to touch is called a thigmotropism (thihg MAH truh pih zum). You might have seen vines growing up the side of a building or on a fence. This happens because the plant has special structures that respond to touch. These structures, called tendrils, can wrap around or cling to objects, as shown in **Figure 7.** A tendril wrapping around an object is an example of positive thigmotropism. Roots display negative thigmotropism. They grow away from objects in soil, enabling them to follow the easiest path through the soil.

Gravity The response of a plant to gravity is called gravitropism. Stems grow away from gravity, while roots grow toward gravity. The seedlings in **Figure 8** are exhibiting both responses. No matter how a seed lands on soil, when it starts to grow, its roots grow down into the soil. The stem grows up. This happens even when a seed is grown in a dark chamber, indicating that these responses can occur independently of light.

 Key Concept Check What types of environmental stimuli do plants respond to? Give three examples.

Response to Touch 🔑

▲ **Figure 7** The tendrils of the vine respond to touch and coil around the blade of grass.

Response to Gravity 🔑

Figure 8 Both of these plant stems are growing away from gravity. The upward growth of a plant's stem is negative gravitropism, and the downward growth of its roots is positive gravitropism.

✓ **Visual Check** How is the plant on the left responding to the pot being placed on its side?

Flowering Responses

You might think all plants respond to light, but in some plants, flowering is actually a response to darkness! **Photoperiodism** *is a plant's response to the number of hours of darkness in its environment.* Scientists once hypothesized that photoperiodism was a response to light. Therefore, these flowering responses are called long-day, short-day, and day-neutral and relate to the number of hours of daylight in a plant's environment.

Long-Day Plants Plants that flower when exposed to less than 10–12 hours of darkness are called long-day plants. The carnations shown in **Figure 9** are examples of long-day plants. This plant usually produces flowers in summer, when the number of hours of daylight is greater than the number of hours of darkness.

Short-Day Plants Short-day plants require 12 or more hours of darkness for flowering to begin. An example of a short-day plant is the poinsettia, shown in **Figure 9.** Poinsettias tend to flower in late summer or early fall when the number of hours of daylight is decreasing and the number of hours of darkness is increasing.

Day-Neutral Plants The flowering of some plants doesn't seem to be affected by the number of hours of darkness. Day-neutral plants flower when they reach maturity and the environmental conditions are right. Plants such as the roses in **Figure 9** are day-neutral plants.

 Reading Check How is the flowering of day-neutral plants affected by exposure to hours of darkness?

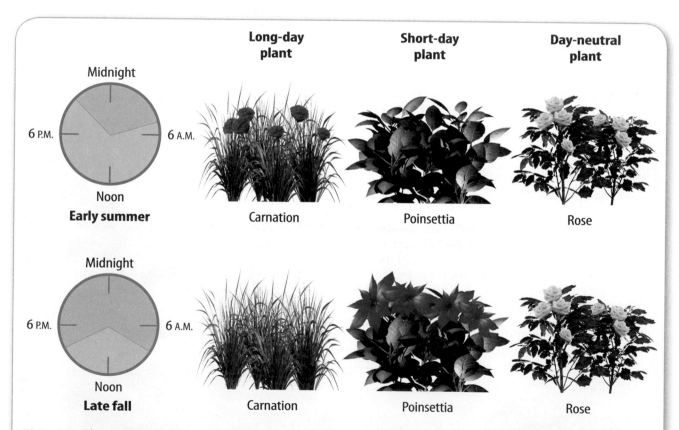

Figure 9 The number of hours of darkness controls flowering in many plants. Long-day plants flower when there are more hours of daylight than darkness, and short-day plants flower when there are more hours of darkness than daylight.

Visual Check What time of year receives more darkness, and what type of plant produces flowers during that season?

Chemical Stimuli

Plants respond to chemical stimuli as well as environmental stimuli. **Plant hormones** *are substances that act as chemical messengers within plants.* These chemicals are produced in tiny amounts. They are called messengers because they usually are produced in one part of a plant and affect another part of that plant.

Auxins

One of the first plant hormones discovered was auxin (AWK sun). There are many different kinds of auxins. Auxins generally cause increased plant growth. They are responsible for phototropism, the growth of a plant toward light. Auxins concentrate on the dark side of a plant's stem, and these cells grow longer. This causes the stem of the plant to grow toward the light, as shown in **Figure 10.**

Ethylene

The plant hormone ethylene helps stimulate the ripening of fruit. Ethylene is a gas that can be produced by fruits, seeds, flowers, and leaves. You might have heard someone say that one rotten apple spoils the whole barrel. This is based on the fact that rotting fruits release ethylene. This can cause other fruits nearby to ripen and possibly rot. Ethylene also can cause plants to drop their leaves.

 Key Concept Check How do plants respond to the chemical stimuli, or hormones, auxin and ethylene?

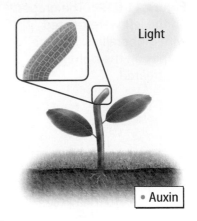
• Auxin
Light

Figure 10 Auxin on the left side of the seedling causes more growth and makes the seedling bend to the right.

Inquiry MiniLab
20 minutes

When will plants flower?

Did you ever think plants could have strategies so that they can germinate, live, grow, reproduce, and continue their species? Photoperiodism is one such strategy.

❶ In your Science Journal, copy the table below to classify plants based on their photoperiodisms.

❷ Choose 8–10 **pictures of flowers.** Record their names in your table. Use the clues on the back of each photo to determine the correct photoperiodism of each plant.

Analyze and Conclude

1. **Interpret Data** Based on your table, which plants would flower during the summer?

2. **Explain** why some plants flower at the same time every year.

3. **Infer** what might happen if short-day plants were placed under light for an hour or two at night.

4. **Key Concept** Why would photoperiodism be an important strategy for flowering plants?

Plant	Season	Short-Day	Long-Day	Day-Neutral

Figure 11 The grapes on the left were treated with gibberellins, and the grapes on the right were not treated.

Math Skills

Use Percentages

A percentage is a ratio that compares a number to 100. For example, if a plant grows 2 cm per day with no chemical stimulus and 3 cm per day with a chemical stimulus, what is the percentage increase in growth?

Subtract the original value from the final value.

3 cm − 2 cm = 1 cm

Set up a ratio between the difference and the original value. Find the decimal equivalent.

$$\frac{1 \text{ cm}}{2 \text{ cm}} = 0.5$$

Multiply by 100 and add a percent sign.

$$0.5 \times 100 = 50\%$$

Practice

Without gibberellins, pea seedlings grew to 2 cm in 3 days. With gibberellins, the seedlings grew to 4 cm in 3 days. What was the percentage increase in growth?

 Review

- **Math Practice**
- **Personal Tutor**

Gibberellins and Cytokinins

Rapidly growing areas of a plant, such as roots and stems, produce gibberellins (jih buh REL unz). These hormones increase the rate of cell division and cell elongation. This results in increased growth of stems and leaves. Gibberellins also can be applied to the outside of plants. As shown in **Figure 11,** applying gibberellins to the outside of plants can have a dramatic effect.

Root tips produce most of the cytokinins (si tuh KI nunz), another type of hormone. Xylem carries cytokinins to other parts of a plant. Cytokinins increase the rate of cell division, and in some plants, cytokinins slow the aging process of flowers and fruits.

Summary of Plant Hormones

Plants produce many different hormones. The hormones you have just read about are groups of similar compounds. Often, two or more hormones interact and produce a plant response. Scientists continue to discover new information about plant hormones.

Humans and Plant Responses

Humans depend on plants for food, fuel, shelter, and clothing. Humans make plants more productive using plant hormones. Some crops now are easier to grow because humans understand how they respond to hormones.

✓ **Reading Check** In what ways are humans dependent on plants?

Lesson 2 Review

Visual Summary

Plants respond to stimuli in their environments in many ways.

Carnation

Photoperiodism occurs in long-day plants and short-day plants. Day-neutral plants are not affected by the number of hours of darkness.

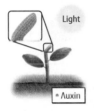

Light

• Auxin

Plant hormones are internal chemical stimuli that produce different responses in plants.

FOLDABLES

Use your lesson Foldable to review the lesson. Save your Foldable for the project at the end of the chapter.

What do you think NOW?

You first read the statements below at the beginning of the chapter.

4. Plants do not produce hormones.

5. Plants can respond to their environments.

6. All plants flower when nights are 10–12 hours long.

Did you change your mind about whether you agree or disagree with the statements? Rewrite any false statements to make them true.

Use Vocabulary

1 **Define** *plant hormone* in your own words.

2 The response of an organism to the number of hours of darkness in its environment is called _____.

3 **Distinguish** between *stimuli* and *tropism*.

Understand Key Concepts

4 **Describe** an example of a plant responding to environmental stimuli.

5 **Distinguish** between a long-day plant and a short-day plant.

6 **Compare** the effect of auxins and gibberellins on plant cells.

7 Which is NOT likely to cause a plant response?
   A. changing the amount of daylight
   B. moving plants away from each other
   C. treating with plant hormones
   D. turning a plant on its side

Interpret Graphics

8 **Identify** Copy the table below and list the plant hormones mentioned in this lesson. Describe the effect of each on plants.

Hormone	Effect on Plants

Critical Thinking

9 **Infer** why the plant shown to the right is growing at an angle.

Math Skills ×÷+−

Review
— Math Practice —

10 When sprayed with gibberellins, the diameter of mature grapes increased from 1.0 cm to 1.75 cm. What was the percent increase in size?

2–3 class periods

Design a Stimulating Environment for Plants

Materials

one quad of plants

Also needed
appropriate materials to perform lab

Safety

Plants usually respond to stimuli in the environment by growing. The response to light is phototropism; plants grow toward the light. The growth response of gravitropism is a little more complicated; stems grow away from the direction of gravity (negative gravitropism), and roots grow in the direction of gravity (positive gravitropism). Thigmotropism is a plant response to touch.

Ask a Question

You have explored tropisms in other labs in this chapter. What questions would you like to answer more thoroughly, or what outcomes would you like to double-check? Do you have another approach in mind to investigate one of the tropisms? Ask a question that you would like to investigate further. Make sure it is testable; think about the variables and equipment you would need.

Make Observations

1. Read and complete a lab safety form.
2. Examine your quad of plants and decide which tropism you want to explore.
3. Make a plan and write it in your Science Journal.
4. Have your teacher approve your plan for your investigation.
5. Choose materials from those provided by your teacher for a simple lab setup.
6. Decide the criteria you will use to show the outcomes you expect.
7. Set up your lab according to your plan.

Form a Hypothesis

8. After observing your plants and lab setup, formulate a hypothesis about the relationship between your selected tropism and a plant's growth. Make a prediction about how the tropism will affect your plants.

194 • Chapter 6
EXTEND

Test Your Hypothesis

9 Make any necessary modifications to your setup so your procedure will move toward your expected outcome.

10 Make a data table like the one to the right in your Science Journal.

11 Make your observations as directed by your procedure, and record in your table.

Analyze and Conclude

12 **Compare** the position of the parts of your plant at the beginning and end of your study. Check to see if the change is easily visible and measurable; try not to jump to conclusions.

13 **Consider** the possible causes of the changes. Determine if it was changing the variable that brought about the effect. Explain.

14 **Relate** how the tropism you modeled could enable plants to meet their needs and survive.

15 **THE BIG IDEA** **The Big Idea** What might happen if the stimulus you provided for the plant was enlarged, minimized, or eliminated?

Communicate Your Results

Prepare a drama to present your findings. Group members or volunteers from the class can wear pictures or signs to indicate their roles. Begin with students role-playing a healthy plant. Add the role of the stimulus, and be sure to identify the tropism and show results in the plant(s).

Inquiry Extension

Phototropism is one of the plant responses to stimuli that you have been able to explore easily by changing the position of the light source or plants in relation to the light source. What might happen if you changed the light source itself? Would your plants react the same way if you put a colored plastic sheet between the light and the plant? Would a red filter cause the same response as a green filter? What if you used different plants? For example, some mustard seeds are fast-germinating. Would these respond in the same way as the other plants?

Time Period	[Variable observed] of Plant			
	1	2	3	4
Day 0 prior to tropism				
Day 1				
Day 2				
Day 3				

Lab Tips

☑ Discuss the possible materials you will use with your lab partner. Remember that the materials should help you learn more about the tropism you selected.

☑ Be creative when deciding how to test the tropism you selected.

☑ Be sure to test only one variable, have a control, and collect data that you can count or measure.

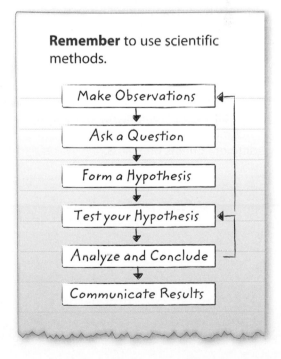

Remember to use scientific methods.

- Make Observations
- Ask a Question
- Form a Hypothesis
- Test your Hypothesis
- Analyze and Conclude
- Communicate Results

Plants transform light energy into chemical energy, respond to stimuli, and maintain homeostasis.

Key Concepts Summary 🔑	Vocabulary
Lesson 1: Energy Processing in Plants	**photosynthesis** p. 180
• The vascular tissues in most plants, xylem and phloem, move materials throughout plants.	**cellular respiration** p. 182

• In **photosynthesis,** plants convert light energy, water, and carbon dioxide into the food-energy molecule glucose through a series of chemical reactions. The process gives off oxygen.

Sunlight energy
Carbon dioxide CO_2
Oxygen O_2
Water H_2O
Sugar $C_6H_{12}O_6$

• **Cellular respiration** is a series of chemical reactions that convert the energy in food molecules into a usable form of energy called ATP.

• Photosynthesis and cellular respiration can be considered opposite processes of each other.

Lesson 2: Plant Responses

	stimulus p. 187
	tropism p. 188
	photoperiodism p. 190
	plant hormone p. 191

• Although plants cannot move from one place to another, they do respond to **stimuli**, or changes in their environments. Plants respond to stimuli in different ways. **Tropisms** are growth responses toward or away from stimuli such as light, touch, and gravity. **Photoperiodism** is a plant's response to the number of hours of darkness in its environment.

• Plants respond to chemical stimuli, or **plant hormones,** such as auxins, ethylene, gibberellins, and cytokinins. Different hormones have different effects on plants.

- **Personal Tutor**
- **Vocabulary eGames**
- **Vocabulary eFlashcards**

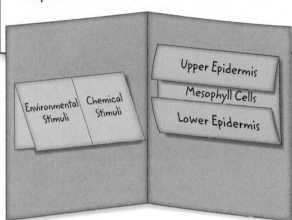 **Chapter Project**

Assemble your lesson Foldables as shown to make a Chapter Project. Use the project to review what you have learned in this chapter.

Use Vocabulary

1 Long-day and short-day plants are examples of plants that respond to _____.

2 The process that uses oxygen and produces carbon dioxide is _____.

3 Any change in an environment that causes an organism to respond is called a(n) _____.

4 Food is produced for plants through the process of _____.

Link Vocabulary and Key Concepts

 **Concepts in Motion** Interactive Concept Map

Copy this concept map, and then use vocabulary terms from the previous page to complete the concept map.

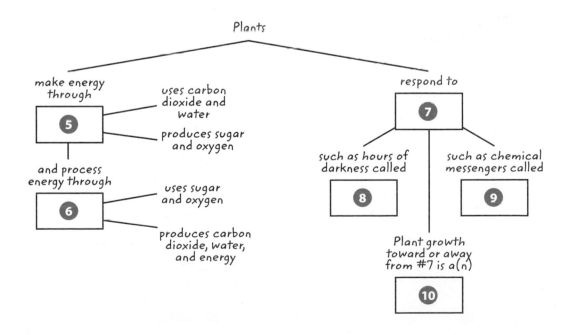

Chapter 6 Review

Understand Key Concepts

1 Which material travels from the roots to the leaves through the xylem?

A. oxygen
B. sugar
C. sunlight
D. water

2 Which organelle is the site of photosynthesis?

A. chloroplast
B. mitochondria
C. nucleus
D. ribosome

3 Which is a product of cellular respiration?

A. ATP
B. light
C. oxygen
D. sugar

Use the image below to answer questions 4 and 5.

4 What type of plant-growth response is shown in the photo above?

A. flowering
B. gravitropism
C. photoperiodism
D. thigmotropism

5 Which stimulus is responsible for this type of growth?

A. gravity
B. light
C. nutrients
D. touch

6 Which molecule is responsible for capturing light energy in a plant?

A. ATP
B. chlorophyll
C. sugar
D. water

Use the image below to answer questions 7 and 8.

7 Which is a product of the process shown above?

A. carbon dioxide
B. sugar
C. sunlight
D. water

8 Where does the energy that drives this process come from?

A. oxygen
B. sugar
C. sunlight
D. water

9 Which is related to an external environmental stimulus?

A. auxins
B. cytokinins
C. gibberellins
D. thigmotropism

10 Which is a plant hormone?

A. chloroplast
B. gibberellin
C. gravitropism
D. phototropism

Critical Thinking

11 Infer which came first—photosynthesis or cellular respiration.

12 Assess the importance of material transport in plants.

13 Construct a table to compare the reactants and products of photosynthesis and cellular respiration.

14 Evaluate the internal structure of a leaf as a location for photosynthesis.

15 Assess the need for plants to respond to their environment.

16 Predict what would happen if a short-day plant were exposed to more hours of daylight.

17 Critique the saying "one rotten apple spoils the whole barrel."

18 Infer from the photo below where the light source is in relation to the plant.

19 Compare and contrast the functions of xylem and phloem.

20 Evaluate the importance of auxins.

21 Predict the effect of an atmosphere with no gravity on a plant growing from a seed.

Writing in Science

22 Write a five-sentence paragraph about the importance of plants in your life. Include a main idea, supporting details, and a concluding sentence.

REVIEW THE BIG IDEA

23 What plant processes have you learned about in this chapter? Make a list.

24 How do these processes, such as the one shown below, help a plant survive?

Math Skills

Review

— **Math Practice** —

Use Percentages

25 Without treatment with gibberellins, 500 out of 1,000 grass seeds germinated. When sprayed with gibberellins, 875 of the seeds germinated. What was the percentage increase?

26 A bunch of bananas ripens (turns from green to yellow) in 42 hours. When the bananas are placed in a bag with an apple, which releases ethylene, the bananas ripen in 21 hours. What is the percentage change in ripening time?

Standardized Test Practice

Record your answers on the answer sheet provided by your teacher or on a sheet of paper.

Multiple Choice

1 Which structure transports sugars throughout a plant?

   A epidermis

   B phloem

   C stomata

   D xylem

2 What is one similarity between plants and animals?

   A Both plants and animals carry on cellular respiration.

   B Both plants and animals carry on photosynthesis.

   C Both plants and animals have chloroplasts.

   D Both plants and animals use xylem and phloem to transport materials.

Use the diagram below to answer question 3.

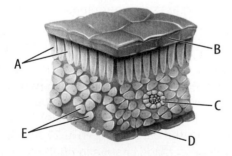

3 Where does most of the photosynthesis in the leaf above take place?

   A cells A and B

   B cells A and E

   C cells B and C

   D cells D and E

4 Which two plant hormones increase the rate of cell division?

   A auxins and cytokinins

   B cytokinins and giberellins

   C ethylene and auxins

   D giberellins and ethylene

5 Which is a product of photosynthesis?

   A ATP

   B glucose

   C light

   D water

Use the image below to answer question 6.

6 Which cellular process occurs within the organelle shown above?

   A cellular respiration

   B photosynthesis

   C transport of phloem

   D transport of xylem

7 What causes a seed that has fallen on the ground to send roots downward and a stem upward?

   A gravitropism

   B photoperiodism

   C phototropism

   D thigmotropism

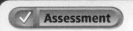

8 How is cellular respiration related to photosynthesis?

A Animals produce sugars through cellular respiration that are broken down by plants through photosynthesis.

B Animals use cellular respiration while plants use photosynthesis.

C Cellular respiration produces sugars, which are stored through photosynthesis.

D Photosynthesis produces sugars, which are broken down in cellular respiration.

Use the diagram below to answer question 9.

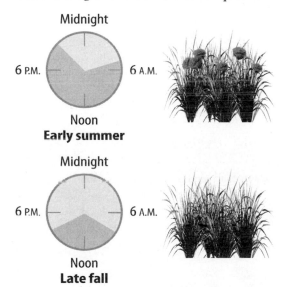

9 What kind of flowering plants are shown in the diagram above?

A day-neutral plants

B long-day plants

C night-neutral plants

D short-day plants

Constructed Response

Use the figure below to answer questions 10 and 11.

10 Describe what is happening in the image above. In your response, identify the environmental stimulus and the plant growth response.

11 Which plant hormone is involved in the growth response shown in the drawing above? Explain how this hormone causes the growth response.

12 Fruit distributors might use technologies to remove ethylene from the area where fruits are stored. How does this practice affect the fruit? Explain your answer.

13 A gardener is having trouble keeping the grass alive under a large oak tree. What is a possible reason why this grass will not grow?

NEED EXTRA HELP?													
If You Missed Question...	1	2	3	4	5	6	7	8	9	10	11	12	13
Go to Lesson...	1	1	1	2	1	1	2	1	2	2	2	2	1

Populations and Communities

THE BIG IDEA How do populations and communities interact and change?

(inquiry) Too Many Pigeons?

This group of pigeons does not depend only on the environment for food. Tourists visiting the area also feed the pigeons. Because so much food is available, more pigeons than normal live in this part of the city.

- Do you think this large number of pigeons affects other organisms in the area?

- How do you think groups of pigeons and other organisms interact and change?

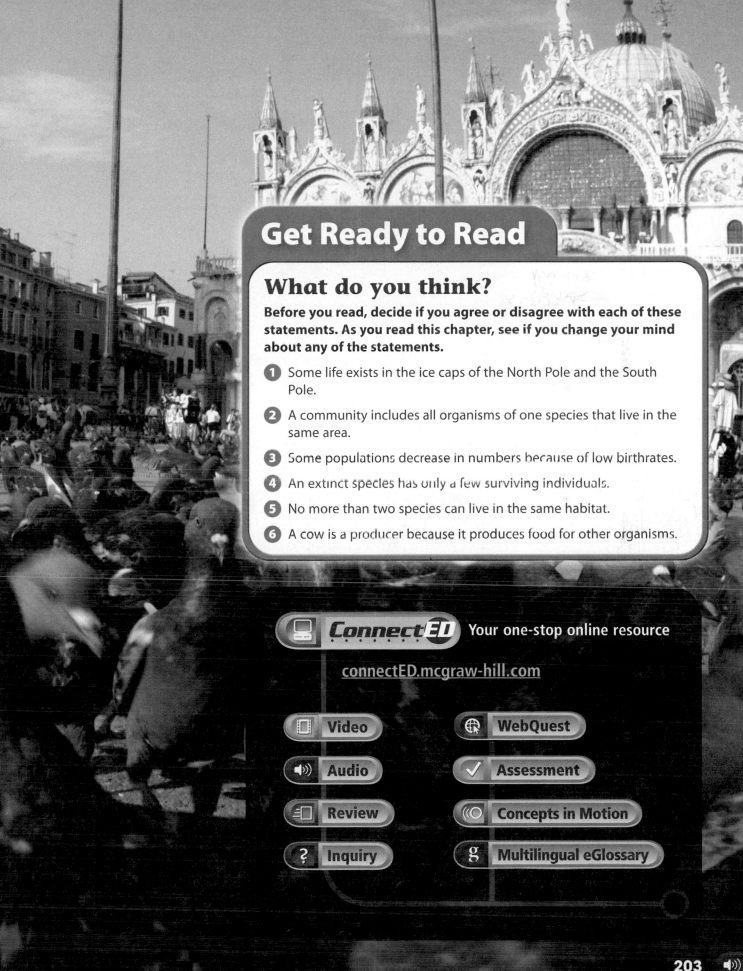

Get Ready to Read

What do you think?

Before you read, decide if you agree or disagree with each of these statements. As you read this chapter, see if you change your mind about any of the statements.

1. Some life exists in the ice caps of the North Pole and the South Pole.

2. A community includes all organisms of one species that live in the same area.

3. Some populations decrease in numbers because of low birthrates.

4. An extinct species has only a few surviving individuals.

5. No more than two species can live in the same habitat.

6. A cow is a producer because it produces food for other organisms.

ConnectED Your one-stop online resource

connectED.mcgraw-hill.com

- Video
- WebQuest
- Audio
- Assessment
- Review
- Concepts in Motion
- Inquiry
- Multilingual eGlossary

Populations

Reading Guide

Key Concepts
ESSENTIAL QUESTIONS

- What defines a population?
- What factors affect the size of a population?

Vocabulary

biosphere p. 205   *Ecosystem* ✓

community p. 206   *Ecology* ✓

population p. 206   *species*

competition p. 207

limiting factor p. 207

population density p. 208

biotic potential p. 208

carrying capacity p. 209

g **Multilingual eGlossary**

Academic Standards for Science

6.3.2 Describe how changes caused by organisms in the habitat where they live can be beneficial or detrimental to themselves or the native plants and animals.

6.3.3 Describe how certain biotic and abiotic factors, such as predators, quantity of light and water, range of temperatures, and soil composition, can limit the number of organisms that an ecosystem can support.

Also covers: 6.NS.3, 6.NS.5, 6.NS.6, 6.NS.7, 6.NS.8, 6.NS.9

Inquiry Looking for Something?

Meerkats live in family groups. They help protect each other by watching for danger from eagles, lions, and other hunters of the Kalahari Desert. What other ways might the meerkats interact?

Inquiry Launch Lab

15 minutes

How many times do you interact?

Every day, you interact with other people in different ways, including talking, writing, or shaking hands. Some interactions involve just one other person, and others happen between many people. Like humans, other organisms interact with each other in their environment.

1. Make a list in your Science Journal of all the ways you have interacted with other people today.

2. Use a **highlighter** to mark the interactions that occurred between you and one other person.

3. Use a **highlighter** of another color to mark interactions that occurred among three or more people.

Think About This

1. Were your interactions mainly with one person or with three or more people?

2. 🔑 **Key Concept** How might your interactions change if the group of people were bigger?

The Biosphere and Ecological Systems

Imagine flying halfway around the world to Africa. When your plane flies over Africa, you might see mountains, rivers, grasslands, and forests. As you get closer to land, you might see a herd of elephants at a watering hole. You also might see a group of meerkats, like the ones on the previous page.

Now imagine hiking through an African forest. You might see monkeys, frogs, insects, spiders, and flowers. Maybe you catch sight of crocodiles sunning themselves by a river or birds perching on trees.

You are exploring Earth's **biosphere** (BI uh sfihr)—*the parts of Earth and the surrounding atmosphere where there is life.* The biosphere includes all the land of the continents and islands. It also includes all of Earth's oceans, lakes, and streams, as well as the ice caps at the North Pole and the South Pole.

Parts of the biosphere with large amounts of plants or algae often contain many other organisms as well. The biosphere's distribution of chlorophyll, a green pigment in plants and algae, is shown in **Figure 1**.

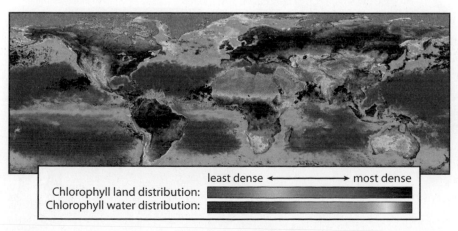

least dense ◄————► most dense

Chlorophyll land distribution:
Chlorophyll water distribution:

Figure 1 The colors in this satellite image represent the densities of chlorophyll, a green pigment found in plants and algae.

✓ **Visual Check** Why might the North Pole have very little green?

What is a population?

The Kalahari Desert in Africa is a part of the Earth's biosphere. A wildlife refuge in the Kalahari Desert is home to several groups of meerkats. Meerkats are small mammals that live in family groups and help each other care for their young.

Meerkats rely on interactions among themselves to survive. They sleep in underground burrows at night and hunt for food during the day. They take turns standing upright to watch for danger and call out warnings to others.

Meerkats are part of an ecosystem, as shown in **Figure 2.** An ecosystem is a group of organisms that lives in an area at one time, as well as the climate, soil, water, and other nonliving parts of the environment. The Kalahari Desert is an ecosystem. The study of all ecosystems on Earth is ecology.

Many species besides meerkats live in the Kalahari Desert. They include scorpions, spiders, insects, snakes, and birds such as eagles and owls. Also, large animals like zebras, giraffes, and lions live there. Plants that grow in the Kalahari Desert include shrubs, grasses, small trees, and melon vines. Together, all these plants, animals, and other organisms form a community. *A **community** is all the populations of different species that live together in the same area at the same time.*

All the meerkats in this refuge form a population. *A **population** is all the organisms of the same species that live in the same area at the same time.* A species is a group of organisms that have similar traits and are able to produce fertile offspring.

 Key Concept Check What defines a population?

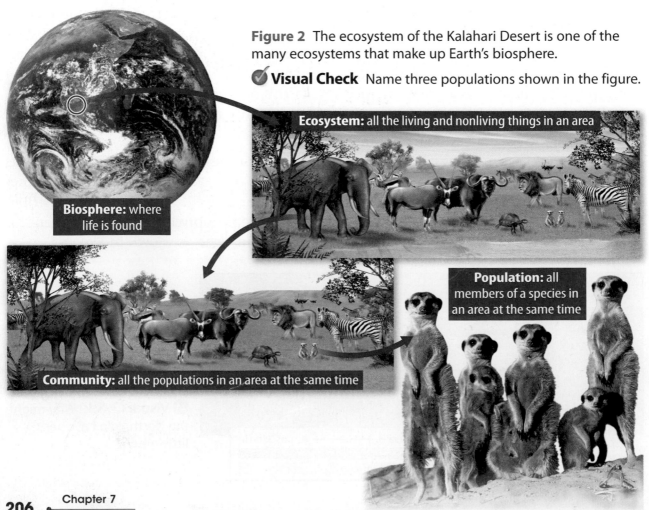

Figure 2 The ecosystem of the Kalahari Desert is one of the many ecosystems that make up Earth's biosphere.

✔**Visual Check** Name three populations shown in the figure.

Biosphere: where life is found

Ecosystem: all the living and nonliving things in an area

Community: all the populations in an area at the same time

Population: all members of a species in an area at the same time

Competition

At times, not enough food is available for every organism in a community. Members of a population, including those in the Kalahari Desert, must compete with other populations and each other for enough food to survive. **Competition** *is the demand for resources, such as food, water, and shelter, in short supply in a community.* When there are not enough resources available to survive, there is more competition in a community.

Population Sizes

If the amount of available food decreases, what do you think happens to a population of meerkats? Some meerkats might move away to find food elsewhere. Female meerkats cannot raise as many young. The population becomes smaller. If there is plenty of food, however, the size of the population grows larger as more meerkats survive to adulthood and live longer. Changes in environmental factors can result in population size changes.

Limiting Factors

Environmental factors, such as available water, food, shelter, sunlight, and temperature, are possible limiting factors for a population. *A* **limiting factor** *is anything that restricts the size of a population.* Available sunlight is a limiting factor for most organisms. If there is not enough sunlight, green plants cannot make food by photosynthesis. Organisms that eat plants are affected if little food is available.

Temperature is a limiting factor for some organisms. When the temperature drops below freezing, many organisms die because it is too cold to carry out their life functions. Disease, predators—animals that eat other animals—and natural disasters such as fires or floods are limiting factors as well.

 Key Concept Check What factors affect the size of a population?

Inquiry MiniLab
15 minutes

What are limiting factors?

Certain factors, called limiting factors, can affect the size of a population.

1. Read and complete a lab safety form.

2. Your teacher will divide your class into groups.

3. Using a **meterstick** and **masking tape,** mark a 1-m square on the floor. Place a piece of paper in the middle of the square.

4. All members of your group will stand entirely within the square. While one member keeps time with a **stopwatch,** members of the group will write the alphabet on the sheet of paper one at a time.

5. In your Science Journal, calculate the average time it took each person to write the alphabet.

Analyze and Conclude

1. **Describe** how the space limitations affected each member's ability to complete the task.

2. **Key Concept** What functions must an organism perform that can be limited by the amount of available space?

Figure 3 A sedated lynx is fitted with a radio collar and then returned to the wild.

WORD ORIGIN · · · · · · · · · ·

population
from Latin *populus*, means "inhabitants"

density
from Latin *densus*, means "thick, crowded"
· · · · · · · · · · · · · · · ·

FOLDABLES

Make a horizontal half book and label it as shown. Use it to organize your notes on the relationship between population size and carrying capacity in an ecosystem.

Carrying Capacity

Measuring Population Size

Sometimes it is difficult to determine the size of a population. How would you count scampering meerkats or wild lynx? One method used to count and monitor animal populations is the capture-mark-and-release method. The lynx in **Figure 3** is a member of a population in Poland that is monitored using this method. Biologists using this method sedate animals and fit them with radio collars before releasing them back into the wild. By counting how many observed lynx are wearing collars, scientists can estimate the size of the lynx population. Biologists also use the collars to track the lynx's movements and monitor their activities.

Suppose you want to know how closely together Cumberland azaleas (uh ZAYL yuhz), a type of flower, grow in the Great Smoky Mountains National Park. **Population density** *is the size of a population compared to the amount of space available.* One way of estimating population density is by sample count. Rather than counting every azalea shrub, you count only those in a representative area, such as 1 km². By multiplying the number of square kilometers in the park by the number of azaleas in 1 km², you find the estimated population density of azalea shrubs in the entire park.

✓ **Reading Check** Describe two ways you can estimate population size.

Biotic Potential

Imagine that a population of raccoons has plenty of food, water, and den space. In addition, there is no disease or danger from other animals. The only limit to the size of this population is the number of offspring the raccoons can produce. **Biotic potential** *is the potential growth of a population if it could grow in perfect conditions with no limiting factors.* No population on Earth ever reaches its biotic potential because no ecosystem has an unlimited supply of natural resources.

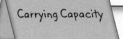

Carrying Capacity

What would happen if a population of meerkats reached its biotic potential? It would stop growing when it reached the limit of available resources that the ecosystem could provide, such as food, water, or shelter. *The largest number of individuals of one species that an environment can support is the* **carrying capacity.** A population grows until it reaches the carrying capacity of an environment, as shown in **Figure 4.** Disease, space, predators, and food are some of the factors that limit the carrying capacity of an ecosystem. However, the carrying capacity of an environment is not constant. It increases and decreases as the amount of available resources increases and decreases. At times, a population can temporarily exceed the carrying capacity of an environment.

✓ **Reading Check** What is carrying capacity?

Overpopulation

When the size of a population becomes larger than the carrying capacity of its ecosystem, overpopulation occurs. Overpopulation can cause problems for organisms. For example, meerkats eat spiders. An overpopulation of meerkats causes the size of the spider population in that community to decrease. Populations of birds and other animals that eat spiders also decrease when the number of spiders decreases.

Elephants in Africa's wild game parks is another example of overpopulation. Elephants searching for food caused the tree damage shown in **Figure 5.** They push over trees to feed on the uppermost leaves. Other species of animals that use the same trees for food and shelter must compete with the elephants. The loss of trees and plants can also damage soil. Trees and plants might not grow in that area again for a long time.

✓ **Reading Check** How can overpopulation affect a community?

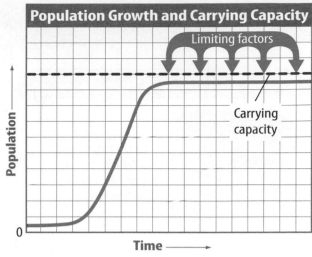

▲ **Figure 4** Carrying capacity is determined in part by limiting factors.

✓ **Visual Check** What factors affect population size in the graph above?

▲ **Figure 5** An overpopulation of elephants can cause damage to trees and other plants as the herd searches for food in the community.

Lesson 1 Review

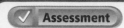

Visual Summary

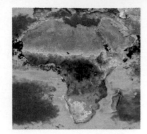

The population density of organisms, including green plants and algae, varies throughout the world.

A community is all the populations of different species that live together in the same area at the same time.

The number of individuals in a population varies as the amount of available resources varies.

FOLDABLES

Use your lesson Foldable to review the lesson. Save your Foldable for the project at the end of the chapter.

What do you think NOW?

You first read the statements below at the beginning of the chapter.

1. Some life exists in the ice caps of the North Pole and the South Pole.

2. A community includes all organisms of one species that live in the same area.

Did you change your mind about whether you agree or disagree with the statements? Rewrite any false statements to make them true.

Use Vocabulary

1 Define *population.*

2 Distinguish between carrying capacity and biotic potential.

3 Food, water, living space, and disease are examples of _____.

Understand Key Concepts

4 Explain how competition could limit the size of a bird population.

5 One example of competition among members of a meerkat population is
   A. fighting over mates.
   B. warning others of danger.
   C. huddling together to stay warm.
   D. teaching young to search for food.

Interpret Graphics

6 Sequence Draw a graphic organizer like the one below to show the sequence of steps in one type of population study.

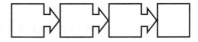

7 Explain the changes in population size at each point marked on the graph below.

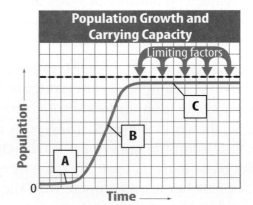

Critical Thinking

8 Explain Is the problem of elephants destroying trees in southern Africa overpopulation, competition, or both?

Familiar Birds in an Unlikely Place

Howling winds blow across the Altiplano—a cold plateau high in the Andes mountain range of South America. There, you might expect to see animals such as llamas, but Felicity Arengo travels to the Altiplano to observe flamingos.

Flamingos usually are associated with tropical regions. However, three species of flamingo—James, Andean, and Chilean—are adapted to the cold, barren Altiplano. Although this region differs from tropical areas where other flamingos live, both have food sources for the birds. The plateau is dotted with salty lakes containing brine shrimp, tiny organisms that flamingos eat.

Scientists have many questions about the flamingos that visit these salty lakes. How large are the flamingo populations? How do they survive when the lakes evaporate? To answer these questions, Arengo and her team visit the lakes and count flamingos there. They also tag flamingos with radio transmitters to track their movements. They have learned that one species, the Andean flamingo, is the rarest flamingo species in the world. Additionally, when the plateau lakes freeze, many flamingos fly to lakes in the lowlands of Argentina, Bolivia, Chile, and Peru.

As human activity changes the Altiplano, flamingos that live there might be in danger. On the plateau, mining operations use and pollute lake water. In the lowlands, ranchers often drain lakes for more land to grow crops or to feed animals.

Arengo and other scientists are working with organizations to protect flamingos' habitats. Scientists have trained park rangers to monitor flamingos' reproductive activities and protect nesting colonies. As scientists collect more data and find new ways to protect flamingos' habitats, a brighter future might be in store for the flamingos of the Altiplano.

▲ Dr. Arengo tags a flamingo with a radio transmitter. Once she releases the flamingo, satellites will track the flamingo's movement.

▲ Flamingos' habitats cover four countries—Argentina, Bolivia, Chile, and Peru. As a well-known species, flamingos help motivate conservation efforts in these countries.

It's Your Turn

BRAINSTORM With classmates, choose an ecosystem in your area that is in need of conservation. Brainstorm what animal would make a good species to represent the ecosystem, and create a poster designed to raise awareness.

Reading Guide

Key Concepts 🔑
ESSENTIAL QUESTIONS

• How do populations change?

• Why do human populations change?

Vocabulary

birthrate p. 213

death rate p. 213

extinct species p. 215

endangered species p. 215

threatened species p. 215

migration p. 216

 **Multilingual eGlossary**

 Video BrainPOP®

Academic Standards for Science

6.3.2 Describe how changes caused by organisms in the habitat where they live can be beneficial or detrimental to themselves or the native plants and animals.

6.3.3 Describe how certain biotic and abiotic factors, such as predators, quantity of light and water, range of temperatures, and soil composition, can limit the number of organisms that an ecosystem can support.

Also covers: 6.NS.4, 6.NS.6, 6.NS.7, 6.NS.8, 6.NS.11

Changing Populations

Inquiry Same Mother?

Have you ever seen newly hatched baby spiders? Baby spiders can have hundreds or even thousands of brothers and sisters. What keeps the spider population from growing out of control?

What events can change a population?

Populations can be affected by human-made and environmental changes, such as floods or a good growing season. A population's size can increase or decrease in response to these changes.

1 Read and complete a lab safety form.

2 Record in your Science Journal the number of **counting objects** you have been given. Each object represents an organism, and all the objects together represent a population.

3 Turn over one of the **event cards** you were given and follow the instructions on the card. Determine the event's impact on your population.

4 Repeat step 3 for four more "seasons," or turns.

Think About This

1. Compare the size of your population with other groups. Do you all have the same number of organisms at the end of five seasons?

2. 🔑 **Key Concept** What effect did the different events have on your population?

How Populations Change

Have you ever seen a cluster of spider eggs? Some female spiders lay hundreds or even thousands of eggs in their lifetime. What happens to a population of spiders when a large group of eggs hatches all at once? The population suddenly becomes larger. It doesn't stay that way for long, though. Many spiders die or become food, like the one being eaten in **Figure 6,** before they grow enough to reproduce. The size of the spider population increases when the eggs hatch but decreases as the spiders die.

A population change can be measured by the population's birthrate and death rate. *A population's* **birthrate** *is the number of off-spring produced over a given time period. The* **death rate** *is the number of individuals that die over the same time period.* If the birthrate is higher than the death rate, the population increases. If the death rate is higher than the birthrate, the population decreases.

Figure 6 Spiders have a high birthrate, but they usually have a high death rate too. Many spiders die or are eaten before they can reproduce.

Exponential Growth

When a population is in ideal conditions with unlimited resources, it grows in a pattern called **exponential** growth. During exponential growth, the larger a population gets, the faster it grows. *E. coli* bacteria are microscopic organisms that undergo exponential growth. This population doubles in size every half hour, as shown in **Figure 7.** It takes only 10 hours for the *E. coli* population to grow from one organism to more than 1 million. Exponential growth cannot continue for long. Eventually, limiting factors stop population growth.

SCIENCE USE V. COMMON USE

exponential
Science Use a mathematical expression that contains a constant raised to a power, such as 2^3 or x^2

Common Use in great amounts

Exponential Population Growth

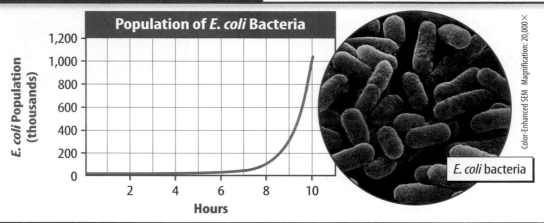

Population of *E. coli* Bacteria

E. coli Population (thousands)

Color-Enhanced SEM Magnification: 20,000×

E. coli bacteria

Hours

Figure 7 When grown in the laboratory, this population of *E. coli* bacteria is given everything it needs to briefly achieve exponential growth.

WORD ORIGIN

extinct
from Latin *extinctus*, means "extinguish"

Population Size Decrease

Population size can increase, but it also can decrease. For example, a population of field mice might decrease in size in the winter because there is less food. Some mice might not be able to find enough food and will starve. More mice will die than will be born, so the population size decreases. When food is plentiful, the population size usually increases.

Natural disasters such as floods, fires, or volcanic eruptions also affect population size. For example, if a hurricane rips away part of a coral reef, the populations of coral and other organisms that live on the reef also decrease in size.

Disease is another cause of population decrease. In the mid-1900s, Dutch elm disease spread throughout the United States and destroyed many thousands of elm trees. Because of the disease, the size of population of elm trees decreased.

Predation—the hunting of organisms for food—also reduces population size. For example, a farmer might bring cats into a barn to reduce the size of a mouse population.

Reading Check What are four reasons that a population might decrease in size?

Extinction If populations continue to decrease in numbers, they disappear. *An extinct species is a species that has died out and no individuals are left.* Extinctions can be caused by predation, natural disasters, or damage to the environment.

Some extinctions in Earth's history were large events that involved many species. Most scientists think the extinction of the dinosaurs about 65 million years ago was caused by a meteorite crashing into Earth. The impact would have sent tons of dust into the atmosphere, blocking sunlight. Without sunlight, plants could not grow. Animals, such as dinosaurs, that ate plants probably starved.

Most extinctions involve fewer species. For example, New Zealand was once home to a large, flightless bird called the giant moa, as shown in **Figure 8.** Humans first settled these islands about 700 years ago. They hunted the moa for food. As the size of the human population increased, the size of the moa population decreased. Within 200 years, all the giant moas had been killed and the species became extinct.

Endangered Species The mountain gorillas shown in **Figure 8** are an example of a species that is endangered. *An **endangered species** is a species whose population is at risk of extinction.*

Threatened Species California sea otters almost became extinct in the early 1900s due to overhunting. In 1977, California sea otters were classified as a **threatened species**—*a species at risk, but not yet endangered.* Laws were passed to protect the otters and by 2007 there were about 3,000 sea otters. Worldwide, there are more than 4,000 species that are classified as endangered or threatened.

 Reading Check What is the difference between an endangered species and a threatened species?

Figure 8 Organisms are classified as extinct, endangered, or threatened.

Extinct The giant moa, a large bird that was nearly four meters tall, was hunted to extinction.

Endangered Just over 700 mountain gorillas remain in the wild in Africa.

Threatened California sea otters are at risk of becoming endangered because there are so few of them remaining in the wild.

How does migration affect population size?

Your class will model a population of birds that migrates during the fall and the spring.

1. Read and complete a lab safety form.

2. Begin at the summer station. Record in your Science Journal the size of the bird population represented by your class. When your teacher signals, move to the fall station.

3. Pick a piece of **paper** out of the **jar.** If the paper has a minus sign, drop out of the game. If it has a plus sign, bring a classmate into the game.

4. Record the size of the remaining population at the fall station.

5. Migrate to the winter station and repeat steps 3 and 4. Move two more times and repeat for spring and summer.

Analyze and Conclude

1. **Draw Conclusions** What might happen if the birds did not migrate each year?

2. 🔑 **Key Concept** How did the population change throughout the year?

Movement

Populations also change when organisms move from place to place. When an animal population becomes overcrowded, some individuals might move to find more food or living space. For example, zebras might overgraze an area and move to areas that are not so heavily grazed.

Plant populations can also move from place to place. Have you ever blown on a dandelion puff full of seeds? Each tiny dandelion seed has a feathery part that enables it to be carried by the wind. Wind often carries seeds far from their parent plants. Animals also help spread plant seeds. For example, some squirrels and woodpeckers collect acorns. They carry the acorns away and store them for a future food source. The animal forgets some acorns, and they sprout and grow into new trees far from their parent trees.

Migration Sometimes an entire population moves from one place to another and later returns to its original location. **Migration** *is the instinctive seasonal movement of a population of organisms from one place to another.* Ducks, geese, and monarch butterflies are examples of organisms that migrate annually. Some fish, frogs, insects, and mammals—including the whales described in **Figure 9**—migrate to find food and shelter.

🔑 **Key Concept Check** List three ways populations change.

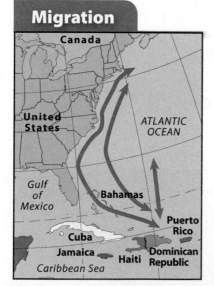

Migration

Figure 9 During the winter, humpback whales mate and give birth in warm ocean waters near the Bahamas. In the summer, they migrate north to food-rich waters along the coast of New England.

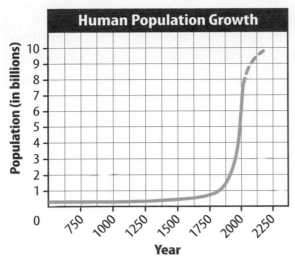

Human Population Growth

Population (in billions)

Year

◀ **Figure 10** The human population has grown faster in the past 150 years than at any time in Earth's history.

☑ **Visual Check** How does this population curve compare with the graph of the *E. coli* population in **Figure 7?**

Human Population Changes

Human population size is affected by the same three factors that determine the sizes of all populations—birthrate, death rate, and movement. But, unlike other species, humans have developed ways to increase the carrying capacity of their environment. Improved crop yields, domesticated farm animals, and timely methods of transporting foods and other resources enable people to survive in all types of environments.

Scientists **estimate** that there were about 300 million humans on Earth a thousand years ago. Today there are more than 6 billion humans on Earth, as shown in **Figure 10.** By 2050 there could be over 9 billion. No one knows when the human population will reach Earth's carrying capacity. However, some scientists estimate Earth's carrying capacity is about 11 billion.

As the human population grows, people need to build more houses and roads and clear more land for crops. This means less living space, food, and other resources for other species. In addition, people use more energy to heat and cool homes; to fuel cars, airplanes, and other forms of transportation; and to produce electricity. This energy use contributes to pollution that affects other populations.

One example of the consequences of human population growth is the destruction of tropical forests. Each year, humans clear thousands of acres of tropical forest to make room for crops and livestock, as shown in **Figure 11.** Clearing tropical forests is harmful because these forests contain a large variety of species that are not in other ecosystems.

☑ **Reading Check** Explain how human population growth affects other species.

ACADEMIC VOCABULARY

estimate
(verb) to determine roughly the size, nature, or extent of something

Figure 11 Tropical forests are cleared for crops and livestock. The habitats of many organisms are destroyed, resulting in many species becoming endangered or extinct. ▼

Math Skills

Use Graphs

Graphs are used to make large amounts of information easy to interpret. Line graphs show how data changes over a period of time. A circle graph, or pie graph, shows how portions of a set of data compare with the whole set. The circle represents 100 percent and each segment represents one part making up the whole. For example, Figure 14 shows all the moves made by people in the United States during 2004–2005. Fifty-seven percent of all moves were within the same county.

Practice

Based on Figure 14,

1. What percentage of the moves were from one state to another?

2. What percentage of the moves were within the same state?

 Review

- **Math Practice**
- **Personal Tutor**

Figure 12 Before vaccinations, many children died in infancy. The use of vaccines has significantly reduced death rates.

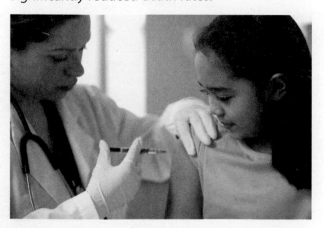

Population Size Increase

Do you know anyone who is more than 100 years old? In 2006, almost 80,000 people living in the United States were at least 100 years old. People are living longer today than in previous generations, and more children reach adulthood. Recall that when the birthrate of a population is higher than its death rate, the population grows. There are several factors that keep the human birthrate higher than its death rate. Some of these factors are discussed below.

Food For some, finding food might be as easy as making a trip to the grocery store, but not everyone can get food as easily. Advances in agriculture have made it possible to produce food for billions of people.

Resources Fossil fuels, cloth, metals, foods, and many other materials are easily transported around the world by planes, trains, trucks, or boats. Today, people have access to more resources because of better transportation methods.

Sanitation As recently as 100 years ago, diseases such as typhoid, cholera, and diphtheria were major causes of death. These diseases spread through unclean water supplies and untreated sewage. Modern water treatment technologies have reduced the occurrence of many diseases. Less expensive and more effective cleaning products are now available to help prevent the spread of disease-causing organisms. As a result, deaths from these illnesses are less common in many countries.

Medical Care Modern medical care is keeping people alive and healthy longer than ever before. As shown in **Figure 12,** scientists have developed vaccines, antibiotics, and other medicines that prevent and treat disease. As a result, fewer people get sick, and human death rates have decreased. Medical technologies and new medicines help people survive heart attacks, cancer, and other major illnesses.

Decreases in Human Population Size

Human populations in some parts of the world are decreasing in size. Diseases such as AIDS and malaria cause high death rates in some countries. Severe drought has resulted in major crop failures and lack of food. Floods, earthquakes, and other natural disasters can cause the deaths of hundreds or even thousands of people at a time. Damage from disasters, such as the damage shown in **Figure 13,** can keep people from living in the area for a long time. All of these factors cause decreases in human population sizes in some areas.

 Reading Check What are three events that can decrease human population size?

Population Movement

Have you ever moved to a different city, state, or country? The size of a human population changes as people move from place to place. The graph in **Figure 14** shows the percentages of each kind of move people make. Like other organisms, populations of humans might move when more resources become available in a different place.

Did your parents, grandparents, or great grandparents come to the United States from another country? Immigration takes place when organisms move into an area. Most of the U.S. population is descended from people who immigrated from Europe, Africa, Asia, and Central and South America.

 Key Concept Check What makes human populations increase or decrease in size?

▲ **Figure 13** Natural disasters such as a tsunami can cause severe damage to people's homes, as well as drastically reduce the population size.

FOLDABLES®

Make a horizontal two-tab book and label it as shown. Use it to summarize why human populations change in size.

| Human Population Increase | Human Population Decrease |

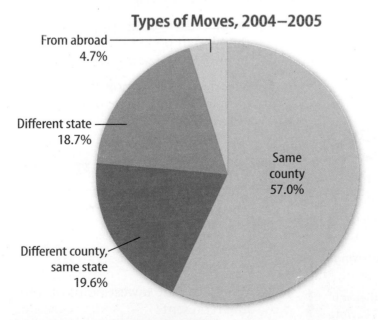

Types of Moves, 2004–2005

- From abroad 4.7%
- Different state 18.7%
- Different county, same state 19.6%
- Same county 57.0%

Source: U.S. Census Bureau, Current Population Survey, 2005 Annual Social and Economic Supplement.

◀ **Figure 14** Populations can move between counties and states or even from another country.

✓ **Visual Check** Which type of move did the largest percentage of the population make?

Lesson 2 Review

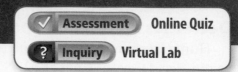
Visual Summary

The birthrate and the death rate of any population affects its population size.

The giant moa is classified as an extinct species because there are no surviving members.

A population that is at risk but not yet endangered is a threatened species.

FOLDABLES

Use your lesson Foldable to review the lesson. Save your Foldable for the project at the end of the chapter.

What do you think NOW?

You first read the statements below at the beginning of the chapter.

3. Some populations decrease in numbers because of low birthrates.

4. An extinct species has only a few surviving individuals.

Did you change your mind about whether you agree or disagree with the statements? Rewrite any false statements to make them true.

Use Vocabulary

1 **Define** *endangered species* in your own words.

2 **Distinguish** between birthrate and death rate.

3 The instinctive movement of a population from one place to another is _____.

Understand Key Concepts

4 Rabbits move into a new field where there is plenty of room to dig new burrows. This is an example of
  A. overpopulation. C. carrying capacity.
  B. immigration. D. competition.

Interpret Graphics

5 **Summarize** Copy and fill in the graphic organizer below to identify the three major factors that affect population size.

Critical Thinking

6 **Predict** what could happen to the size of the human population if a cure for all cancers were discovered.

7 **Recommend** an action humans could take to help prevent the extinction of tropical organisms.

Math Skills

Review
Math Practice

Use the graph in the Skill Practice on the next page to answer these questions.

8 What does each unit on the *y*-axis represent?

9 What does the lowest point on the blue line represent?

How do populations change in size?

Birthrate and death rate change the size of a population. In the 1700s the death rate of sea otters in central California was extremely high because many people hunted them. By the 1930s only about 50 sea otters remained. Today, the Marine Mammal Protection Act protects sea otters from being hunted. Every spring, scientists survey the central California Coast to determine the numbers of adult and young sea otters (called pups) in the population. The numbers on the graph indicate population sizes at the end of a breeding season.

Learn It

Most scientists collect some type of data when testing a hypothesis. Once data are collected, scientists look for patterns or trends in the data and draw conclusions. This process is called **interpreting data.**

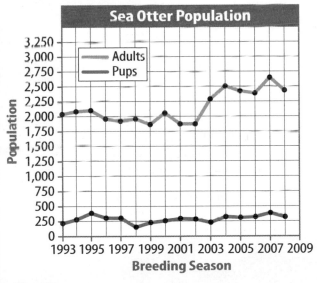

Try It

1 The above graph shows changes in adult and pup sea otter populations over many years. Assume that the number of pups seen during the survey represents all the pups that were born and survived in one year— the birthrate. For example, in the 1997 breeding season, the birthrate was 300.

2 In your Science Journal, make a table showing the population size and the birthrate for the 2001 breeding season. Repeat for 2002, 2003, and 2004.

3 In each breeding season, the population increases by the number of pups born and decreases by the number of sea otters that die. Use the following equation to find the death rate for 2002.

Death rate in 2002 = population size in 2001 + birthrate in 2002 − population size in 2002

Apply It

4 Calculate the death rate in 2004 and compare it to the death rate in 2002.

5 What environmental factors might account for the difference in the death rate between 2002 and 2004?

6 How do you think the population size will change in 2009 and 2010?

7 **Key Concept** Determine how the birthrate compared to the death rate in 2002 and 2004. Explain how these rates affected the population sizes in 2002 and 2004.

Lesson 3

Communities

Reading Guide

Key Concepts 🔑
ESSENTIAL QUESTIONS

- What defines a community?
- How do the populations in a community interact?

Vocabulary

habitat p. 223

niche p. 223

producer p. 224

consumer p. 224

symbiosis p. 227

mutualism p. 227

commensalism p. 228

parasitism p. 228

g Multilingual eGlossary

Academic Standards for Science

6.3.1 Describe specific relationships (predator/prey, consumer/producer or parasite/host) between organisms and determine whether these relationships are competitive or mutually beneficial.

Also covers: 6.3.2, 6.3.3, 6.3.4, 6.3.5, 6.NS.1, 6.NS.7, 6.NS.8, 6.NS.11

Inquiry Time for Lunch?

This Hoopoe (HOO poo) has captured its next meal. Some of the energy needed by this bird for its life processes will come from the energy stored in the body of the lizard. Where did the lizard get its energy?

What are the roles in your school community?

Within a community, different organisms have different roles. Trees produce their own food from the environment. Then, they become food for other organisms. Mushrooms break down dead organisms and make the nutrients useful to other living things. Think about the members of your school community such as the students, teachers, and custodians. What roles do they have?

1. Draw a table with two columns in your Science Journal. Label one column *Community Member* and the other column *Role in the Community*.

2. Fill in the table with examples from your school.

Community Member	Role in the Community
Principal	Manages school staff including students and teachers

Think About This

1. Are there any community members who have more than one role?

2. What is your role in the school community?

3. **Key Concept** Explain how it is beneficial for members of a community to have different roles.

Communities, Habitats, and Niches

High in a rain forest tree, a two-toed sloth munches leaves. Ants crawl on a branch, carrying away a dead beetle. Two birds build a nest. A flowering vine twists around the tree trunk. These organisms are part of a rain forest community. You read in Lesson 1 that a community is made up of all the species that live in the same ecosystem at the same time.

The place within an ecosystem where an organism lives is its **habitat.** A habitat, like the one in **Figure 15,** provides all the resources an organism needs, including food and shelter. A habitat also has the right temperature, water, and other conditions the organism needs to survive.

The rain forest tree described above is a habitat for sloths, insects, birds, vines, and many other species. Each species uses the habitat in a different way. *A* **niche** *(NICH) is what a species does in its habitat to survive.* For example, butterflies feed on flower nectar. Sloths eat leaves. Ants eat insects or plants. These species have different niches in the same environment. Each organism shown in **Figure 15** has its own niche on the tree. The plants anchor themselves to the tree and can capture more sunlight. Termites use the tree for food.

Key Concept Check What is a community?

WORD ORIGIN · · · · · · · · · · · ·

habitat
from Latin *habitus,* means "to live, dwell"

Figure 15 This tree trunk is a habitat for ferns.

Inquiry MiniLab

20 minutes

How can you model a food web? 🥽 🧴 ✂️ ✋

Populations interact through feeding relationships. A food web shows overlapping feeding relationships in a community.

1. Read and complete a lab safety form.

2. On a sheet of **paper,** make a list of at least 10 different organisms within a community of your choice. Include a variety of producers and consumers.

3. Use **scissors** to cut out the name of each organism on your list.

4. **Glue** the names onto a piece of **construction paper.**

5. Use **yarn** and glue to connect organisms that have feeding relationships. For example, a piece of yarn would connect a rabbit and grass.

Analyze and Conclude

1. **Use Models** Add the label *Sun* to your model. Which organisms would be connected to the Sun?

2. **Infer** Imagine that you removed three organisms from your food web. How would this affect the community?

3. 🔑 **Key Concept** Which organisms in your model interact through feeding relationships?

Energy in Communities

Sloths are the slowest mammals on Earth. They hardly make a sound, and they sleep 15 to 20 hours a day. Squirrel monkeys, however, chatter as they swing through treetops hunting for fruit, insects, and eggs. Sloths might appear to use no energy at all. However, sloths, squirrel monkeys, and all other organisms need energy to live. All living things use energy and carry out life processes such as growth and reproduction.

Energy Roles

How an organism obtains energy is an important part of its niche. Almost all the energy available to life on Earth originally came from the Sun. However, some organisms, such as those that live near deep-sea vents, are exceptions. They obtain energy from chemicals such as hydrogen sulfide.

Producers *are organisms that get energy from the environment, such as sunlight, and make their own food.* For example, most plants are producers that get their energy from sunlight. They use the process of photosynthesis and make sugar molecules that they use for food. Producers near deep-sea vents use hydrogen sulfide and carbon dioxide and make sugar molecules.

Consumers *are organisms that get energy by eating other organisms.* Consumers are also classified by the type of organisms they eat. Herbivores get their energy by eating plants. Cows and sheep are herbivores. Carnivores get their energy by eating other consumers. Harpy eagles, lions, and wolves are carnivores. Omnivores, such as most humans, get their energy by eating producers and consumers. Detritivores (dee TRI tuh vorz) get their energy by eating dead organisms or parts of dead organisms. Some bacteria and some fungi are detritivores.

Reading Check Identify a producer, an herbivore, a carnivore, and an omnivore.

Energy Flow

A food chain is a way of showing how energy moves through a community. In a rain forest community, energy flows from the Sun to a rain forest tree, a producer. The tree uses the energy and grows, producing leaves and other plant structures. Energy moves to consumers, such as the sloth that eats the leaves of the tree, and then to the eagle that eats the sloth. When the eagle dies, detritivores, such as bacteria, feed on its body. That food chain can be written like this:

Sun ⟶ leaves ⟶ sloth ⟶ eagle ⟶ bacteria

A food chain shows only part of the energy flow in a community. A food web, like the one in **Figure 16,** shows many food chains within a community and how they overlap.

 Key Concept Check Identify a food chain in a community near your home. List the producers and consumers in your food chain.

Figure 16 Organisms in a rain forest community get their energy in different ways.

✅ **Visual Check** List the members of two different food chains shown in the figure.

Food Web

⊟ Review **Personal Tutor**

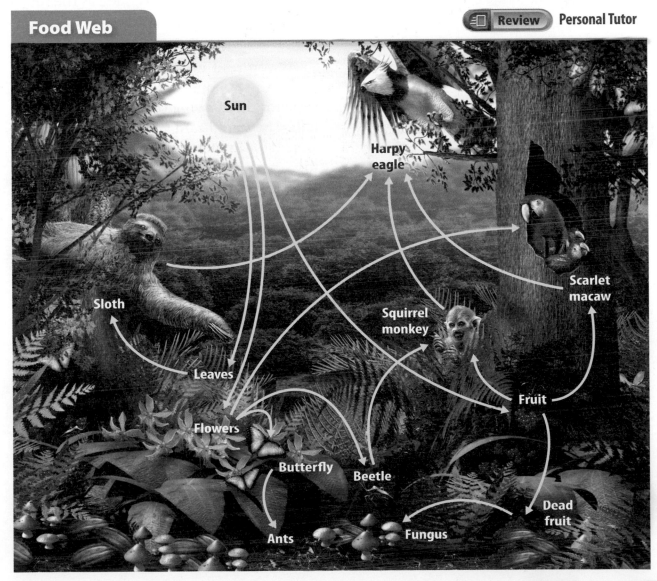

Sun

Harpy eagle

Sloth

Scarlet macaw

Squirrel monkey

Leaves

Fruit

Flowers

Butterfly

Beetle

Ants

Fungus

Dead fruit

Predator—Prey Relationships

Cooperative Relationships

Symbiotic Relationships

REVIEW VOCABULARY

predator
an organism that survives by hunting another

Relationships in Communities

The populations that make up a community interact with each other in a variety of ways. Some species have feeding relationships—they either eat or are eaten by another species. Some species interact with another species to get the food or shelter they need.

Predator-Prey Relationships

Hungry squirrel monkeys quarrel over a piece of fruit. They don't notice the harpy eagle above them. Suddenly, the eagle swoops down and grabs one of the monkeys in its talons. Harpy eagles and monkeys have a predator-prey relationship. The eagle, like other **predators,** hunts other animals for food. The hunted animals, such as the squirrel monkey or the lizard shown at the beginning of this lesson, are called prey.

As you read in Lesson 1, predators help prevent prey populations from growing too large for the carrying capacity of the ecosystem. The sand lizard, shown in **Figure 17,** is a predator in most of Europe. Like all predators, they often capture weak or injured individuals of a prey population. When the weak members of a population are removed, there are more resources available for the remaining members. This helps keep the prey population healthy.

 Reading Check Why are predators important to a prey population?

Figure 17 Sand lizards eat slugs, spiders, insects, fruits, and flowers.

Visual Check Which type of consumers are sand lizards?

Figure 18 Leaf-cutter ants cooperate while growing food. They work together and cut apart leaves. The ants carry the leaves to an underground nest. The ants' only food is a species of fungus that grows on the leaves.

Cooperative Relationships

The members of some populations work together in cooperative relationships for their survival, like the leaf-cutter ants shown in **Figure 18**. As you read in Lesson 1, meerkats cooperate with each other and raise young and watch for predators. Squirrel monkeys benefit in a similar way by living in groups. They cooperate as they hunt for food and watch for danger.

Symbiotic Relationships

Some species have such close relationships that they are almost always found living together. *A close, long-term relationship between two species that usually involves an exchange of food or energy is called* **symbiosis** (sihm bee OH sus). There are three types of symbiosis— mutualism, commensalism, and parasitism.

Mutualism Boxer crabs and sea anemones share a mutualistic partnership, as shown in **Figure 19**. *A symbiotic relationship in which both partners benefit is called* **mutualism**. Boxer crabs and sea anemones live in tropical coral reef communities. The crabs carry sea anemones in their claws. The sea anemones have stinging cells that help the crabs fight off predators. The sea anemones eat leftovers from the crabs' meals.

◄ **Figure 19** Boxer crabs and sea anemones have a mutualistic relationship because both partners benefit from the relationship.

▲ **Figure 20** Epiphytes and trees share a commensal relationship.

Figure 21 Hunting wasps are examples of parasites. The larvae use the paralyzed spider as food while they mature. ▼

Commensalism *A symbiotic relationship that benefits one species but does not harm or benefit the other is* **commensalism.** Plants called epiphytes (EH puh fites), shown in **Figure 20,** grow on the trunks of trees and other objects. The roots of an epiphyte anchor it to the object. The plant's nutrients are absorbed from the air. Epiphytes benefit from attaching to tree trunks by getting more living space and sunlight. The trees are neither helped nor harmed by the plants. Orchids are another example of epiphytes that have commensal relationships with trees.

Parasitism *A symbiotic relationship that benefits one species and harms the other is* **parasitism.** The species that benefits is the parasite. The species that is harmed is the host. Heartworms, tapeworms, fleas, and lice are parasites that feed on a host organism, such as a human or a dog. The parasites benefit by getting food. The host usually is not killed, but it can be weakened. For example, heartworms in a dog can cause the heart to work harder. Eventually, the heart can fail, killing the host. Other common parasites include the fungi that cause ringworm and toenail fungus. The fungi that cause these ailments feed on keratin (KER ah tihn), a protein in skin and nails.

The larvae of the hunting wasp is another example of a parasite. The female wasp, shown in **Figure 21,** stings a spider to paralyze it. Then she lays eggs in its body. When the eggs hatch into larvae, they eat the paralyzed spider's body. Another example of parasitism is the strangler fig. The seeds of the strangler fig sprout on the branches of a host tree. The young strangler fig sends roots into the tree and down into the ground below. The host tree provides the fig with nutrients and a trunk for support. Strangler figs grow fast and they can kill a host tree.

 Key Concept Check List five ways species in a community interact.

Lesson 3 Review

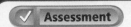

Visual Summary

Each organism in a community has its own habitat and niche within the ecosystem.

Within a community, each organism must obtain energy for life processes. Some organisms are producers and some are consumers.

Some organisms have cooperative relationships and some have symbiotic relationships. The hunting wasp and spider have a symbiotic relationship.

FOLDABLES

Use your lesson Foldable to review the lesson. Save your Foldable for the project at the end of the chapter.

What do you think NOW?

You first read the statements below at the beginning of the chapter.

5. No more than two species can live in the same habitat.

6. A cow is a producer because it produces food for other organisms.

Did you change your mind about whether you agree or disagree with the statements? Rewrite any false statements to make them true.

Use Vocabulary

1 **Define** *symbiosis*.

2 **Distinguish** between producers and consumers.

Understand Key Concepts

3 **Explain** how energy from the Sun flows through a rain forest community.

4 **Compare and contrast** predator-prey relationships and cooperative relationships.

5 A shrimp removes and eats the parasites from the gills of a fish. The fish stays healthier because the parasites are removed. This relationship is

A. commensalism.   C. mutualism.
B. competition.   D. parasitism.

Interpret Graphics

6 **Organize Information** Copy and fill in the table below with details about the three different types of symbiosis.

7 **Identify** the type of diagram shown below and explain what it means.

Critical Thinking

8 **Predict** what could happen to a population of ants if anteaters, a predator of the ants, disappeared.

9 **Decide** which type of symbiosis this is: Bacteria live in the skin under the eyes of deep-sea fish. The bacteria give off light that helps the fish find food. The bacteria get food from the fish.

How can you model a symbiotic relationship?

As you read earlier, organisms in communities can have many different types of relationships. Symbiotic relationships occur when two organisms live in direct contact and form a relationship. Symbiotic relationships include mutualism, commensalism, and parasitism. Although communities around the world have symbiotic relationships, coral reef communities often include all three types of symbiosis. Many of the organisms in these communities, such as clownfish, sea anemones, and even microscopic copepods, have some type of symbiotic relationship. In this lab, you will research and model one type of symbiosis in a coral reef community.

Question

How do you model a symbiotic relationship and determine its type?

Procedure

1. Read and complete a lab safety form.

2. Get a card from your teacher with the name of an organism that has a symbiotic relationship. Find your partner(s) in the symbiotic relationship.

3. With your partner, brainstorm what type of symbiotic relationship your organism and your partner's organism might have. List and explain your choice(s) in your Science Journal.

4 Using your library and reference books, research your organism with your partner.

5 Develop a visual presentation, such as a skit, a slide presentation, or a series of posters with your partner showing how your symbiotic relationship works and how your organisms interact with other members of the community.

6 Show your presentation to the class.

Analyze and Conclude

7 **Identify** What type of symbiotic relationship did your organism have? What was your organism's role in the relationship?

8 **Compare** How would your organism interact in the community if its partner were not present?

9 **Contrast** What other organisms in a coral reef community have the same type of symbiotic relationship as your organism? If none, explain why.

10 **The Big Idea** How did your organism interact with other members of its population and community?

Communicate Your Results

Make a poster illustrating all the symbiotic relationships you and your classmates studied. Determine what type of relationship each example had. Identify which organisms are hosts, if any.

Inquiry Extension

All of the organisms your class studied are part of the coral reef ecosystem. Create a food web showing how the organisms obtained energy.

Lab Tips

☑ Think about your organism's niche in the ecosystem.

☑ Carefully select resources for accuracy.

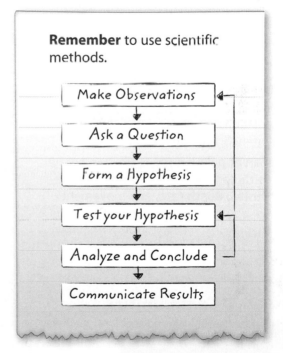

Remember to use scientific methods.

Make Observations
↓
Ask a Question
↓
Form a Hypothesis
↓
Test your Hypothesis
↓
Analyze and Conclude
↓
Communicate Results

Chapter 7 Study Guide

THE BIG IDEA A community contains many populations that interact in their energy roles and in their competition for resources. Populations can increase, decrease, and move, affecting the community.

Key Concepts Summary 🔑

	Vocabulary
### Lesson 1: Populations  • A **population** is all the organisms of the same species that live in the same area at the same time. • Population sizes vary due to **limiting factors** such as environmental factors and available resources. • Population size usually does not exceed the **carrying capacity** of the ecosystem.	**biosphere** p. 205 **community** p. 206 **population** p. 206 **competition** p. 207 **limiting factor** p. 207 **population density** p. 208 **biotic potential** p. 208 **carrying capacity** p. 209
### Lesson 2: Changing Populations • Populations of living things can increase, decrease, or move. • Populations can decrease until they are threatened, endangered, or extinct. • Human population size is affected by the same three factors as other populations— **birthrate**, **death rate**, and movement. 	**birthrate** p. 213 **death rate** p. 213 **extinct species** p. 215 **endangered species** p. 215 **threatened species** p. 215 **migration** p. 216
### Lesson 3: Communities  • A community is all the populations of different species that live together in the same area at the same time. • The place within an ecosystem where an organism lives is its **habitat** and what an organism does in its habitat to survive is its **niche.** • Three types of relationships within a community are predator-prey, cooperative, and symbiotic.	**habitat** p. 223 **niche** p. 223 **producer** p. 224 **consumer** p. 224 **symbiosis** p. 227 **mutualism** p. 227 **commensalism** p. 228 **parasitism** p. 228

FOLDABLES

Assemble your lesson Foldables as shown to make a Chapter Project. Use the project to review what you have learned in this chapter.

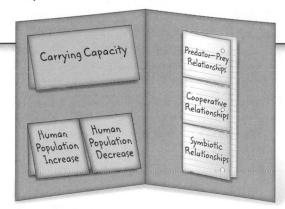

Use Vocabulary

① The struggle in a community for the same resources is _____.

② The part of Earth that supports life is the _____.

③ The instinctive movement of a population is _____.

④ A(n) _____ species is one at risk of becoming endangered.

⑤ A(n) _____ is an organism that gets energy from the environment.

⑥ The largest number of offspring that can be produced when there are no limiting factors is the _____.

Link Vocabulary and Key Concepts

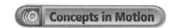 **Concepts in Motion** Interactive Concept Map

Copy this concept map, and then use vocabulary terms from the previous page to complete the concept map.

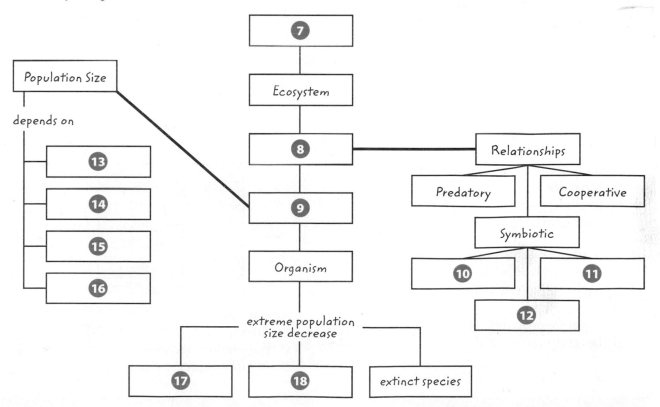

Understand Key Concepts

1 What does the line indicated by the red arrow in the graph below represent?

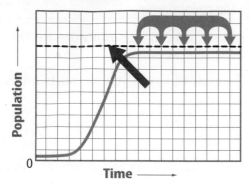

A. competition
B. biotic potential
C. carrying capacity
D. limiting factors

2 The need for organisms to rely on the same resources causes

A. competition.
B. biotic potential.
C. carrying capacity.
D. population growth.

3 The number of organisms in a specific area is

A. a community.
B. the carrying capacity.
C. the population density.
D. the population growth.

4 The number of robins that hatch in a year is the population's

A. biotic potential.
B. birthrate.
C. carrying capacity.
D. exponential growth.

5 A robin population that reaches its biotic potential probably shows

A. exponential growth.
B. low growth.
C. negative growth.
D. no growth.

6 An organism that uses sunlight to make food molecules is a(n)

A. carnivore.
B. consumer.
C. herbivore.
D. producer.

7 Which is NOT part of Earth's biosphere?

A. low atmosphere
B. surface of the Moon
C. bottom of the Pacific ocean
D. North American continent

8 Which is a limiting factor for a cottontail rabbit population on the prairie in Oklahoma?

A. a large amount of food
B. a large amount of shelter space
C. an abundance of coyotes in the area
D. an unpolluted river in the ecosystem

9 Which factor does NOT normally affect human population size?

A. birthrate
B. death rate
C. population movement
D. lack of resources

10 What type of overall population change is shown below?

A. immigration
B. migration
C. population decrease
D. population increase

Critical Thinking

11 **Select and draw** three food chains from the food web shown.

12 **Give an Example** What problems might result from overpopulation of pigeons in a city park?

13 **Describe** What are some possible solutions that a city might use to solve a pigeon overpopulation problem?

14 **Decide** Would sample counting or capture-mark-and-release at a specified time and place be the best method for measuring each of these populations: birds, whales, bluebonnet flowers, and oak trees?

15 **Compare and contrast** the feeding habits of carnivores, omnivores, and producers.

16 **Classify** Decide whether each of these relationships is mutualism, commensalism, or parasitism.

- Butterfly pollinates flower while drinking nectar.
- Tapeworm feeds on contents of dog's intestines.
- Fish finds shelter in coral reef.

17 **Draw** a food web that describes energy flow in this community. Insects eat leaves. Spiders eat insects. Birds eat insects and spiders. Frogs eat insects. Birds eat frogs.

Writing in Science

18 **Write** a two-page story that explains how an imaginary population becomes threatened with extinction.

REVIEW THE BIG IDEA

19 Describe three different types of relationships in a community between two different populations of organisms.

20 Do you think this large number of pigeons affects other organisms in the community? Explain your answer.

Math Skills

Review

Math Practice

Use Graphs
Use the graph to answer the questions.

21 During what range of years did the population change the least?

22 The dotted line represents a prediction. What does it predict about population growth beyond the present time?

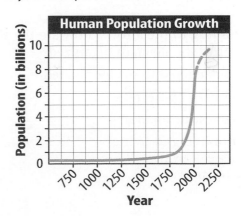

Human Population Growth

Standardized Test Practice

Record your answers on the answer sheet provided by your teacher or on a sheet of paper.

Multiple Choice

1 Which is defined as the demand for resources in short supply in a community?

   A biotic potential

   B competition

   C density

   D limiting factor

Use the diagram below to answer questions 2 and 3.

2 In the diagram above, which number represents an ecosystem?

   A 1

   B 2

   C 3

   D 4

3 According to the arrows, how are the elements of the diagram organized?

   A endangered to overpopulated

   B farthest to nearest

   C largest to smallest

   D nonliving to living

4 Which is NOT a possible result of overpopulation?

   A damage to soil

   B increased carrying capacity

   C loss of trees and plants

   D more competition

Use the diagram below to answer question 5.

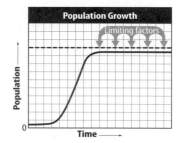

5 What does the dashed line in the diagram represent?

   A biotic potential

   B carrying capacity

   C overpopulation

   D population density

6 What does a population undergo when it has no limiting factors?

   A exponential growth

   B extinction

   C migration

   D population movement

7 What is the term for all species living in the same ecosystem at the same time?

   A biosphere

   B community

   C habitat

   D population

Use the diagram below to answer question 8.

Types of Moves, 2004–2005

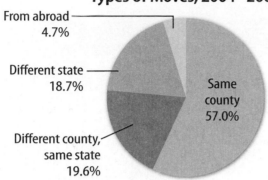

From abroad
4.7%

Different state
18.7%

Same county
57.0%

Different county, same state
19.6%

Source: U.S. Census Bureau, Current Population Survey, 2005 Annual Social and Economic Supplement.

8 According to the diagram, about how many of those who moved remained within the same state?

   A 20 percent

   B 39 percent

   C 57 percent

   D 77 percent

9 Which type of relationship includes mutualism and parasitism?

   A competition

   B cooperation

   C predation

   D symbiosis

10 Which is a population?

   A all meerkats in a refuge

   B all the types of birds in a forest

   C all the types of cats in a zoo

   D all the types of insects in a swamp

Constructed Response

Use the table below to answer questions 11 and 12.

Growth	Decline

11 In the table, list four factors that contribute to human population growth and four factors that lead to population decline.

12 Select one factor from each column in the table above. Which has the greatest effect on human population today? Explain your reasoning.

13 Describe a negative consequence of human population growth. How can humans minimize the effect of this change?

Use the diagram below to answer question 14.

sunlight → grasses → antelope → lion → bacteria

14 Explain how each organism in the food chain above gets energy. How might the other organisms be affected if the antelope population declines due to disease?

NEED EXTRA HELP?														
If You Missed Question...	1	2	3	4	5	6	7	8	9	10	11	12	13	14
Go to Lesson...	1	1	1	1	1	2	1	2	3	1	2	2	2	3

Chapter 8

Biomes and Ecosystems

THE BIG IDEA

How do Earth's biomes and ecosystems differ?

Inquiry Modern Art?

Although it might look like a piece of art, this structure was designed to replicate several ecosystems. When Biosphere 2 was built in the 1980s near Tucson, Arizona, it included a rain forest, a desert, a grassland, a coral reef, and a wetland. Today, it is used mostly for research and education.

- How realistic do you think Biosphere 2 is?

- Is it possible to make artificial environments as complex as those in nature?

- How do Earth's biomes and ecosystems differ?

Get Ready to Read

What do you think?

Before you read, decide if you agree or disagree with each of these statements. As you read this chapter, see if you change your mind about any of the statements.

1 Deserts can be cold.

2 There are no rain forests outside the tropics.

3 Estuaries do not protect coastal areas from erosion.

4 Animals form coral reefs.

5 An ecosystem never changes.

6 Nothing grows in the area where a volcano has erupted.

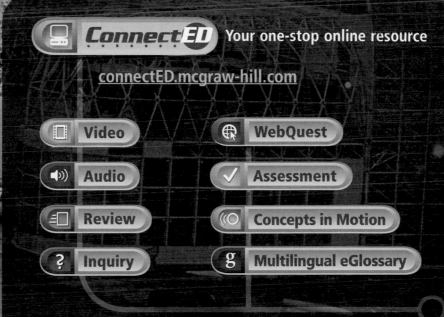

ConnectED Your one-stop online resource

connectED.mcgraw-hill.com

- Video
- Audio
- Review
- Inquiry
- WebQuest
- Assessment
- Concepts in Motion
- Multilingual eGlossary

Land Biomes

Reading Guide

Key Concepts 🔑
ESSENTIAL QUESTIONS

- How do Earth's land biomes differ?
- How do humans impact land biomes?

Vocabulary

biome p. 241

desert p. 242

grassland p. 243

temperate p. 245

taiga p. 247

tundra p. 247

 Multilingual eGlossary

 Video **BrainPOP®**

Academic Standards for Science

6.3.2 Describe how changes caused by organisms in the habitat where they live can be beneficial or detrimental to themselves or the native plants and animals.

6.3.3 Describe how certain biotic and abiotic factors, such as predators, quantity of light and water, range of temperatures, and soil composition, can limit the number of organisms that an ecosystem can support.

Also covers: 6.NS.1, 6.NS.3, 6.NS.5, 6.NS.7, 6.NS.11

Inquiry Plant or Animal?

Believe it or not, this is a flower. One of the largest flowers in the world, *Rafflesia* (ruh FLEE zhuh), grows naturally in the tropical rain forests of southeast Asia. What do you think would happen if you planted a seed from this plant in a desert? Would it survive?

What is the climate in China?

Beijing, China, and New York, New York, are about the same distance from the equator but on opposite sides of Earth. How do temperature and rainfall compare for these two cities?

1. Locate Beijing and New York on a world map.

2. Copy the table to the right in your Science Journal. From the data and charts provided, find and record the average high and low temperatures in January and in June for each city.

3. Record the average rainfall in January and in June for each city.

High Temperature (°C)	January	June
Beijing		
New York		
Low Temperature (°C)	January	June
Beijing		
New York		
Rainfall (mm)	January	June
Beijing		
New York		

Think About This

1. What are the temperature and rainfall ranges for each city?

2. 🔑 **Key Concept** How do you think the climates of these cities differ year-round?

Land Ecosystems and Biomes

When you go outside, you might notice people, grass, flowers, birds, and insects. You also are probably aware of nonliving things, such as air, sunlight, and water. The living or once-living parts of an environment are the biotic parts. The nonliving parts that the living parts need to survive are the abiotic parts. The biotic and abiotic parts of an environment together make up an ecosystem.

Earth's continents have many different ecosystems, from deserts to rain forests. Scientists classify similar ecosystems in large geographic areas as biomes. *A* **biome** *is a geographic area on Earth that contains ecosystems with similar biotic and abiotic features.* As shown in **Figure 1,** Earth has seven major land biomes. Areas classified as the same biome have similar climates and organisms.

Figure 1 Earth contains seven major biomes.

Concepts in Motion Animation

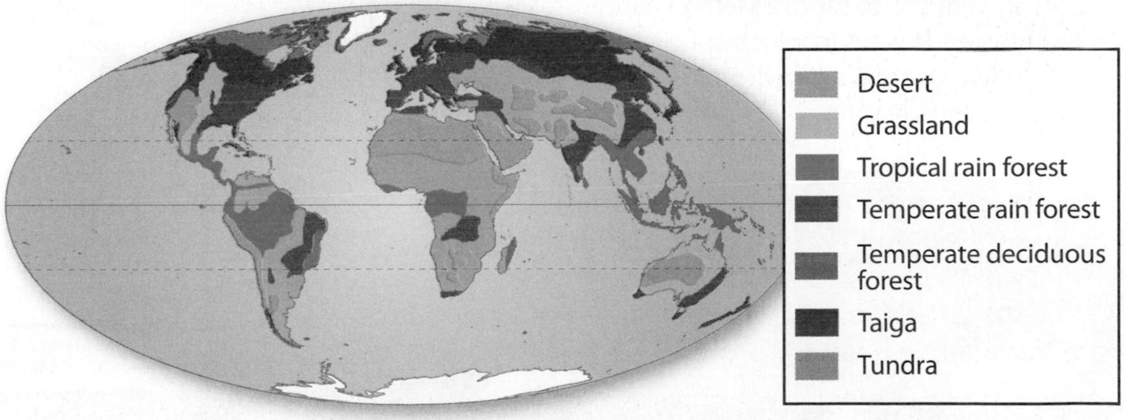

- Desert
- Grassland
- Tropical rain forest
- Temperate rain forest
- Temperate deciduous forest
- Taiga
- Tundra

How hot is sand?

If you have ever walked barefoot on a sandy beach on a sunny day, you know how hot sand can be. But how hot is the sand below the surface?

1. Read and complete a lab safety form.

2. Position a **desk lamp** over a **container** of **sand** that is at least 7 cm deep.

3. Place one **thermometer** on the surface of the sand and bury the tip of another **thermometer** about 5 cm below the surface. Record the temperature on each thermometer in your Science Journal.

4. Turn on the lamp and record the temperatures again after 10 minutes.

Analyze and Conclude

1. **Describe** the temperatures of the sand at the surface and below the surface.

2. **Predict** what would happen to the temperature of the sand at night.

3. 🔑 **Key Concept** Desert soil contains a high percentage of sand. Based on your results, predict ways in which species are adapted to living in an environment where the soil is mostly sand.

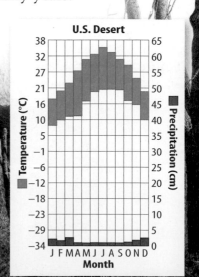

Deserts *are biomes that receive very little rain.* They are on nearly every continent and are Earth's driest ecosystems.

- Most deserts are hot during the day and cold at night. Others, like those in Antarctica, remain cold all of the time.

- Rainwater drains away quickly because of thin, porous soil. Large patches of ground are bare.

Biodiversity

- Animals include lizards, bats, woodpeckers, and snakes. Most animals avoid activity during the hottest parts of the day.

- Plants include spiny cactus and thorny shrubs. Shallow roots absorb water quickly. Some plants have accordion-like stems that expand and store water. Small leaves or spines reduce the loss of water.

Human Impact

- Cities, farms, and recreational areas in deserts use valuable water.

- Desert plants grow slowly. When they are damaged by people or livestock, recovery takes many years.

U.S. Desert

Temperature (°C): 38, 32, 27, 21, 16, 10, 5, −1, −6, −12, −18, −23, −29, −34

Precipitation (cm): 65, 60, 55, 50, 45, 40, 35, 30, 25, 20, 15, 10, 5, 0

Month: J F M A M J J A S O N D

Black-footed ferret

Grassland *biomes are areas where grasses are the dominant plants.* Also called prairies, savannas, and meadows, grasslands are the world's "breadbaskets." Wheat, corn, oats, rye, barley, and other important cereal crops are grasses. They grow well in these areas.

- Grasslands have a wet and a dry season.

- Deep, fertile soil supports plant growth.

- Grass roots form a thick mass, called sod, which helps soil absorb and hold water during periods of drought.

✓ Reading Check Why are grasslands called "breadbaskets"?

Biodiversity

- Trees grow along moist banks of streams and rivers. Wildflowers bloom during the wet season.

- In North America, large herbivores, such as bison and elk, graze here. Insects, birds, rabbits, prairie dogs, and snakes find shelter in the grasses.

- Predators in North American grasslands include hawks, ferrets, coyotes, and wolves.

- African savannas are grasslands that contain giraffes, zebras, and lions. Australian grasslands are home to kangaroos, wallabies, and wild dogs.

Human Impact

- People plow large areas of grassland to raise cereal crops. This reduces habitat for wild species.

- Because of hunting and loss of habitat, large herbivores—such as bison—are now uncommon in many grasslands.

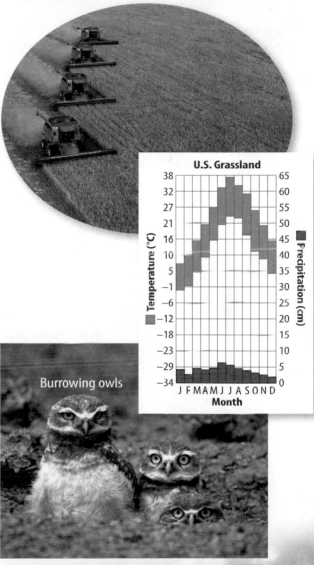
Burrowing owls

U.S. Grassland

Tropical Rain Forest Biome

Ocelot

Toucan

The forests that grow near the equator are called tropical rain forests. These forests receive large amounts of rain and have dense growths of tall, leafy trees.

- Weather is warm and wet year-round.

- The soil is shallow and easily washed away by rain.

- Less than 1 percent of the sunlight that reaches the top of forest trees also reaches the forest floor.

- Half of Earth's species live in tropical rain forests. Most live in the canopy—the uppermost part of the forest.

✓ **Reading Check** Where do most organisms live in a tropical rain forest?

Biodiversity

- Few plants live on the dark forest floor.

- Vines climb the trunks of tall trees.

- Mosses, ferns, and orchids live on branches in the canopy.

- Insects make up the largest group of tropical animals. They include beetles, termites, ants, bees, and butterflies.

- Larger animals include parrots, toucans, snakes, frogs, flying squirrels, fruit bats, monkeys, jaguars, and ocelots.

Human Impact

- People have cleared more than half of Earth's tropical rain forests for lumber, farms, and ranches. Poor soil does not support rapid growth of new trees in cleared areas.

- Some organizations are working to encourage people to use less wood harvested from rain forests.

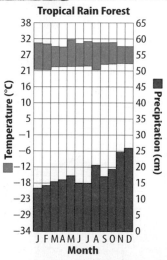

Tropical Rain Forest
(Temperature (°C) / Precipitation (cm) vs. Month: J F M A M J J A S O N D)

Temperate Rain Forest Biome

Regions of Earth between the tropics and the polar circles are **temperate** *regions*. Temperate regions have relatively mild climates with distinct seasons. Several biomes are in temperate regions, including rain forests. Temperate rain forests are moist ecosystems mostly in coastal areas. They are not as warm as tropical rain forests.

- Winters are mild and rainy.

- Summers are cool and foggy.

- Soil is rich and moist.

Elk

Biodiversity

- Forests are dominated by spruce, hemlock, cedar, fir, and redwood trees, which can grow very large and tall.

- Fungi, ferns, mosses, vines, and small flowering plants grow on the moist forest floor.

- Animals include mosquitoes, butterflies, frogs, salamanders, woodpeckers, owls, eagles, chipmunks, raccoons, deer, elk, bears, foxes, and cougars.

Human Impact

- Temperate rain forest trees are a source of lumber. Logging can destroy the habitat of forest species.

- Rich soil enables cut forests to grow back. Tree farms help provide lumber without destroying habitat.

 Key Concept Check In what ways do humans affect temperate rain forests?

FOLDABLES®

Use a sheet of paper to make a horizontal two-tab book. Record what you learn about desert and temperate rain forest biomes under the tabs, and use the information to compare and contrast these biomes.

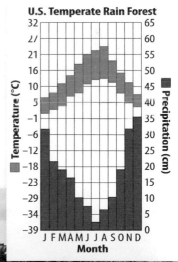

Temperate deciduous forests grow in temperate regions where winter and summer climates have more variation than those in temperate rain forests. These forests are the most common forest ecosystems in the United States. They contain mostly deciduous trees, which lose their leaves in the fall.

- Winter temperatures are often below freezing. Snow is common.

- Summers are hot and humid.

- Soil is rich in nutrients and supports a large amount of diverse plant growth.

Biodiversity

- Most plants, such as maples, oaks, birches, and other deciduous trees, stop growing during the winter and begin growing again in the spring.

- Animals include snakes, ants, butterflies, birds, raccoons, opossums, and foxes.

- Some animals, including chipmunks and bats, spend the winter in hibernation.

- Many birds and some butterflies, such as the monarch, migrate to warmer climates for the winter.

Human Impact

Over the past several hundred years, humans have cleared thousands of acres of Earth's deciduous forests for farms and cities. Today, much of the clearing has stopped and some forests have regrown.

 Key Concept Check How are temperate deciduous rain forests different from temperate rain forests?

U.S. Temperate Deciduous Forest

Temperature (°C) / Precipitation (cm) — Month: J F M A M J J A S O N D

Red fox

Taiga Biome

A **taiga** (TI guh) *is a forest biome consisting mostly of cone-bearing evergreen trees.* The taiga biome exists only in the northern hemisphere. It occupies more space on Earth's continents than any other biome.

• Winters are long, cold, and snowy. Summers are short, warm, and moist.

• Soil is thin and acidic.

Biodiversity

• Evergreen trees, such as spruce, pine, and fir, are thin and shed snow easily.

• Animals include owls, mice, moose, bears, and other cold-adapted species.

• Abundant insects in summer attract many birds, which migrate south in winter.

Human Impact

• Tree harvesting reduces taiga habitat.

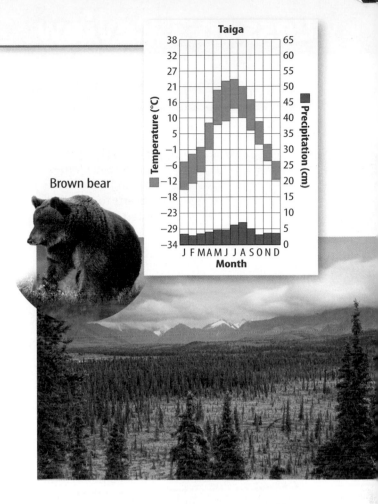

Brown bear

Tundra Biome

A **tundra** (TUN druh) *biome is cold, dry, and treeless.* Most tundra is south of the North Pole, but it also exists in mountainous areas at high altitudes.

• Winters are long, dark, and freezing; summers are short and cool; the growing season is only 50–60 days.

• Permafrost—a layer of permanently frozen soil—prevents deep root growth.

Biodiversity

• Plants include shallow-rooted mosses, lichens, and grasses.

• Many animals hibernate or migrate south during winter. Few animals, including lemmings, live in tundras year-round.

Human Impact

• Drilling for oil and gas can interrupt migration patterns.

Lemming

Lesson 1 Review

✓ Assessment Online Quiz
? Inquiry Virtual Lab

Visual Summary

Earth has seven major land biomes, ranging from hot, dry deserts to cold, forested taigas.

Half of Earth's species live in rain forest biomes.

Temperate deciduous forests are the most common forest biome in the United States.

Use your lesson Foldable to review the lesson. Save your Foldable for the project at the end of the chapter.

What do you think NOW?

You first read the statements below at the beginning of the chapter.

1. Deserts can be cold.

2. There are no rain forests outside the tropics.

Did you change your mind about whether you agree or disagree with the statements? Rewrite any false statements to make them true.

Use Vocabulary

1. **Define** *biome* using your own words.

2. **Distinguish** between tropical rain forests and temperate rain forests.

3. A cold, treeless biome is a(n) _____.

Understand Key Concepts

4. **Explain** why tundra soil cannot support the growth of trees.

5. **Give examples** of how plants and animals adapt to temperate deciduous ecosystems.

Interpret Graphics

6. **Determine** What is the average annual rainfall for the biome represented by the chart to the right?

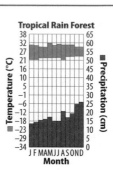

Tropical Rain Forest

7. **Summarize Information** Copy the graphic organizer below and fill it in with animals and plants of the biome you live in.

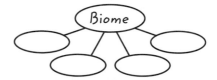

Critical Thinking

8. **Plan** an enclosed zoo exhibit for a desert ecosystem. What abiotic factors should you consider?

9. **Recommend** one or more actions people can take to reduce habitat loss in tropical and taiga forests.

Which biome is it?

Materials

biome data

You have read about the major land biomes found on Earth. Within each biome are ecosystems with similar biotic and abiotic factors. In this lab, you will **interpret data** describing a particular area on Earth to identify which biome it belongs to.

Learn It

Scientists collect and present data in a variety of forms, including graphs and tables. In this activity, you will interpret data in a graph and apply the information to the ideas you learned in the lesson.

Try It

1 Examine the temperature and precipitation data in the graph given you by your teacher.

2 Create a table from these data in your Science Journal. Calculate the average temperature and precipitation during the winter and the summer.

3 Examine the image of the biome and identify some plants and animals in the image.

4 Compare your data to the information on land biomes presented in Lesson 1. Which biome is the most similar?

Apply It

5 Which land biome did your data come from? Why did you choose this biome?

6 Are the data in your graph identical to the data in the graph of the biome in Lesson 1 to which it belongs? Why or why not?

7 Describe this biome. What do you think your biome will be like six months from now?

8 🔑 **Key Concept** How might humans affect the organisms in your biome?

Lesson 2

Aquatic Ecosystems

Reading Guide

Key Concept 🔑
ESSENTIAL QUESTIONS

- How do Earth's aquatic ecosystems differ?
- How do humans impact aquatic ecosystems?

Vocabulary

salinity p. 251

wetland p. 254

estuary p. 255

intertidal zone p. 257

coral reef p. 257

 Multilingual eGlossary

Academic Standards for Science

6.3.2 Describe how changes caused by organisms in the habitat where they live can be beneficial or detrimental to themselves or the native plants and animals.

6.3.3 Describe how certain biotic and abiotic factors, such as predators, quantity of light and water, range of temperatures, and soil composition, can limit the number of organisms that an ecosystem can support.

Also covers: 6.NS.7, 6.NS.11

Inquiry Floating Trees?

These plants, called mangroves, are one of the few types of plants that grow in salt water. They usually live along ocean coastlines in tropical ecosystems. What other organisms do you think live near mangroves?

What happens when rivers and oceans mix?

Freshwater and saltwater ecosystems have different characteristics. What happens in areas where freshwater rivers and streams flow into oceans?

1. Read and complete a lab safety form.

2. In a **plastic tub,** add 100 g of **salt** to 2 L of water. Stir with a **long-handled spoon** until the salt dissolves.

3. In another **container,** add 5 drops of **blue food coloring** to 1 L of water. Gently pour the colored water into one corner of the plastic tub. Observe how the color of the water changes in the tub.

4. Observe the tub again in 5 minutes.

Think About This

1. What bodies of water do the containers represent?

2. What happened to the water in the tub after 5 minutes? What do you think happens to the salt content of the water?

3. **Key Concept** How do you think the biodiversity of rivers and oceans differ? What organisms do you think might live at the place where the two meet?

Aquatic Ecosystems

If you've ever spent time near an ocean, a river, or another body of water, you might know that water is full of life. There are four major types of water, or aquatic, ecosystems: freshwater, wetland, estuary, and ocean. Each type of ecosystem contains a unique variety of organisms. Whales, dolphins, and corals live only in ocean ecosystems. Catfish and trout live only in freshwater ecosystems. Many other organisms that do not live under water, such as birds and seals, also depend on aquatic ecosystems for food and shelter.

Important abiotic factors in aquatic ecosystems include temperature, sunlight, and dissolved oxygen gas. Aquatic species have adaptations that enable them to use the oxygen in water. The gills of a fish separate oxygen from water and move it into the fish's bloodstream. Mangrove plants, pictured on the previous page, take in oxygen through small pores in their leaves and roots.

Salinity (say LIH nuh tee) is another important abiotic factor in aquatic ecosystems. **Salinity** *is the amount of salt dissolved in water.* Water in saltwater ecosystems has high salinity compared to water in freshwater ecosystems, which contains little salt.

Math Skills

Use Proportions

Salinity is measured in parts per thousand (PPT). One PPT water contains 1 g salt and 1,000 g water. Use proportions to calculate salinity. What is the salinity of 100 g of water with 3.5 g of salt?

$$\frac{3.5 \text{ g salt}}{100 \text{ g seawater}} = \frac{x \text{ g salt}}{1,000 \text{ g seawater}}$$

$$100\,x = 3500$$

$$x = \frac{3500}{100} = 35 \text{ PPT}$$

Practice

A sample contains 0.1895 g of salt per 50 g of seawater. What is its salinity?

 Review

• **Math Practice**
• **Personal Tutor**

Great Blue Heron

Freshwater ecosystems include streams, rivers, ponds, and lakes. Streams are usually narrow, shallow, and fast-flowing. Rivers are larger, deeper, and flow more slowly.

- Streams form from underground sources of water, such as springs or from runoff from rain and melting snow.

- Stream water is often clear. Soil particles are quickly washed downstream.

- Oxygen levels in streams are high because air mixes into the water as it splashes over rocks.

- Rivers form when streams flow together.

- Soil that washes into a river from streams or nearby land can make river water muddy. Soil also introduces nutrients, such as nitrogen, into rivers.

- Slow-moving river water has higher levels of nutrients and lower levels of dissolved oxygen than fast-moving water.

Salmon

Biodiversity

- Willows, cottonwoods, and other water-loving plants grow along streams and on riverbanks.

- Species adapted to fast-moving water include trout, salmon, crayfish, and many insects.

- Species adapted to slow-moving water include snails and catfish.

Stonefly larva

Human Impact

- People take water from streams and rivers for drinking, laundry, bathing, crop irrigation, and industrial purposes.

- Hydroelectric plants use the energy in flowing water to generate electricity. Dams stop the water's flow.

- Runoff from cities, industries, and farms is a source of pollution.

Freshwater: Ponds and Lakes

Ponds and lakes contain freshwater that is not flowing downhill. These bodies of water form in low areas on land.

- Ponds are shallow and warm.
- Sunlight reaches the bottom of most ponds.
- Pond water is often high in nutrients.
- Lakes are larger and deeper than ponds.
- Sunlight penetrates into the top few feet of lake water. Deeper water is dark and cold.

Biodiversity

- Plants surround ponds and lake shores.
- Surface water in ponds and lakes contains plants, algae, and microscopic organisms that use sunlight for photosynthesis.
- Organisms living in shallow water near shorelines include cattails, reeds, insects, crayfish, frogs, fish, and turtles.
- Fewer organisms live in the deeper, colder water of lakes where there is little sunlight.
- Lake fish include perch, trout, bass, and walleye.

Smallmouth bass

✓ **Reading Check** Why do few organisms live in the deep water of lakes?

Human Impact

- Humans fill in ponds and lakes with sediment to create land for houses and other structures.
- Runoff from farms, gardens, and roads washes pollutants into ponds and lakes, disrupting food webs.

🔑 **Key Concept Check** How do ponds and lakes differ?

Common loon

Some types of aquatic ecosystems have mostly shallow water. **Wetlands** *are aquatic ecosystems that have a thin layer of water covering soil that is wet most of the time.* Wetlands contain freshwater, salt water, or both. They are among Earth's most fertile ecosystems.

• Freshwater wetlands form at the edges of lakes and ponds and in low areas on land. Saltwater wetlands form along ocean coasts.

• Nutrient levels and biodiversity are high.

• Wetlands trap sediments and purify water. Plants and microscopic organisms filter out pollution and waste materials.

Biodiversity

• Water-tolerant plants include grasses and cattails. Few trees live in saltwater wetlands. Trees in freshwater wetlands include cottonwoods, willows, and swamp oaks.

• Insects are abundant and include flies, mosquitoes, dragonflies, and butterflies.

• More than one-third of North American bird species, including ducks, geese, herons, loons, warblers, and egrets, use wetlands for nesting and feeding.

• Other animals that depend on wetlands for food and breeding grounds include alligators, turtles, frogs, snakes, salamanders, muskrats, and beavers.

Human Impact

• In the past, many people considered wetlands as unimportant environments. Water was drained away to build homes and roads and to raise crops.

• Today, many wetlands are being preserved, and drained wetlands are being restored.

 Key Concept Check How do humans impact wetlands?

Estuaries (ES chuh wer eez) *are regions along coastlines where streams or rivers flow into a body of salt water.* Most estuaries form along coastlines, where freshwater in rivers meets salt water in oceans. Estuary ecosystems have varying degrees of salinity.

- Salinity depends on rainfall, the amount of freshwater flowing from land, and the amount of salt water pushed in by tides.

- Estuaries help protect coastal land from flooding and erosion. Like wetlands, estuaries purify water and filter out pollution.

- Nutrient levels and biodiversity are high.

Biodiversity

- Plants that grow in salt water include mangroves, pickleweeds, and seagrasses.

- Animals include worms, snails, and many species that people use for food, including oysters, shrimp, crabs, and clams.

- Striped bass, salmon, flounder, and many other ocean fish lay their eggs in estuaries.

- Many species of birds depend on estuaries for breeding, nesting, and feeding.

Human Impact

- Large portions of estuaries have been filled with soil to make land for roads and buildings.

- Destruction of estuaries reduces habitat for estuary species and exposes the coastline to flooding and storm damage.

WORD ORIGIN ·······················

estuary
from Latin *aestuarium*, means "a tidal marsh or opening."

···································

FOLDABLES®

Make a horizontal two-tab book and label it as shown. Use it to compare how biodiversity and human impact differ in wetlands and estuaries.

Wetlands | Estuaries

Harvest mouse

Sunlit zone

200 m

Twilight zone

Continental shelf

1,000 m

Dark zone

3,800 m

Seafloor

Jellyfish

Fur seal

Most of Earth's surface is covered by ocean water with high salinity. The oceans contain different types of ecosystems. If you took a boat trip several kilometers out to sea, you would be in the open ocean—one type of ocean ecosystem. The open ocean extends from the steep edges of continental shelves to the deepest parts of the ocean. The amount of light in the water depends on depth.

- Photosynthesis can take place only in the uppermost, or sunlit, zone. Very little sunlight reaches the twilight zone. None reaches the deepest water, known as the dark zone.

- Decaying matter and nutrients float down from the sunlit zone, through the twilight and dark zones, to the seafloor.

Biodiversity

- Microscopic algae and other producers in the sunlit zone form the base of most ocean food chains. Other organisms living in the sunlit zone are jellyfish, tuna, mackerel, and dolphins.

- Many species of fish stay in the twilight zone during the day and swim to the sunlit zone at night to feed.

- Sea cucumbers, brittle stars, and other bottom-dwelling organisms feed on decaying matter that drifts down from above.

- Many organisms in the dark zone live near cracks in the seafloor where lava erupts and new seafloor forms.

✓ **Reading Check** Which organisms are at the base of most ocean food chains?

Human Impact

- Overfishing threatens many ocean fish.

- Trash discarded from ocean vessels or washed into oceans from land is a source of pollution. Animals such as seals become tangled in plastic or mistake it for food.

Ocean: Coastal Oceans

Sea stars

Coastal oceans include several types of ecosystems, including continental shelves and intertidal zones. *The **intertidal zone** is the ocean shore between the lowest low tide and the highest high tide.*

- Sunlight reaches the bottom of shallow coastal ecosystems.

- Nutrients washed in from rivers and streams contribute to high biodiversity.

Biodiversity

- The coastal ocean is home to mussels, fish, crabs, sea stars, dolphins, and whales.

- Intertidal species have adaptations for surviving exposure to air during low tides and to heavy waves during high tides.

Human Impact

- Oil spills and other pollution harm coastal organisms.

Ocean: Coral Reefs

Another ocean ecosystem with high biodiversity is the coral reef. *A **coral reef** is an underwater structure made from outside skeletons of tiny, soft-bodied animals called coral.*

- Most coral reefs form in shallow tropical oceans.

- Coral reefs protect coastlines from storm damage and erosion.

Biodiversity

- Coral reefs provide food and shelter for many animals, including parrotfish, groupers, angelfish, eels, shrimp, crabs, scallops, clams, worms, and snails.

Human Impact

- Pollution, overfishing, and harvesting of coral threaten coral reefs.

---

inquiry MiniLab   **15 minutes**

How do ocean ecosystems differ?

Ocean ecosystems include open oceans, coastal oceans, and coral reefs—each one a unique environment with distinctive organisms.

1. Read and complete a lab safety form.

2. In a **large plastic tub,** use **rocks** and **sand** to make a structure representing an open ocean, a coastal ocean, or a coral reef.

3. Fill the tub with **water.**

4. Make waves by gently moving your hand back and forth in the water.

Analyze and Conclude

1. **Observe** What happened to your structure when you made waves? How might a hurricane affect the organisms that live in the ecosystem you modeled?

2. **Key Concept** Compare your results with results of those who modeled other ecosystems. Suggest what adaptations species might have in each ecosystem.

Grouper

Lesson 2 Review

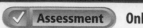

Visual Summary

 Freshwater ecosystems include ponds and lakes.

 Wetlands can be salt-water ecosystems or freshwater ecosystems.

 Coral reefs and coastal ecosystems have high levels of biodiversity.

FOLDABLES

Use your lesson Foldable to review the lesson. Save your Foldable for the project at the end of the chapter.

What do you think NOW?

You first read the statements below at the beginning of the chapter.

3. Estuaries do not protect coastal areas from erosion.

4. Animals form coral reefs.

Did you change your mind about whether you agree or disagree with the statements? Rewrite any false statements to make them true.

Use Vocabulary

1. **Define** the term *salinity*.

2. **Distinguish** between a wetland and an estuary.

3. An ocean ecosystem formed from the skeletons of animals is a(n) _____.

Understand Key Concepts

4. Which ecosystem contains both salt water and freshwater?
   - A. estuary
   - B. lake
   - C. pond
   - D. stream

5. **Describe** what might happen to a coastal area if its estuary were filled in to build houses.

Interpret Graphics

6. **Describe** Copy the drawing to the right and label the light zones. Describe characteristics of each zone.

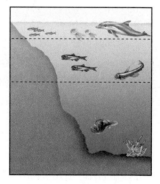

Critical Thinking

7. **Recommend** actions people might take to prevent pollutants from entering coastal ecosystems.

Math Skills

 Review
— Math Practice —

8. The salinity of the Baltic Sea is about 10 PPT. What weight of salt is present in 2,000 g of seawater?

Saving an Underwater Wilderness

A researcher takes a water sample from a marine reserve. ▼

How do scientists help protect coral reefs?

Pollution and human activities, such as mining and tourism, have damaged many ecosystems, including coral reefs. Scientists and conservation groups are working together to help protect and restore coral reefs and areas that surround them. One way is to create marine reserves where no fishing or collection of organisms is allowed.

A team of scientists, including marine ecologists Dr. Dan Brumbaugh and Kate Holmes from the American Museum of Natural History, are investigating how well reserves are working. These scientists compare how many fish of one species live both inside and outside reserves. Their results indicate that more species of fish and greater numbers of each species live inside reserves than outside—one sign that reefs in the area are improving.

Reef ecosystems do not have to be part of a reserve in order to improve, however. Scientists can work with local governments to find ways to limit damage to reef ecosystems. One way is to prevent overfishing by limiting the number of fish caught. Other ways include eliminating the use of destructive fishing practices that can harm reefs and reducing runoff from farms and factories.

By creating marine reserves, regulating fishing practices, and reducing runoff, humans can help reefs that were once in danger become healthy again.

Kate Holmes examines a coral reef. ▶

It's Your Turn

COMPOSE Write a letter to a town near a marine reserve describing why it is important to maintain a protected area.

Reading Guide

Key Concepts 🔑
ESSENTIAL QUESTIONS

- How do land ecosystems change over time?
- How do aquatic ecosystems change over time?

Vocabulary

ecological succession p. 261

climax community p. 261

pioneer species p. 262

eutrophication p. 264

 Multilingual eGlossary

 Video

- **Science Video**
- **What's Science Got to do With It?**

Academic Standards for Science

6.3.2 Describe how changes caused by organisms in the habitat where they live can be beneficial or detrimental to themselves or the native plants and animals.

6.3.3 Describe how certain biotic and abiotic factors, such as predators, quantity of light and water, range of temperatures, and soil composition, can limit the number of organisms that an ecosystem can support.

Also covers: 6.NS.1, 6.NS.2, 6.NS.7, 6.NS.8, 6.NS.10

How Ecosystems Change

Inquiry) How did this happen?

This object was once part of a mining system used to move copper and iron ore. Today, so many forest plants have grown around it that it is barely recognizable. How do you think this happened? What do you think this object will look like after 500 more years?

How do communities change?
An ecosystem can change over time. Change usually happens so gradually that you might not notice differences from day to day.

1 Your teacher has given you **two pictures of ecosystem communities.** One is labeled *A* and the other is labeled *B*.

2 Imagine community A changed and became like community B. On a blank piece of **paper,** draw what you think community A might look like midway in its change to becoming like community B.

Think About This
1. What changes did you imagine? How long do you think it would take for community A to become like community B?

2. 🔑 **Key Concept** Summarize the changes you think would happen as the community changed from A to B.

How Land Ecosystems Change

Have you ever seen weeds growing up through cracks in a concrete sidewalk? If they were not removed, the weeds would keep growing. The crack would widen, making room for more weeds. Over time, the sidewalk would break apart. Shrubs and vines would move in. Their leaves and branches would grow large enough to cover the concrete. Eventually, trees could start growing there.

This process is an example of **ecological succession**—*the process of one ecological community gradually changing into another.* Ecological succession occurs in a series of steps. These steps can usually be predicted. For example, small plants usually grow first. Larger plants, such as trees, usually grow last.

The final stage of ecological succession in a land ecosystem is a **climax community**—*a stable community that no longer goes through major ecological changes.* Climax communities differ depending on the type of biome they are in. In a tropical forest biome, a climax community would be a mature tropical forest. In a grassland biome, a climax community would be a mature grassland. Climax communities are usually stable over hundreds of years. As plants in a climax community die, new plants of the same species grow and take their places. The community will continue to contain the same kinds of plants as long as the climate remains the same.

🔑 **Key Concept Check** What is a climax community?

FOLDABLES

Fold a sheet of paper into fourths. Use two sections on one side of the paper to describe and illustrate what land might look like before secondary succession and the other side to describe and illustrate the land after secondary succession is complete.

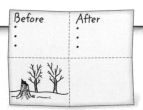

REVIEW VOCABULARY
community
all the organisms that live in one area at the same time

SCIENCE USE V. COMMON USE

pioneer
Science Use the first species that colonize new or undisturbed land

Common Use the first human settlers in an area

Primary Succession

What do you think happens to a lava-filled landscape when a volcanic eruption is over? As shown in **Figure 2**, volcanic lava eventually becomes new soil that supports plant growth. Ecological succession in new areas of land with little or no soil, such as on a lava flow, a sand dune, or exposed rock, is primary succession. *The first species that colonize new or undisturbed land are* **pioneer species.** The lichens and mosses in **Figure 2** are pioneer species.

Figure 2 Following a volcanic eruption, a landscape undergoes primary succession.

During a volcanic eruption, molten lava flows over the ground and into the water. After the eruption is over, the lava cools and hardens into bare rock.

Lichen spores carried on the wind settle on the rock. Lichens release acid that helps break down the rock and create soil. Lichens add nutrients to the soil as they die and decay.

Airborne spores from mosses and ferns settle onto the thin soil and add to the soil when they die. The soil gradually becomes thick enough to hold water. Insects and other small organisms move into the area.

After many years the soil is deep and has enough nutrients for grasses, wildflowers, shrubs, and trees. The new ecosystem provides habitats for many animals. Eventually, a climax community develops.

Secondary Succession

In areas where existing ecosystems have been disturbed or destroyed, secondary succession can occur. One example is forestland in New England that early colonists cleared hundreds of years ago. Some of the cleared land was not planted with crops. This land gradually grew back to a climax forest community of beech and maple trees, as illustrated in **Figure 3.**

 Reading Check Where does secondary succession occur?

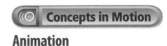 **Concepts in Motion**

Animation

Figure 3 When disturbed land grows back, secondary succession occurs.

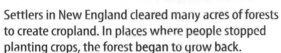

Settlers in New England cleared many acres of forests to create cropland. In places where people stopped planting crops, the forest began to grow back.

Seeds of grasses, wildflowers, and other plants quickly began to sprout and grow. Young shrubs and trees also started growing. These plants provided habitats for insects and other small animals, such as mice.

White pines and poplars were the first trees in the area to grow to their full height. They provided shade and protection to slower growing trees, such as beech and maple.

Eventually, a climax community of beech and maple trees developed. As older trees die, new beech and maple seedlings grow and replace them.

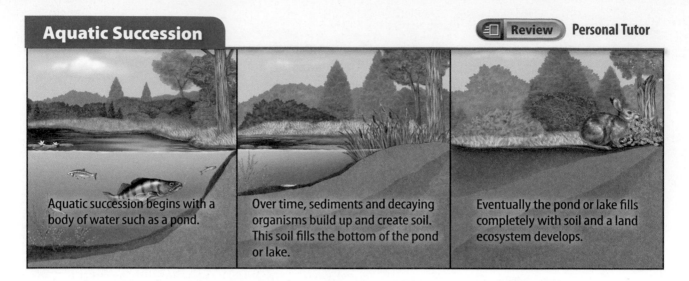

Aquatic succession begins with a body of water such as a pond.

Over time, sediments and decaying organisms build up and create soil. This soil fills the bottom of the pond or lake.

Eventually the pond or lake fills completely with soil and a land ecosystem develops.

Figure 4 The water in a pond is slowly replaced by soil. Eventually, land plants take over and the pond disappears.

How Freshwater Ecosystems Change

Like land ecosystems, freshwater ecosystems change over time in a natural, predictable process. This process is called aquatic succession.

Aquatic Succession

Aquatic succession is illustrated in **Figure 4.** Sediments carried by rainwater and streams accumulate on the bottoms of ponds, lakes, and wetlands. The decomposed remains of dead organisms add to the buildup of soil. As time passes, more and more soil accumulates. Eventually, so much soil has collected that the water disappears and the area becomes land.

 Key Concept Check What happens to a pond, a lake, or a wetland over time?

Eutrophication

As decaying organisms fall to the bottom of a pond, a lake, or a wetland, they add nutrients to the water. **Eutrophication** (yoo troh fuh KAY shun) *is the process of a body of water becoming nutrient-rich.*

WORD ORIGIN
eutrophication
from Greek *eutrophos*, means "nourishing"

Eutrophication is a natural part of aquatic succession. However, humans also contribute to eutrophication. The fertilizers that farmers use on crops and the waste from farm animals can be very high in nutrients. So can other forms of pollution. When fertilizers and pollution run off into a pond or lake, nutrient concentrations increase. High nutrient levels support large populations of algae and other microscopic organisms. These organisms use most of the dissolved oxygen in the water and less oxygen is available for fish and other pond or lake organisms. As a result, many of these organisms die. Their bodies decay and add to the buildup of soil, speeding up succession.

Lesson 3 Review

Visual Summary

Ecosystems change in predictable ways through ecological succession.

The final stage of ecological succession in a land ecosystem is a climax community.

The final stage of aquatic succession is a land ecosystem.

FOLDABLES

Use your lesson Foldable to review the lesson. Save your Foldable for the project at the end of the chapter.

What do you think NOW?

You first read the statements below at the beginning of the chapter.

5. An ecosystem never changes.

6. Nothing grows in the area where a volcano has erupted.

Did you change your mind about whether you agree or disagree with the statements? Rewrite any false statements to make them true.

Use Vocabulary

1 **Define** *pioneer species* in your own words.

2 The process of one ecological community changing into another is _____.

3 **Compare and contrast** succession and eutrophication in freshwater ecosystems.

Understand Key Concepts

4 **Draw** a picture of what your school might look like in 500 years if it were abandoned.

5 Which process occurs after a forest fire?
   A. eutrophication
   B. photosynthesis
   C. primary succession
   D. secondary succession

Interpret Graphics

6 **Determine** What kind of succession—primary or secondary—might occur in the environment pictured to the right? Explain.

7 **Summarize Information** Copy the graphic organizer below and fill it with the types of succession an ecosystem can go through.

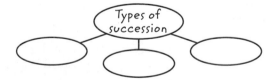

Critical Thinking

8 **Reflect** What kinds of abiotic factors might cause a grassland climax community to slowly become a forest?

9 **Recommend** actions people can take to help prevent the loss of wetland and estuary habitats.

A Biome for Radishes

Materials

paper towels

small jar

plastic wrap

jar lid

radish seeds

desk lamp

magnifying lens

Safety

Biomes contain plant and animal species adapted to particular climate conditions. Many organisms can live only in one type of biome. Others can survive in more than one biome. A radish is a plant grown around the world. How do you think radish seeds grow in different biomes? In this lab, you will model four different biomes and ecosystems—a temperate deciduous forest, a temperate rain forest, a desert, and a pond—and determine which biome the radishes grow best in.

Ask a Question

Which biome do radishes grow best in?

Make Observations

1 Read and complete a lab safety form.

2 Fold two pieces of paper towel lengthwise. Place the paper towels on opposite sides of the top of a small jar, as shown, with one end of each towel inside the jar and one end outside. Add water until about 10 cm of the paper towels are in the water. The area inside the jar models a pond ecosystem.

3 Place a piece of plastic wrap loosely over the end of one of the the paper towels hanging over the jar's edge. Do not completely cover the paper towel. This paper towel models a temperate rain forest ecosystem. The paper towel without plastic wrap models a temperate deciduous forest.

4 Place the jar lid upside-down on the top of the jar. The area in the lid models a desert.

Form a Hypothesis

5 Observe the four biomes and ecosystems you have modeled. Based on your observations and your knowledge of the abiotic factors a plant requires, hypothesize which biome or ecosystem you think radish seeds will grow best in.

By permission of TOPS Learning Systems, www.topscience.org.

Test Your Hypothesis

6 Place three radish seeds in each biome: pond, temperate forest, temperate rain forest, and desert. Gently press the seeds to the paper towel until they stick.

7 Place your jar near a window or under a desk lamp that can be turned on during the day.

8 In your Science Journal, record your observations of the seeds and the paper towel.

9 After five days, use a magnifying lens to observe the seeds and the paper towels again. Record your observations.

Analyze and Conclude

10 **Compare and Contrast** How did the appearance of the seeds change after five days in each model biome?

11 **Critique** Evaluate your hypothesis. Did the seeds grow the way you expected? In which biome did the seeds grow the most?

12 🔵 **The Big Idea** In the biome with the most growth, what characteristics do you think made the seeds grow best?

Communicate Your Results

Working in a group of three or four, create a table showing results for each biome. Present the table to the class.

In this lab, you determined which biome produced the most growth of radish seeds. Seeds of different species might sprout in several different biomes. However, not all sprouted seeds grow to adulthood. Design a lab to test what conditions are necessary for radishes to grow to adulthood.

By permission of TOPS Learning Systems, www.topscience.org.

Lab Tips

☑ Do not eat the radish seeds.

☑ If your seeds fall off the paper towel strips, do not replace them.

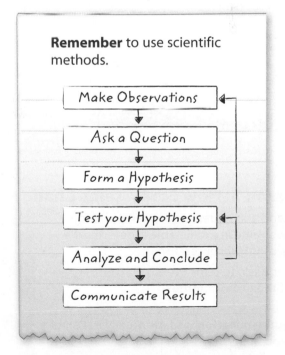

Remember to use scientific methods.

Make Observations

Ask a Question

Form a Hypothesis

Test your Hypothesis

Analyze and Conclude

Communicate Results

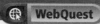
 THE BIG IDEA

Each of Earth's land biomes and aquatic ecosystems is characterized by distinct environments and organisms. Biomes and ecosystems change by natural processes of ecological succession and by human activities.

Key Concepts Summary 🔑	Vocabulary
Lesson 1: Land Biomes • Each land **biome** has a distinct climate and contains animals and plants well adapted to the environment. Biomes include **deserts**, **grasslands**, tropical rain forests, **temperate** rain forests, deciduous forests, **taigas**, and **tundras.** • Humans affect land biomes through agriculture, construction, and other activities. 	**biome** p. 241 **desert** p. 242 **grassland** p. 243 **temperate** p. 245 **taiga** p. 247 **tundra** p. 247
Lesson 2: Aquatic Ecosystems 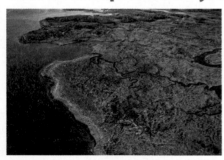 • Earth's aquatic ecosystems include freshwater and saltwater ecosystems. **Wetlands** can contain either salt water or freshwater. The **salinity** of **estuaries** varies. • Human activities such as construction and fishing can affect aquatic ecosystems.	**salinity** p. 251 **wetland** p. 254 **estuary** p. 255 **intertidal zone** p. 257 **coral reef** p. 257
Lesson 3: How Ecosystems Change • Land and aquatic ecosystems change over time in predictable processes of **ecological succession.** • Land ecosystems eventually form **climax communities.** • Freshwater ecosystems undergo **eutrophication** and eventually become land ecosystems. 	**ecological succession** p. 261 **climax community** p. 261 **pioneer species** p. 262 **eutrophication** p. 264

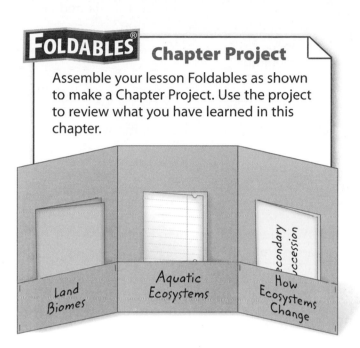

FOLDABLES **Chapter Project**

Assemble your lesson Foldables as shown to make a Chapter Project. Use the project to review what you have learned in this chapter.

Land Biomes

Aquatic Ecosystems

How Ecosystems Change

Secondary Succession

Use Vocabulary

Choose the vocabulary word that fits each description.

1 group of ecosystems with similar climate

2 area between the tropics and the polar circles

3 land biome with a layer of permafrost

4 the amount of salt dissolved in water

5 area where a river empties into an ocean

6 coastal zone between the highest high tide and the lowest low tide

7 process of one ecological community gradually changing into another

8 a stable community that no longer goes through major changes

9 the first species to grow on new or disturbed land

Link Vocabulary and Key Concepts

((O)) **Concepts in Motion** **Interactive Concept Map**

Copy this concept map, and then use vocabulary terms from the previous page and other terms from this chapter to complete the concept map.

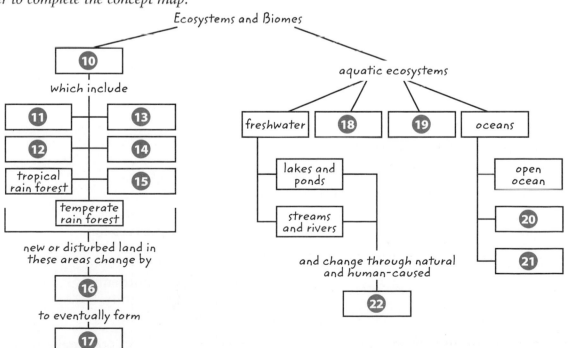

Understand Key Concepts

1 Where would you find plants with stems that can store large amounts of water?

A. desert
B. grassland
C. taiga
D. tundra

2 What does the pink area on the map below represent?

A. taiga
B. tundra
C. temperate deciduous forest
D. temperate rain forest

3 Where would you find trees that have no leaves during the winter?

A. estuary
B. tundra
C. temperate deciduous forest
D. temperate rain forest

4 Which biomes have rich, fertile soil?

A. grassland and taiga
B. grassland and tundra
C. grassland and tropical rain forest
D. grassland and temperate deciduous forest

5 Which is NOT a freshwater ecosystem?

A. oceans
B. ponds
C. rivers
D. streams

6 Where would you find species adapted to withstand strong wave action?

A. estuaries
B. wetlands
C. intertidal zone
D. twilight zone

7 Which ecosystem has flowing water?

A. estuary
B. lake
C. stream
D. wetland

8 Which ecosystems help protect coastal areas from flood damage?

A. estuaries
B. ponds
C. rivers
D. streams

9 Which organism below would be the first to settle an area that has been buried in lava?

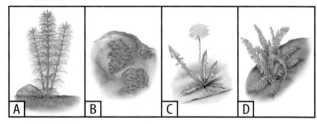

A. A
B. B
C. C
D. D

10 What is a forest called that has had the same species of trees for 200 years?

A. climax community
B. pioneer species
C. primary succession
D. secondary succession

11 What is eutrophication?

A. decreasing nutrients
B. decreasing salinity
C. increasing nutrients
D. increasing salinity

Critical Thinking

12 **Compare** mammals that live in tundra biomes with those that live in desert biomes. What adaptations does each group have that help them survive?

13 **Analyze** You are invited to go on a trip to South America. Before you leave, you read a travel guide that says the country you will be visiting has hot summers, cold winters, and many wheat farms. What biome will you be visiting? Explain your reasoning.

14 **Contrast** How are ecosystems in the deep water of lakes and oceans different?

15 **Analyze** Which type of ocean ecosystem is likely to have the highest levels of dissolved oxygen? Why?

16 **Hypothesize** Why are the first plants that appear in primary succession small?

17 **Interpret Graphics** The following climate data were recorded for a forest ecosystem. To which biome does this ecosystem likely belong?

Climate Data	June	July	August
Average temperature (°C)	16.0	16.5	17.0
Average rainfall (cm)	3.0	2.0	2.0

Writing in Science

18 **Write** a paragraph explaining the succession process that might occur in a small pond on a cow pasture. Include a main idea, supporting details, and concluding sentence.

REVIEW **THE BIG IDEA**

19 Earth contains a wide variety of organisms that live in different conditions. How do Earth's biomes and ecosystems differ?

20 The photo below shows Biosphere 2, built in Arizona as an artificial Earth. Imagine that you have been asked to build a biome of your choice for Biosphere 3. What biotic and abiotic features should you consider?

Math Skills

Review
Math Practice

Use Proportions

21 At its highest salinity, the water in Utah's Great Salt Lake contained about 14.5 g of salt in 50 g of lake water. What was the salinity of the lake?

22 The seawater in Puget Sound off the coast of Oregon has a salinity of about 24 PPT. What weight of water is there in 1,000 g of seawater?

Standardized Test Practice

Record your answers on the answer sheet provided by your teacher or on a sheet of paper.

Multiple Choice

1 Which aquatic ecosystem contains a mixture of freshwater and salt water?

   A coral reef

   B estuary

   C pond

   D river

Use the diagram below to answer question 2.

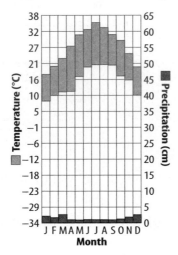

2 The diagram above most likely illustrates the climate of which biome?

   A desert

   B grassland

   C tropical rain forest

   D tundra

3 Which occurs during the first stage of ecological succession?

   A eutrophication

   B settlement

   C development of climax community

   D growth of pioneer species

4 Which biome has lost more than half its trees to logging activity?

   A grassland

   B taiga

   C temperate deciduous forest

   D tropical rain forest

Use the diagram below to answer question 5.

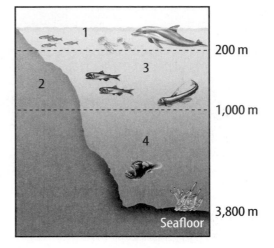

5 In the diagram above, where might you find microscopic photosynthetic organisms?

   A 1

   B 2

   C 3

   D 4

6 During aquatic succession, freshwater ponds

   A become saltwater.

   B fill with soil.

   C gain organisms.

   D increase in depth.

Use the diagram below to answer question 7.

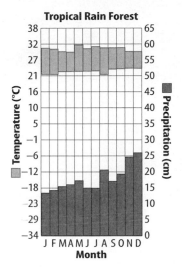

Tropical Rain Forest

Constructed Response

Use the table below to answer questions 9 and 10.

Land Biome	Climate and Plant Life	Location
Desert		
Grassland		
Taiga		
Temperate deciduous forest		
Temperate rain forest		
Tropical rain forest		
Tundra		

7 Based on the diagram above, which is true of the tropical rain forest biome?

   A Precipitation increases as temperatures rise.

   B Rainfall is greatest mid-year.

   C Temperatures rise at year-end.

   D Temperatures vary less than rainfall amounts.

8 Which aquatic biome typically has many varieties of nesting ducks, geese, herons, and egrets?

   A coral reefs

   B intertidal zones

   C lakes

   D wetlands

9 Briefly describe the characteristics of Earth's seven land biomes. List one example of each biome, including its location.

10 How does human activity affect each land biome?

Use the table below to answer question 11.

Aquatic Ecosystem	Aquatic Animal
Coastal ocean	
Coral reefs	
Estuaries	
Lakes and ponds	
Open ocean	

11 Complete the table above with the name of an aquatic animal that lives in each of Earth's aquatic ecosystems.

NEED EXTRA HELP?											
If You Missed Question...	1	2	3	4	5	6	7	8	9	10	11
Go to Lesson...	2	1	2	3	2	2	2	2	1	1	2

Student Resources

For Students and Parents/Guardians

These resources are designed to help you achieve success in science. You will find useful information on laboratory safety, math skills, and science skills. In addition, science reference materials are found in the Reference Handbook. You'll find the information you need to learn and sharpen your skills in these resources.

Table of Contents

Scientific Methods

Scientists use an orderly approach called the scientific method to solve problems. This includes organizing and recording data so others can understand them. Scientists use many variations in this method when they solve problems.

Identify a Question

The first step in a scientific investigation or experiment is to identify a question to be answered or a problem to be solved. For example, you might ask which gasoline is the most efficient.

Gather and Organize Information

After you have identified your question, begin gathering and organizing information. There are many ways to gather information, such as researching in a library, interviewing those knowledgeable about the subject, testing and working in the laboratory and field. Fieldwork is investigations and observations done outside of a laboratory.

Researching Information Before moving in a new direction, it is important to gather the information that already is known about the subject. Start by asking yourself questions to determine exactly what you need to know. Then you will look for the information in various reference sources, like the student is doing in **Figure 1.** Some sources may include textbooks, encyclopedias, government documents, professional journals, science magazines, and the Internet. Always list the sources of your information.

Figure 1 The Internet can be a valuable research tool.

Evaluate Sources of Information Not all sources of information are reliable. You should evaluate all of your sources of information, and use only those you know to be dependable. For example, if you are researching ways to make homes more energy efficient, a site written by the U.S. Department of Energy would be more reliable than a site written by a company that is trying to sell a new type of weatherproofing material. Also, remember that research always is changing. Consult the most current resources available to you. For example, a 1985 resource about saving energy would not reflect the most recent findings.

Sometimes scientists use data that they did not collect themselves, or conclusions drawn by other researchers. This data must be evaluated carefully. Ask questions about how the data were obtained, if the investigation was carried out properly, and if it has been duplicated exactly with the same results. Would you reach the same conclusion from the data? Only when you have confidence in the data can you believe it is true and feel comfortable using it.

SCIENCE SKILL HANDBOOK

MATH SKILL HANDBOOK

FOLDABLES HANDBOOK

REFERENCE HANDBOOK

GLOSSARY/ GLOSARIO

INDEX

Interpret Scientific Illustrations As you research a topic in science, you will see drawings, diagrams, and photographs to help you understand what you read. Some illustrations are included to help you understand an idea that you can't see easily by yourself, like the tiny particles in an atom in **Figure 2.** A drawing helps many people to remember details more easily and provides examples that clarify difficult concepts or give additional information about the topic you are studying. Most illustrations have labels or a caption to identify or to provide more information.

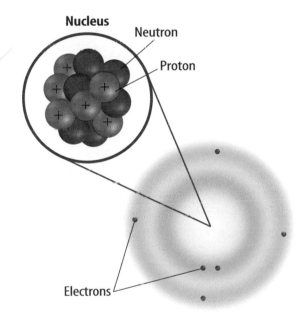

Figure 2 This drawing shows an atom of carbon with its six protons, six neutrons, and six electrons.

Concept Maps One way to organize data is to draw a diagram that shows relationships among ideas (or concepts). A concept map can help make the meanings of ideas and terms more clear, and help you understand and remember what you are studying. Concept maps are useful for breaking large concepts down into smaller parts, making learning easier.

Network Tree A type of concept map that not only shows a relationship, but how the concepts are related is a network tree, shown in **Figure 3.** In a network tree, the words are written in the ovals, while the description of the type of relationship is written across the connecting lines.

When constructing a network tree, write down the topic and all major topics on separate pieces of paper or notecards. Then arrange them in order from general to specific. Branch the related concepts from the major concept and describe the relationship on the connecting line. Continue to more specific concepts until finished.

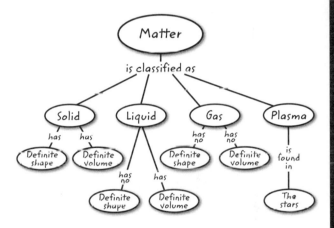

Figure 3 A network tree shows how concepts or objects are related.

Events Chain Another type of concept map is an events chain. Sometimes called a flow chart, it models the order or sequence of items. An events chain can be used to describe a sequence of events, the steps in a procedure, or the stages of a process.

When making an events chain, first find the one event that starts the chain. This event is called the initiating event. Then, find the next event and continue until the outcome is reached, as shown in **Figure 4.**

SCIENCE SKILL HANDBOOK

MATH SKILL HANDBOOK

FOLDABLES HANDBOOK

REFERENCE HANDBOOK

GLOSSARY/ GLOSARIO

INDEX

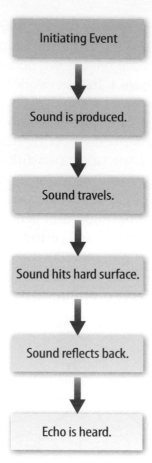

Figure 4 Events-chain concept maps show the order of steps in a process or event. This concept map shows how a sound makes an echo.

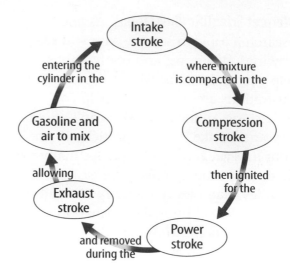

Figure 5 A cycle map shows events that occur in a cycle.

Spider Map A type of concept map that you can use for brainstorming is the spider map. When you have a central idea, you might find that you have a jumble of ideas that relate to it but are not necessarily clearly related to each other. The spider map on sound in **Figure 6** shows that if you write these ideas outside the main concept, then you can begin to separate and group unrelated terms so they become more useful.

Cycle Map A specific type of events chain is a cycle map. It is used when the series of events do not produce a final outcome, but instead relate back to the beginning event, such as in **Figure 5.** Therefore, the cycle repeats itself.

To make a cycle map, first decide what event is the beginning event. This is also called the initiating event. Then list the next events in the order that they occur, with the last event relating back to the initiating event. Words can be written between the events that describe what happens from one event to the next. The number of events in a cycle map can vary, but usually contain three or more events.

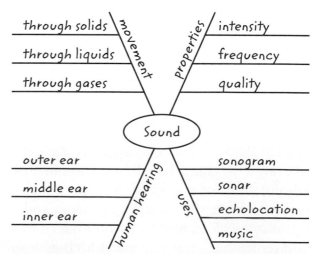

Figure 6 A spider map allows you to list ideas that relate to a central topic but not necessarily to one another.

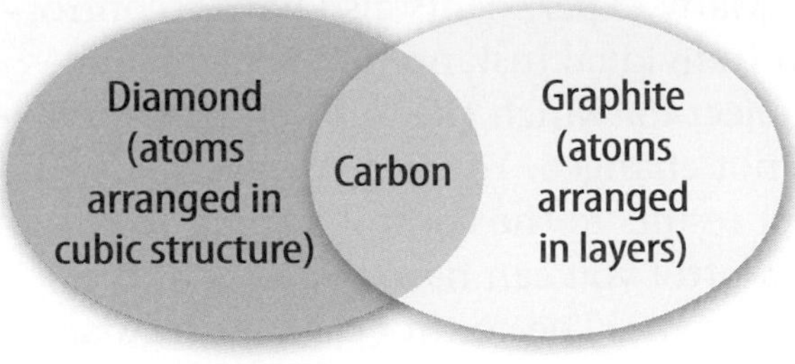

Figure 7 This Venn diagram compares and contrasts two substances made from carbon.

Venn Diagram To illustrate how two subjects compare and contrast you can use a Venn diagram. You can see the characteristics that the subjects have in common and those that they do not, shown in **Figure 7.**

To create a Venn diagram, draw two overlapping ovals that that are big enough to write in. List the characteristics unique to one subject in one oval, and the characteristics of the other subject in the other oval. The characteristics in common are listed in the overlapping section.

Make and Use Tables One way to organize information so it is easier to understand is to use a table. Tables can contain numbers, words, or both.

To make a table, list the items to be compared in the first column and the characteristics to be compared in the first row. The title should clearly indicate the content of the table, and the column or row heads should be clear. Notice that in **Table 1** the units are included.

Table 1 Recyclables Collected During Week			
Day of Week	Paper (kg)	Aluminum (kg)	Glass (kg)
Monday	5.0	4.0	12.0
Wednesday	4.0	1.0	10.0
Friday	2.5	2.0	10.0

Make a Model One way to help you better understand the parts of a structure, the way a process works, or to show things too large or small for viewing is to make a model. For example, an atomic model made of a plastic-ball nucleus and pipe-cleaner electron shells can help you visualize how the parts of an atom relate to each other. Other types of models can be devised on a computer or represented by equations.

Form a Hypothesis

A possible explanation based on previous knowledge and observations is called a hypothesis. After researching gasoline types and recalling previous experiences in your family's car you form a hypothesis—our car runs more efficiently because we use premium gasoline. To be valid, a hypothesis has to be something you can test by using an investigation.

Predict When you apply a hypothesis to a specific situation, you predict something about that situation. A prediction makes a statement in advance, based on prior observation, experience, or scientific reasoning. People use predictions to make everyday decisions. Scientists test predictions by performing investigations. Based on previous observations and experiences, you might form a prediction that cars are more efficient with premium gasoline. The prediction can be tested in an investigation.

Design an Experiment A scientist needs to make many decisions before beginning an investigation. Some of these include: how to carry out the investigation, what steps to follow, how to record the data, and how the investigation will answer the question. It also is important to address any safety concerns.

SCIENCE SKILL HANDBOOK

MATH SKILL HANDBOOK

FOLDABLES HANDBOOK

REFERENCE HANDBOOK

GLOSSARY/ GLOSARIO

INDEX

SCIENCE SKILL HANDBOOK

MATH SKILL HANDBOOK

FOLDABLES HANDBOOK

REFERENCE HANDBOOK

GLOSSARY/ GLOSARIO

INDEX

Test the Hypothesis

Now that you have formed your hypothesis, you need to test it. Using an investigation, you will make observations and collect data, or information. This data might either support or not support your hypothesis. Scientists collect and organize data as numbers and descriptions.

Follow a Procedure In order to know what materials to use, as well as how and in what order to use them, you must follow a procedure. **Figure 8** shows a procedure you might follow to test your hypothesis.

Procedure

Step 1 Use regular gasoline for two weeks.

Step 2 Record the number of kilometers between fill-ups and the amount of gasoline used.

Step 3 Switch to premium gasoline for two weeks.

Step 4 Record the number of kilometers between fill-ups and the amount of gasoline used.

Figure 8 A procedure tells you what to do step by step.

Identify and Manipulate Variables and Controls

In any experiment, it is important to keep everything the same except for the item you are testing. The one factor you change is called the independent variable. The change that results is the dependent variable. Make sure you have only one independent variable, to assure yourself of the cause of the changes you observe in the dependent variable. For example, in your gasoline experiment the type of fuel is the independent variable. The dependent variable is the efficiency.

Many experiments also have a control—an individual instance or experimental subject for which the independent variable is not changed. You can then compare the test results to the control results. To design a control you can have two cars of the same type. The control car uses regular gasoline for four weeks. After you are done with the test, you can compare the experimental results to the control results.

Collect Data

Whether you are carrying out an investigation or a short observational experiment, you will collect data, as shown in **Figure 9.** Scientists collect data as numbers and descriptions and organize it in specific ways.

Observe Scientists observe items and events, then record what they see. When they use only words to describe an observation, it is called qualitative data. Scientists' observations also can describe how much there is of something. These observations use numbers, as well as words, in the description and are called quantitative data. For example, if a sample of the element gold is described as being "shiny and very dense" the data are qualitative. Quantitative data on this sample of gold might include "a mass of 30 g and a density of 19.3 g/cm^3."

Figure 9 Collecting data is one way to gather information directly.

Figure 10 Record data neatly and clearly so it is easy to understand.

When you make observations you should examine the entire object or situation first, and then look carefully for details. It is important to record observations accurately and completely. Always record your notes immediately as you make them, so you do not miss details or make a mistake when recording results from memory. Never put unidentified observations on scraps of paper. Instead they should be recorded in a notebook, like the one in **Figure 10.** Write your data neatly so you can easily read it later. At each point in the experiment, record your observations and label them. That way, you will not have to determine what the figures mean when you look at your notes later. Set up any tables that you will need to use ahead of time, so you can record any observations right away. Remember to avoid bias when collecting data by not including personal thoughts when you record observations. Record only what you observe.

Estimate Scientific work also involves estimating. To estimate is to make a judgment about the size or the number of something without measuring or counting. This is important when the number or size of an object or population is too large or too difficult to accurately count or measure.

Sample Scientists may use a sample or a portion of the total number as a type of estimation. To sample is to take a small, representative portion of the objects or organisms of a population for research. By making careful observations or manipulating variables within that portion of the group, information is discovered and conclusions are drawn that might apply to the whole population. A poorly chosen sample can be unrepresentative of the whole. If you were trying to determine the rainfall in an area, it would not be best to take a rainfall sample from under a tree.

Measure You use measurements every day. Scientists also take measurements when collecting data. When taking measurements, it is important to know how to use measuring tools properly. Accuracy also is important.

Length To measure length, the distance between two points, scientists use meters. Smaller measurements might be measured in centimeters or millimeters.

Length is measured using a metric ruler or meter stick. When using a metric ruler, line up the 0-cm mark with the end of the object being measured and read the number of the unit where the object ends. Look at the metric ruler shown in **Figure 11.** The centimeter lines are the long, numbered lines, and the shorter lines are millimeter lines. In this instance, the length would be 4.50 cm.

Figure 11 This metric ruler has centimeter and millimeter divisions.

SCIENCE SKILL HANDBOOK

MATH SKILL HANDBOOK

FOLDABLES HANDBOOK

REFERENCE HANDBOOK

GLOSSARY/ GLOSARIO

INDEX

SCIENCE SKILL HANDBOOK

MATH SKILL HANDBOOK

FOLDABLES HANDBOOK

REFERENCE HANDBOOK

GLOSSARY/ GLOSARIO

INDEX

Mass The SI unit for mass is the kilogram (kg). Scientists can measure mass using units formed by adding metric prefixes to the unit gram (g), such as milligram (mg). To measure mass, you might use a triple-beam balance similar to the one shown in **Figure 12.** The balance has a pan on one side and a set of beams on the other side. Each beam has a rider that slides on the beam.

When using a triple-beam balance, place an object on the pan. Slide the largest rider along its beam until the pointer drops below zero. Then move it back one notch. Repeat the process for each rider proceeding from the larger to smaller until the pointer swings an equal distance above and below the zero point. Sum the masses on each beam to find the mass of the object. Move all riders back to zero when finished.

Instead of putting materials directly on the balance, scientists often take a tare of a container. A tare is the mass of a container into which objects or substances are placed for measuring their masses. To mass objects or substances, find the mass of a clean container. Remove the container from the pan, and place the object or substances in the container. Find the mass of the container with the materials in it. Subtract the mass of the empty container from the mass of the filled container to find the mass of the materials you are using.

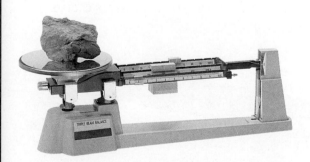

Figure 12 A triple-beam balance is used to determine the mass of an object.

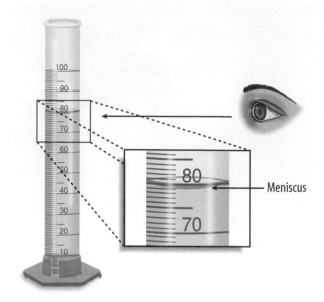

Figure 13 Graduated cylinders measure liquid volume.

Liquid Volume To measure liquids, the unit used is the liter. When a smaller unit is needed, scientists might use a milliliter. Because a milliliter takes up the volume of a cube measuring 1 cm on each side it also can be called a cubic centimeter ($cm^3 = cm \times cm \times cm$).

You can use beakers and graduated cylinders to measure liquid volume. A graduated cylinder, shown in **Figure 13,** is marked from bottom to top in milliliters. In lab, you might use a 10-mL graduated cylinder or a 100-mL graduated cylinder. When measuring liquids, notice that the liquid has a curved surface. Look at the surface at eye level, and measure the bottom of the curve. This is called the meniscus. The graduated cylinder in **Figure 13** contains 79.0 mL, or 79.0 cm^3, of a liquid.

Temperature Scientists often measure temperature using the Celsius scale. Pure water has a freezing point of 0°C and boiling point of 100°C. The unit of measurement is degrees Celsius. Two other scales often used are the Fahrenheit and Kelvin scales.

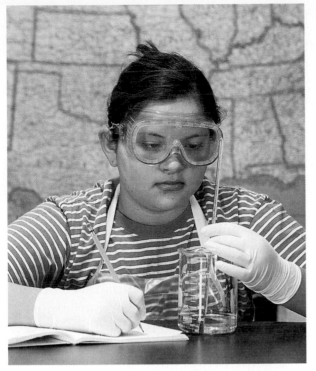

Figure 14 A thermometer measures the temperature of an object.

Scientists use a thermometer to measure temperature. Most thermometers in a laboratory are glass tubes with a bulb at the bottom end containing a liquid such as colored alcohol. The liquid rises or falls with a change in temperature. To read a glass thermometer like the thermometer in **Figure 14,** rotate it slowly until a red line appears. Read the temperature where the red line ends.

Form Operational Definitions
An operational definition defines an object by how it functions, works, or behaves. For example, when you are playing hide and seek and a tree is home base, you have created an operational definition for a tree.

Objects can have more than one operational definition. For example, a ruler can be defined as a tool that measures the length of an object (how it is used). It can also be a tool with a series of marks used as a standard when measuring (how it works).

Analyze the Data

To determine the meaning of your observations and investigation results, you will need to look for patterns in the data. Then you must think critically to determine what the data mean. Scientists use several approaches when they analyze the data they have collected and recorded. Each approach is useful for identifying specific patterns.

Interpret Data
The word *interpret* means "to explain the meaning of something." When analyzing data from an experiment, try to find out what the data show. Identify the control group and the test group to see whether or not changes in the independent variable have had an effect. Look for differences in the dependent variable between the control and test groups.

Classify
Sorting objects or events into groups based on common features is called classifying. When classifying, first observe the objects or events to be classified. Then select one feature that is shared by some members in the group, but not by all. Place those members that share that feature in a subgroup. You can classify members into smaller and smaller subgroups based on characteristics. Remember that when you classify, you are grouping objects or events for a purpose. Keep your purpose in mind as you select the features to form groups and subgroups.

Compare and Contrast
Observations can be analyzed by noting the similarities and differences between two or more objects or events that you observe. When you look at objects or events to see how they are similar, you are comparing them. Contrasting is looking for differences in objects or events.

SCIENCE SKILL HANDBOOK

MATH SKILL HANDBOOK

FOLDABLES HANDBOOK

REFERENCE HANDBOOK

GLOSSARY/ GLOSARIO

INDEX

SCIENCE SKILL HANDBOOK

MATH SKILL HANDBOOK

FOLDABLES HANDBOOK

REFERENCE HANDBOOK

GLOSSARY/ GLOSARIO

INDEX

Recognize Cause and Effect A cause is a reason for an action or condition. The effect is that action or condition. When two events happen together, it is not necessarily true that one event caused the other. Scientists must design a controlled investigation to recognize the exact cause and effect.

Draw Conclusions

When scientists have analyzed the data they collected, they proceed to draw conclusions about the data. These conclusions are sometimes stated in words similar to the hypothesis that you formed earlier. They may confirm a hypothesis, or lead you to a new hypothesis.

Infer Scientists often make inferences based on their observations. An inference is an attempt to explain observations or to indicate a cause. An inference is not a fact, but a logical conclusion that needs further investigation. For example, you may infer that a fire has caused smoke. Until you investigate, however, you do not know for sure.

Apply When you draw a conclusion, you must apply those conclusions to determine whether the data supports the hypothesis. If your data do not support your hypothesis, it does not mean that the hypothesis is wrong. It means only that the result of the investigation did not support the hypothesis. Maybe the experiment needs to be redesigned, or some of the initial observations on which the hypothesis was based were incomplete or biased. Perhaps more observation or research is needed to refine your hypothesis. A successful investigation does not always come out the way you originally predicted.

Avoid Bias Sometimes a scientific investigation involves making judgments. When you make a judgment, you form an opinion. It is important to be honest and not to allow any expectations of results to bias your judgments. This is important throughout the entire investigation, from researching to collecting data to drawing conclusions.

Communicate

The communication of ideas is an important part of the work of scientists. A discovery that is not reported will not advance the scientific community's understanding or knowledge. Communication among scientists also is important as a way of improving their investigations.

Scientists communicate in many ways, from writing articles in journals and magazines that explain their investigations and experiments, to announcing important discoveries on television and radio. Scientists also share ideas with colleagues on the Internet or present them as lectures, like the student is doing in **Figure 15.**

Figure 15 A student communicates to his peers about his investigation.

These safety symbols are used in laboratory and field investigations in this book to indicate possible hazards. Learn the meaning of each symbol and refer to this page often. *Remember to wash your hands thoroughly after completing lab procedures.*

PROTECTIVE EQUIPMENT   Do not begin any lab without the proper protection equipment.

| GOGGLES | Proper eye protection must be worn when performing or observing science activities which involve items or conditions as listed below. | APRON | Wear an approved apron when using substances that could stain, wet, or destroy cloth. | SOAP | Wash hands with soap and water before removing goggles and after all lab activities. | GLOVES | Wear gloves when working with biological materials, chemicals, animals, or materials that can stain or irritate hands. |

LABORATORY HAZARDS

Symbols	Potential Hazards	Precaution	Response
DISPOSAL	contamination of classroom or environment due to improper disposal of materials such as chemicals and live specimens	• DO NOT dispose of hazardous materials in the sink or trash can. • Dispose of wastes as directed by your teacher.	• If hazardous materials are disposed of improperly, notify your teacher immediately.
EXTREME TEMPERATURE	skin burns due to extremely hot or cold materials such as hot glass, liquids, or metals; liquid nitrogen; dry ice	• Use proper protective equipment, such as hot mitts and/or tongs, when handling objects with extreme temperatures.	• If injury occurs, notify your teacher immediately.
SHARP OBJECTS	punctures or cuts from sharp objects such as razor blades, pins, scalpels, and broken glass	• Handle glassware carefully to avoid breakage. • Walk with sharp objects pointed downward, away from you and others.	• If broken glass or injury occurs, notify your teacher immediately.
ELECTRICAL	electric shock or skin burn due to improper grounding, short circuits, liquid spills, or exposed wires	• Check condition of wires and apparatus for fraying or uninsulated wires, and broken or cracked equipment. • Use only GFCI-protected outlets	• DO NOT attempt to fix electrical problems. Notify your teacher immediately.
CHEMICAL	skin irritation or burns, breathing difficulty, and/or poisoning due to touching, swallowing, or inhalation of chemicals such as acids, bases, bleach, metal compounds, iodine, poinsettias, pollen, ammonia, acetone, nail polish remover, heated chemicals, mothballs, and any other chemicals labeled or known to be dangerous	• Wear proper protective equipment such as goggles, apron, and gloves when using chemicals. • Ensure proper room ventilation or use a fume hood when using materials that produce fumes. • NEVER smell fumes directly. • NEVER taste or eat any material in the laboratory.	• If contact occurs, immediately flush affected area with water and notify your teacher. • If a spill occurs, leave the area immediately and notify your teacher.
FLAMMABLE	unexpected fire due to liquids or gases that ignite easily such as rubbing alcohol	• Avoid open flames, sparks, or heat when flammable liquids are present.	• If a fire occurs, leave the area immediately and notify your teacher.
OPEN FLAME	burns or fire due to open flame from matches, Bunsen burners, or burning materials	• Tie back loose hair and clothing. • Keep flame away from all materials. • Follow teacher instructions when lighting and extinguishing flames. • Use proper protection, such as hot mitts or tongs, when handling hot objects.	• If a fire occurs, leave the area immediately and notify your teacher.
ANIMAL SAFETY	injury to or from laboratory animals	• Wear proper protective equipment such as gloves, apron, and goggles when working with animals. • Wash hands after handling animals.	• If injury occurs, notify your teacher immediately.
BIOLOGICAL	infection or adverse reaction due to contact with organisms such as bacteria, fungi, and biological materials such as blood, animal or plant materials	• Wear proper protective equipment such as gloves, goggles, and apron when working with biological materials. • Avoid skin contact with an organism or any part of the organism. • Wash hands after handling organisms.	• If contact occurs, wash the affected area and notify your teacher immediately.
FUME	breathing difficulties from inhalation of fumes from substances such as ammonia, acetone, nail polish remover, heated chemicals, and mothballs	• Wear goggles, apron, and gloves. • Ensure proper room ventilation or use a fume hood when using substances that produce fumes. • NEVER smell fumes directly.	• If a spill occurs, leave area and notify your teacher immediately.
IRRITANT	irritation of skin, mucous membranes, or respiratory tract due to materials such as acids, bases, bleach, pollen, mothballs, steel wool, and potassium permanganate	• Wear goggles, apron, and gloves. • Wear a dust mask to protect against fine particles.	• If skin contact occurs, immediately flush the affected area with water and notify your teacher.
RADIOACTIVE	excessive exposure from alpha, beta, and gamma particles	• Remove gloves and wash hands with soap and water before removing remainder of protective equipment.	• If cracks or holes are found in the container, notify your teacher immediately.

SCIENCE SKILL HANDBOOK

MATH SKILL HANDBOOK

FOLDABLES HANDBOOK

REFERENCE HANDBOOK

GLOSSARY/ GLOSARIO

INDEX

Safety in the Science Laboratory

Introduction to Science Safety

The science laboratory is a safe place to work if you follow standard safety procedures. Being responsible for your own safety helps to make the entire laboratory a safer place for everyone. When performing any lab, read and apply the caution statements and safety symbol listed at the beginning of the lab.

General Safety Rules

1. Complete the *Lab Safety Form* or other safety contract BEFORE starting any science lab.

2. Study the procedure. Ask your teacher any questions. Be sure you understand safety symbols shown on the page.

3. Notify your teacher about allergies or other health conditions which can affect your participation in a lab.

4. Learn and follow use and safety procedures for your equipment. If unsure, ask your teacher.

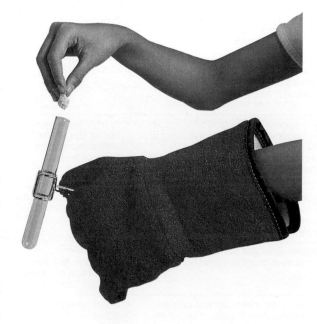

5. Never eat, drink, chew gum, apply cosmetics, or do any personal grooming in the lab. Never use lab glassware as food or drink containers. Keep your hands away from your face and mouth.

6. Know the location and proper use of the safety shower, eye wash, fire blanket, and fire alarm.

Prevent Accidents

1. Use the safety equipment provided to you. Goggles and a safety apron should be worn during investigations.

2. Do NOT use hair spray, mousse, or other flammable hair products. Tie back long hair and tie down loose clothing.

3. Do NOT wear sandals or other open-toed shoes in the lab.

4. Remove jewelry on hands and wrists. Loose jewelry, such as chains and long necklaces, should be removed to prevent them from getting caught in equipment.

5. Do not taste any substances or draw any material into a tube with your mouth.

6. Proper behavior is expected in the lab. Practical jokes and fooling around can lead to accidents and injury.

7. Keep your work area uncluttered.

Laboratory Work

1. Collect and carry all equipment and materials to your work area before beginning a lab.

2. Remain in your own work area unless given permission by your teacher to leave it.

SCIENCE SKILL HANDBOOK

MATH SKILL HANDBOOK

FOLDABLES HANDBOOK

REFERENCE HANDBOOK

GLOSSARY/ GLOSARIO

INDEX

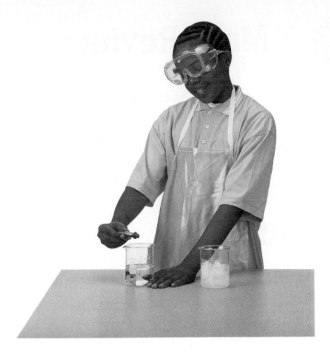

3. Always slant test tubes away from yourself and others when heating them, adding substances to them, or rinsing them.

4. If instructed to smell a substance in a container, hold the container a short distance away and fan vapors towards your nose.

5. Do NOT substitute other chemicals/substances for those in the materials list unless instructed to do so by your teacher.

6. Do NOT take any materials or chemicals outside of the laboratory.

7. Stay out of storage areas unless instructed to be there and supervised by your teacher.

Laboratory Cleanup

1. Turn off all burners, water, and gas, and disconnect all electrical devices.

2. Clean all pieces of equipment and return all materials to their proper places.

3. Dispose of chemicals and other materials as directed by your teacher. Place broken glass and solid substances in the proper containers. Never discard materials in the sink.

4. Clean your work area.

5. Wash your hands with soap and water thoroughly BEFORE removing your goggles.

Emergencies

1. Report any fire, electrical shock, glassware breakage, spill, or injury, no matter how small, to your teacher immediately. Follow his or her instructions.

2. If your clothing should catch fire, STOP, DROP, and ROLL. If possible, smother it with the fire blanket or get under a safety shower. NEVER RUN.

3. If a fire should occur, turn off all gas and leave the room according to established procedures.

4. In most instances, your teacher will clean up spills. Do NOT attempt to clean up spills unless you are given permission and instructions to do so.

5. If chemicals come into contact with your eyes or skin, notify your teacher immediately. Use the eyewash, or flush your skin or eyes with large quantities of water.

6. The fire extinguisher and first-aid kit should only be used by your teacher unless it is an extreme emergency and you have been given permission.

7. If someone is injured or becomes ill, only a professional medical provider or someone certified in first aid should perform first-aid procedures.

SCIENCE SKILL HANDBOOK

MATH SKILL HANDBOOK

FOLDABLES HANDBOOK

REFERENCE HANDBOOK

GLOSSARY/ GLOSARIO

INDEX

Use Fractions

A fraction compares a part to a whole. In the fraction $\frac{2}{3}$, the 2 represents the part and is the numerator. The 3 represents the whole and is the denominator.

Reduce Fractions To reduce a fraction, you must find the largest factor that is common to both the numerator and the denominator, the greatest common factor (GCF). Divide both numbers by the GCF. The fraction has then been reduced, or it is in its simplest form.

Example

Twelve of the 20 chemicals in the science lab are in powder form. What fraction of the chemicals used in the lab are in powder form?

Step 1 Write the fraction.

$$\frac{\text{part}}{\text{whole}} = \frac{12}{20}$$

Step 2 To find the GCF of the numerator and denominator, list all of the factors of each number.

Factors of 12: 1, 2, 3, 4, 6, 12 (the numbers that divide evenly into 12)

Factors of 20: 1, 2, 4, 5, 10, 20 (the numbers that divide evenly into 20)

Step 3 List the common factors.

1, 2, 4

Step 4 Choose the greatest factor in the list. The GCF of 12 and 20 is 4.

Step 5 Divide the numerator and denominator by the GCF.

$$\frac{12 \div 4}{20 \div 4} = \frac{3}{5}$$

In the lab, $\frac{3}{5}$ of the chemicals are in powder form.

Practice Problem At an amusement park, 66 of 90 rides have a height restriction. What fraction of the rides, in its simplest form, has a height restriction?

Add and Subtract Fractions with Like Denominators To add or subtract fractions with the same denominator, add or subtract the numerators and write the sum or difference over the denominator. After finding the sum or difference, find the simplest form for your fraction.

Example 1

In the forest outside your house, $\frac{1}{8}$ of the animals are rabbits, $\frac{3}{8}$ are squirrels, and the remainder are birds and insects. How many are mammals?

Step 1 Add the numerators.

$$\frac{1}{8} + \frac{3}{8} = \frac{(1+3)}{8} = \frac{4}{8}$$

Step 2 Find the GCF.

$$\frac{4}{8} \text{ (GCF, 4)}$$

Step 3 Divide the numerator and denominator by the GCF.

$$\frac{4 \div 4}{8 \div 4} = \frac{1}{2}$$

$\frac{1}{2}$ of the animals are mammals.

Example 2

If $\frac{7}{16}$ of the Earth is covered by freshwater, and $\frac{1}{16}$ of that is in glaciers, how much freshwater is not frozen?

Step 1 Subtract the numerators.

$$\frac{7}{16} - \frac{1}{16} = \frac{(7-1)}{16} = \frac{6}{16}$$

Step 2 Find the GCF.

$$\frac{6}{16} \text{ (GCF, 2)}$$

Step 3 Divide the numerator and denominator by the GCF.

$$\frac{6 \div 2}{16 \div 2} = \frac{3}{8}$$

$\frac{3}{8}$ of the freshwater is not frozen.

Practice Problem A bicycle rider is riding at a rate of 15 km/h for $\frac{4}{9}$ of his ride, 10 km/h for $\frac{2}{9}$ of his ride, and 8 km/h for the remainder of the ride. How much of his ride is he riding at a rate greater than 8 km/h?

SCIENCE SKILL HANDBOOK

MATH SKILL HANDBOOK

FOLDABLES HANDBOOK

REFERENCE HANDBOOK

GLOSSARY/ GLOSARIO

INDEX

Add and Subtract Fractions with Unlike Denominators To add or subtract fractions with unlike denominators, first find the least common denominator (LCD). This is the smallest number that is a common multiple of both denominators. Rename each fraction with the LCD, and then add or subtract. Find the simplest form if necessary.

Example 1

A chemist makes a paste that is $\frac{1}{2}$ table salt (NaCl), $\frac{1}{3}$ sugar ($C_6H_{12}O_6$), and the remainder is water (H_2O). How much of the paste is a solid?

Step 1 Find the LCD of the fractions.

$$\frac{1}{2} + \frac{1}{3} \text{ (LCD, 6)}$$

Step 2 Rename each numerator and each denominator with the LCD.

Step 3 Add the numerators.

$$\frac{3}{6} + \frac{2}{6} = \frac{(3+2)}{6} = \frac{5}{6}$$

$\frac{5}{6}$ of the paste is a solid.

Example 2

The average precipitation in Grand Junction, CO, is $\frac{7}{10}$ inch in November, and $\frac{3}{5}$ inch in December. What is the total average precipitation?

Step 1 Find the LCD of the fractions.

$$\frac{7}{10} + \frac{3}{5} \text{ (LCD, 10)}$$

Step 2 Rename each numerator and each denominator with the LCD.

Step 3 Add the numerators.

$$\frac{7}{10} + \frac{6}{10} = \frac{(7+6)}{10} = \frac{13}{10}$$

$\frac{13}{10}$ inches total precipitation, or $1\frac{3}{10}$ inches.

Practice Problem On an electric bill, about $\frac{1}{8}$ of the energy is from solar energy and about $\frac{1}{10}$ is from wind power. How much of the total bill is from solar energy and wind power combined?

Example 3

In your body, $\frac{7}{10}$ of your muscle contractions are involuntary (cardiac and smooth muscle tissue). Smooth muscle makes $\frac{3}{15}$ of your muscle contractions. How many of your muscle contractions are made by cardiac muscle?

Step 1 Find the LCD of the fractions.

$$\frac{7}{10} - \frac{3}{15} \text{ (LCD, 30)}$$

Step 2 Rename each numerator and each denominator with the LCD.

$$\frac{7 \times 3}{10 \times 3} = \frac{21}{30}$$
$$\frac{3 \times 2}{15 \times 2} = \frac{6}{30}$$

Step 3 Subtract the numerators.

$$\frac{21}{30} - \frac{6}{30} = \frac{(21-6)}{30} = \frac{15}{30}$$

Step 4 Find the GCF.

$$\frac{15}{30} \text{ (GCF, 15)}$$
$$\frac{1}{2}$$

$\frac{1}{2}$ of all muscle contractions are cardiac muscle.

Example 4

Tony wants to make cookies that call for $\frac{3}{4}$ of a cup of flour, but he only has $\frac{1}{3}$ of a cup. How much more flour does he need?

Step 1 Find the LCD of the fractions.

$$\frac{3}{4} - \frac{1}{3} \text{ (LCD, 12)}$$

Step 2 Rename each numerator and each denominator with the LCD.

$$\frac{3 \times 3}{4 \times 3} = \frac{9}{12}$$
$$\frac{1 \times 4}{3 \times 4} = \frac{4}{12}$$

Step 3 Subtract the numerators.

$$\frac{9}{12} - \frac{4}{12} = \frac{(9-4)}{12} = \frac{5}{12}$$

$\frac{5}{12}$ of a cup of flour

Practice Problem Using the information provided to you in Example 3 above, determine how many muscle contractions are voluntary (skeletal muscle).

SCIENCE SKILL HANDBOOK

MATH SKILL HANDBOOK

FOLDABLES HANDBOOK

REFERENCE HANDBOOK

GLOSSARY/ GLOSARIO

INDEX

SCIENCE SKILL HANDBOOK

MATH SKILL HANDBOOK

FOLDABLES HANDBOOK

REFERENCE HANDBOOK

GLOSSARY/ GLOSARIO

INDEX

Multiply Fractions To multiply with fractions, multiply the numerators and multiply the denominators. Find the simplest form if necessary.

Example

Multiply $\frac{3}{5}$ by $\frac{1}{3}$.

Step 1 Multiply the numerators and denominators.

$$\frac{3}{5} \times \frac{1}{3} = \frac{(3 \times 1)}{(5 \times 3)} \frac{3}{15}$$

Step 2 Find the GCF.

$$\frac{3}{15} \text{ (GCF, 3)}$$

Step 3 Divide the numerator and denominator by the GCF.

$$\frac{3 \div 3}{15 \div 3} = \frac{1}{5}$$

$\frac{3}{5}$ multiplied by $\frac{1}{3}$ is $\frac{1}{5}$.

Practice Problem Multiply $\frac{3}{14}$ by $\frac{5}{16}$.

Find a Reciprocal Two numbers whose product is 1 are called multiplicative inverses, or reciprocals.

Example

Find the reciprocal of $\frac{3}{8}$.

Step 1 Inverse the fraction by putting the denominator on top and the numerator on the bottom.

$$\frac{8}{3}$$

The reciprocal of $\frac{3}{8}$ is $\frac{8}{3}$.

Practice Problem Find the reciprocal of $\frac{4}{9}$.

Divide Fractions To divide one fraction by another fraction, multiply the dividend by the reciprocal of the divisor. Find the simplest form if necessary.

Example 1

Divide $\frac{1}{9}$ by $\frac{1}{3}$.

Step 1 Find the reciprocal of the divisor.

The reciprocal of $\frac{1}{3}$ is $\frac{3}{1}$.

Step 2 Multiply the dividend by the reciprocal of the divisor.

$$\frac{\frac{1}{9}}{\frac{1}{3}} = \frac{1}{9} \times \frac{3}{1} = \frac{(1 \times 3)}{(9 \times 1)} = \frac{3}{9}$$

Step 3 Find the GCF.

$$\frac{3}{9} \text{ (GCF, 3)}$$

Step 4 Divide the numerator and denominator by the GCF.

$$\frac{3 \div 3}{9 \div 3} = \frac{1}{3}$$

$\frac{1}{9}$ divided by $\frac{1}{3}$ is $\frac{1}{3}$.

Example 2

Divide $\frac{3}{5}$ by $\frac{1}{4}$.

Step 1 Find the reciprocal of the divisor.

The reciprocal of $\frac{1}{4}$ is $\frac{4}{1}$.

Step 2 Multiply the dividend by the reciprocal of the divisor.

$$\frac{\frac{3}{5}}{\frac{1}{4}} = \frac{3}{5} \times \frac{4}{1} = \frac{(3 \times 4)}{(5 \times 1)} = \frac{12}{5}$$

$\frac{3}{5}$ divided by $\frac{1}{4}$ is $\frac{12}{5}$ or $2\frac{2}{5}$.

Practice Problem Divide $\frac{3}{11}$ by $\frac{7}{10}$.

Use Ratios

When you compare two numbers by division, you are using a ratio. Ratios can be written 3 to 5, 3:5, or $\frac{3}{5}$. Ratios, like fractions, also can be written in simplest form.

Ratios can represent one type of probability, called odds. This is a ratio that compares the number of ways a certain outcome occurs to the number of possible outcomes. For example, if you flip a coin 100 times, what are the odds that it will come up heads? There are two possible outcomes, heads or tails, so the odds of coming up heads are 50:100. Another way to say this is that 50 out of 100 times the coin will come up heads. In its simplest form, the ratio is 1:2.

Example 1

A chemical solution contains 40 g of salt and 64 g of baking soda. What is the ratio of salt to baking soda as a fraction in simplest form?

Step 1 Write the ratio as a fraction.

$$\frac{salt}{baking\ soda} = \frac{40}{64}$$

Step 2 Express the fraction in simplest form. The GCF of 40 and 64 is 8.

$$\frac{40}{64} = \frac{40 \div 8}{64 \div 8} = \frac{5}{8}$$

The ratio of salt to baking soda in the sample is 5:8.

Example 2

Sean rolls a 6-sided die 6 times. What are the odds that the side with a 3 will show?

Step 1 Write the ratio as a fraction.

$$\frac{number\ of\ sides\ with\ a\ 3}{number\ of\ possible\ sides} = \frac{1}{6}$$

Step 2 Multiply by the number of attempts.

$$\frac{1}{6} \times 6\ attempts = \frac{6}{6}\ attempts = 1$$
attempt

1 attempt out of 6 will show a 3.

Practice Problem Two metal rods measure 100 cm and 144 cm in length. What is the ratio of their lengths in simplest form?

Use Decimals

A fraction with a denominator that is a power of ten can be written as a decimal. For example, 0.27 means $\frac{27}{100}$. The decimal point separates the ones place from the tenths place.

Any fraction can be written as a decimal using division. For example, the fraction $\frac{5}{8}$ can be written as a decimal by dividing 5 by 8. Written as a decimal, it is 0.625.

Add or Subtract Decimals When adding and subtracting decimals, line up the decimal points before carrying out the operation.

Example 1

Find the sum of 47.68 and 7.80.

Step 1 Line up the decimal places when you write the numbers.

$$\begin{array}{r} 47.68 \\ + 7.80 \\ \hline \end{array}$$

Step 2 Add the decimals.

$$\begin{array}{r} {}^{1\ 1}47.68 \\ + 7.80 \\ \hline 55.48 \end{array}$$

The sum of 47.68 and 7.80 is 55.48.

Example 2

Find the difference of 42.17 and 15.85.

Step 1 Line up the decimal places when you write the number.

$$\begin{array}{r} 42.17 \\ -15.85 \\ \hline \end{array}$$

Step 2 Subtract the decimals.

$$\begin{array}{r} {}^{3\,11}42.17 \\ -15.85 \\ \hline 26.32 \end{array}$$

The difference of 42.17 and 15.85 is 26.32.

Practice Problem Find the sum of 1.245 and 3.842.

SCIENCE SKILL HANDBOOK

MATH SKILL HANDBOOK

FOLDABLES HANDBOOK

REFERENCE HANDBOOK

GLOSSARY/ GLOSARIO

INDEX

SCIENCE SKILL HANDBOOK

MATH SKILL HANDBOOK

FOLDABLES HANDBOOK

REFERENCE HANDBOOK

GLOSSARY/ GLOSARIO

INDEX

Multiply Decimals To multiply decimals, multiply the numbers like numbers without decimal points. Count the decimal places in each factor. The product will have the same number of decimal places as the sum of the decimal places in the factors.

Example

Multiply 2.4 by 5.9.

Step 1 Multiply the factors like two whole numbers.

$24 \times 59 = 1416$

Step 2 Find the sum of the number of decimal places in the factors. Each factor has one decimal place, for a sum of two decimal places.

Step 3 The product will have two decimal places.

14.16

The product of 2.4 and 5.9 is 14.16.

Practice Problem Multiply 4.6 by 2.2.

Divide Decimals When dividing decimals, change the divisor to a whole number. To do this, multiply both the divisor and the dividend by the same power of ten. Then place the decimal point in the quotient directly above the decimal point in the dividend. Then divide as you do with whole numbers.

Example

Divide 8.84 by 3.4.

Step 1 Multiply both factors by 10.

$3.4 \times 10 = 34, 8.84 \times 10 = 88.4$

Step 2 Divide 88.4 by 34.

```
        2.6
   34)88.4
      -68
       204
      -204
         0
```

8.84 divided by 3.4 is 2.6.

Practice Problem Divide 75.6 by 3.6.

Use Proportions

An equation that shows that two ratios are equivalent is a proportion. The ratios $\frac{2}{4}$ and $\frac{5}{10}$ are equivalent, so they can be written as $\frac{2}{4} = \frac{5}{10}$. This equation is a proportion.

When two ratios form a proportion, the cross products are equal. To find the cross products in the proportion $\frac{2}{4} = \frac{5}{10}$, multiply the 2 and the 10, and the 4 and the 5. Therefore $2 \times 10 = 4 \times 5$, or $20 = 20$.

Because you know that both ratios are equal, you can use cross products to find a missing term in a proportion. This is known as solving the proportion.

Example

The heights of a tree and a pole are proportional to the lengths of their shadows. The tree casts a shadow of 24 m when a 6-m pole casts a shadow of 4 m. What is the height of the tree?

Step 1 Write a proportion.

$$\frac{\text{height of tree}}{\text{height of pole}} = \frac{\text{length of tree's shadow}}{\text{length of pole's shadow}}$$

Step 2 Substitute the known values into the proportion. Let h represent the unknown value, the height of the tree.

$$\frac{h}{6} \times \frac{24}{4}$$

Step 3 Find the cross products.

$$h \times 4 = 6 \times 24$$

Step 4 Simplify the equation.

$$4h \times 144$$

Step 5 Divide each side by 4.

$$\frac{4h}{4} \times \frac{144}{4}$$

$$h = 36$$

The height of the tree is 36 m.

Practice Problem The ratios of the weights of two objects on the Moon and on Earth are in proportion. A rock weighing 3 N on the Moon weighs 18 N on Earth. How much would a rock that weighs 5 N on the Moon weigh on Earth?

Use Percentages

The word *percent* means "out of one hundred." It is a ratio that compares a number to 100. Suppose you read that 77 percent of Earth's surface is covered by water. That is the same as reading that the fraction of Earth's surface covered by water is $\frac{77}{100}$. To express a fraction as a percent, first find the equivalent decimal for the fraction. Then, multiply the decimal by 100 and add the percent symbol.

Example 1

Express $\frac{13}{20}$ as a percent.

Step 1   Find the equivalent decimal for the fraction.

$$\begin{array}{r} 0.65 \\ 20\overline{)13.00} \\ \underline{12\,0} \\ 1\,00 \\ \underline{1\,00} \\ 0 \end{array}$$

Step 2   Rewrite the fraction $\frac{13}{20}$ as 0.65.

Step 3   Multiply 0.65 by 100 and add the % symbol.

$$0.65 \times 100 = 65 = 65\%$$

So, $\frac{13}{20} = 65\%$.

This also can be solved as a proportion.

Example 2

Express $\frac{13}{20}$ as a percent.

Step 1   Write a proportion.

$$\frac{13}{20} = \frac{x}{100}$$

Step 2   Find the cross products.

$$1300 = 20x$$

Step 3   Divide each side by 20.

$$\frac{1300}{20} = \frac{20x}{20}$$

$$65\% = x$$

Practice Problem In one year, 73 of 365 days were rainy in one city. What percent of the days in that city were rainy?

Solve One-Step Equations

A statement that two expressions are equal is an equation. For example, $A = B$ is an equation that states that A is equal to B.

An equation is solved when a variable is replaced with a value that makes both sides of the equation equal. To make both sides equal the inverse operation is used. Addition and subtraction are inverses, and multiplication and division are inverses.

Example 1

Solve the equation $x - 10 = 35$.

Step 1   Find the solution by adding 10 to each side of the equation.

$$x - 10 = 35$$
$$x - 10 + 10 = 35 - 10$$
$$x = 45$$

Step 2   Check the solution.

$$x - 10 = 35$$
$$45 - 10 = 35$$
$$35 = 35$$

Both sides of the equation are equal, so $x = 45$.

Example 2

In the formula $a = bc$, find the value of c if $a = 20$ and $b = 2$.

Step 1   Rearrange the formula so the unknown value is by itself on one side of the equation by dividing both sides by b.

$$a = bc$$
$$\frac{a}{b} = \frac{bc}{b}$$
$$\frac{a}{b} = c$$

Step 2   Replace the variables a and b with the values that are given.

$$\frac{a}{b} = c$$
$$\frac{20}{2} = c$$
$$10 = c$$

Step 3   Check the solution.

$$a = bc$$
$$20 = 2 \times 10$$
$$20 = 20$$

Both sides of the equation are equal, so $c = 10$ is the solution when $a = 20$ and $b = 2$.

Practice Problem In the formula $h = gd$, find the value of d if $g = 12.3$ and $h = 17.4$.

SCIENCE SKILL HANDBOOK

MATH SKILL HANDBOOK

FOLDABLES HANDBOOK

REFERENCE HANDBOOK

GLOSSARY/ GLOSARIO

INDEX

Use Statistics

The branch of mathematics that deals with collecting, analyzing, and presenting data is statistics. In statistics, there are three common ways to summarize data with a single number— the mean, the median, and the mode.

The **mean** of a set of data is the arithmetic average. It is found by adding the numbers in the data set and dividing by the number of items in the set.

The **median** is the middle number in a set of data when the data are arranged in numerical order. If there were an even number of data points, the median would be the mean of the two middle numbers.

The **mode** of a set of data is the number or item that appears most often.

Another number that often is used to describe a set of data is the range. The **range** is the difference between the largest number and the smallest number in a set of data.

Example

The speeds (in m/s) for a race car during five different time trials are 39, 37, 44, 36, and 44.

To find the mean:

Step 1 Find the sum of the numbers.

$39 + 37 + 44 + 36 + 44 = 200$

Step 2 Divide the sum by the number of items, which is 5.

$200 \div 5 = 40$

The mean is 40 m/s.

To find the median:

Step 1 Arrange the measures from least to greatest.

36, 37, 39, 44, 44

Step 2 Determine the middle measure.

36, 37, 39, 44, 44

The median is 39 m/s.

To find the mode:

Step 1 Group the numbers that are the same together.

44, 44, 36, 37, 39

Step 2 Determine the number that occurs most in the set.

44, 44, 36, 37, 39

The mode is 44 m/s.

To find the range:

Step 1 Arrange the measures from greatest to least.

44, 44, 39, 37, 36

Step 2 Determine the greatest and least measures in the set.

44, 44, 39, 37, 36

Step 3 Find the difference between the greatest and least measures.

$44 - 36 = 8$

The range is 8 m/s.

Practice Problem Find the mean, median, mode, and range for the data set 8, 4, 12, 8, 11, 14, 16.

A **frequency table** shows how many times each piece of data occurs, usually in a survey. **Table 1** below shows the results of a student survey on favorite color.

Table 1 **Student Color Choice**		
Color	**Tally**	**Frequency**
red	IIII	4
blue	ʇʜʅ	5
black	II	2
green	III	3
purple	ʇʜʅ II	7
yellow	ʇʜʅ I	6

Based on the frequency table data, which color is the favorite?

Use Geometry

The branch of mathematics that deals with the measurement, properties, and relationships of points, lines, angles, surfaces, and solids is called geometry.

Perimeter The **perimeter** (P) is the distance around a geometric figure. To find the perimeter of a rectangle, add the length and width and multiply that sum by two, or $2(l + w)$. To find perimeters of irregular figures, add the length of the sides.

Example 1

Find the perimeter of a rectangle that is 3 m long and 5 m wide.

Step 1 You know that the perimeter is 2 times the sum of the width and length.

$P = 2(3 \text{ m} + 5 \text{ m})$

Step 2 Find the sum of the width and length.

$P = 2(8 \text{ m})$

Step 3 Multiply by 2.

$P = 16 \text{ m}$

The perimeter is 16 m.

Example 2

Find the perimeter of a shape with sides measuring 2 cm, 5 cm, 6 cm, 3 cm.

Step 1 You know that the perimeter is the sum of all the sides.

$P = 2 + 5 + 6 + 3$

Step 2 Find the sum of the sides.

$P = 2 + 5 + 6 + 3$

$P = 16$

The perimeter is 16 cm.

Practice Problem Find the perimeter of a rectangle with a length of 18 m and a width of 7 m.

Practice Problem Find the perimeter of a triangle measuring 1.6 cm by 2.4 cm by 2.4 cm.

Area of a Rectangle The **area** (A) is the number of square units needed to cover a surface. To find the area of a rectangle, multiply the length times the width, or $l \times w$. When finding area, the units also are multiplied. Area is given in square units.

Example

Find the area of a rectangle with a length of 1 cm and a width of 10 cm.

Step 1 You know that the area is the length multiplied by the width.

$A = (1 \text{ cm} \times 10 \text{ cm})$

Step 2 Multiply the length by the width. Also multiply the units.

$A = 10 \text{ cm}^2$

The area is 10 cm^2.

Practice Problem Find the area of a square whose sides measure 4 m.

Area of a Triangle To find the area of a triangle, use the formula:

$A = \frac{1}{2}(\text{base} \times \text{height})$

The base of a triangle can be any of its sides. The height is the perpendicular distance from a base to the opposite endpoint, or vertex.

Example

Find the area of a triangle with a base of 18 m and a height of 7 m.

Step 1 You know that the area is $\frac{1}{2}$ the base times the height.

$A = \frac{1}{2}(18 \text{ m} \times 7 \text{ m})$

Step 2 Multiply $\frac{1}{2}$ by the product of 18×7. Multiply the units.

$A = \frac{1}{2}(126 \text{ m}^2)$

$A = 63 \text{ m}^2$

The area is 63 m^2.

Practice Problem Find the area of a triangle with a base of 27 cm and a height of 17 cm.

SCIENCE SKILL HANDBOOK

MATH SKILL HANDBOOK

FOLDABLES HANDBOOK

REFERENCE HANDBOOK

GLOSSARY/ GLOSARIO

INDEX

SCIENCE SKILL HANDBOOK

MATH SKILL HANDBOOK

FOLDABLES HANDBOOK

REFERENCE HANDBOOK

GLOSSARY/ GLOSARIO

INDEX

Circumference of a Circle The **diameter** (*d*) of a circle is the distance across the circle through its center, and the **radius** (r) is the distance from the center to any point on the circle. The radius is half of the diameter. The distance around the circle is called the **circumference** (C). The formula for finding the circumference is:

$C = 2\pi r$ or $C = \pi d$

The circumference divided by the diameter is always equal to 3.1415926… This nonterminating and nonrepeating number is represented by the Greek letter π (pi). An approximation often used for π is 3.14.

Example 1

Find the circumference of a circle with a radius of 3 m.

Step 1 You know the formula for the circumference is 2 times the radius times π.

$C = 2\pi(3)$

Step 2 Multiply 2 times the radius.

$C = 6\pi$

Step 3 Multiply by π.

$C \approx 19$ m

The circumference is about 19 m.

Example 2

Find the circumference of a circle with a diameter of 24.0 cm.

Step 1 You know the formula for the circumference is the diameter times π.

$C = \pi(24.0)$

Step 2 Multiply the diameter by π.

$C \approx 75.4$ cm

The circumference is about 75.4 cm.

Practice Problem Find the circumference of a circle with a radius of 19 cm.

Area of a Circle The formula for the area of a circle is: $A = \pi r^2$

Example 1

Find the area of a circle with a radius of 4.0 cm.

Step 1 $A = \pi(4.0)^2$

Step 2 Find the square of the radius.

$A = 16\pi$

Step 3 Multiply the square of the radius by π.

$A \approx 50$ cm^2

The area of the circle is about 50 cm^2.

Example 2

Find the area of a circle with a radius of 225 m.

Step 1 $A = \pi(225)^2$

Step 2 Find the square of the radius.

$A = 50625\pi$

Step 3 Multiply the square of the radius by π.

$A \approx 159043.1$

The area of the circle is about 159043.1 m^2.

Example 3

Find the area of a circle whose diameter is 20.0 mm.

Step 1 Remember that the radius is half of the diameter.

$A = \pi\left(\frac{20.0}{2}\right)^2$

Step 2 Find the radius.

$A = \pi(10.0)^2$

Step 3 Find the square of the radius.

$A = 100\pi$

Step 4 Multiply the square of the radius by π.

$A \approx 314$ mm^2

The area of the circle is about 314 mm^2.

Practice Problem Find the area of a circle with a radius of 16 m.

Volume The measure of space occupied by a solid is the **volume** (*V*). To find the volume of a rectangular solid multiply the length times width times height, or $V = l \times w \times h$. It is measured in cubic units, such as cubic centimeters (cm^3).

Example

Find the volume of a rectangular solid with a length of 2.0 m, a width of 4.0 m, and a height of 3.0 m.

Step 1 You know the formula for volume is the length times the width times the height.

$$V = 2.0 \text{ m} \times 4.0 \text{ m} \times 3.0 \text{ m}$$

Step 2 Multiply the length times the width times the height.

$$V = 24 \text{ m}^3$$

The volume is 24 m^3.

Practice Problem Find the volume of a rectangular solid that is 8 m long, 4 m wide, and 4 m high.

To find the volume of other solids, multiply the area of the base times the height.

Example 1

Find the volume of a solid that has a triangular base with a length of 8.0 m and a height of 7.0 m. The height of the entire solid is 15.0 m.

Step 1 You know that the base is a triangle, and the area of a triangle is $\frac{1}{2}$ the base times the height, and the volume is the area of the base times the height.

$$V = \left[\frac{1}{2}(b \times h)\right] \times 15$$

Step 2 Find the area of the base.

$$V = \left[\frac{1}{2}(8 \times 7)\right] \times 15$$

$$V = \left(\frac{1}{2} \times 56\right) \times 15$$

Step 3 Multiply the area of the base by the height of the solid.

$$V = 28 \times 15$$

$$V = 420 \text{ m}^3$$

The volume is 420 m^3.

Example 2

Find the volume of a cylinder that has a base with a radius of 12.0 cm, and a height of 21.0 cm.

Step 1 You know that the base is a circle, and the area of a circle is the square of the radius times π, and the volume is the area of the base times the height.

$$V = (\pi r^2) \times 21$$

$$V = (\pi 12^2) \times 21$$

Step 2 Find the area of the base.

$$V = 144\pi \times 21$$

$$V = 452 \times 21$$

Step 3 Multiply the area of the base by the height of the solid.

$$V \approx 9,500 \text{ cm}^3$$

The volume is about 9,500 cm^3.

Example 3

Find the volume of a cylinder that has a diameter of 15 mm and a height of 4.8 mm.

Step 1 You know that the base is a circle with an area equal to the square of the radius times π. The radius is one-half the diameter. The volume is the area of the base times the height.

$$V = (\pi r^2) \times 4.8$$

$$V = \left[\pi\left(\frac{1}{2} \times 15\right)^2\right] \times 4.8$$

$$V = (\pi 7.5^2) \times 4.8$$

Step 2 Find the area of the base.

$$V = 56.25\pi \times 4.8$$

$$V \approx 176.71 \times 4.8$$

Step 3 Multiply the area of the base by the height of the solid.

$$V \approx 848.2$$

The volume is about 848.2 mm^3.

Practice Problem Find the volume of a cylinder with a diameter of 7 cm in the base and a height of 16 cm.

SCIENCE SKILL HANDBOOK

MATH SKILL HANDBOOK

FOLDABLES HANDBOOK

REFERENCE HANDBOOK

GLOSSARY/ GLOSARIO

INDEX

Science Applications

SCIENCE SKILL HANDBOOK

MATH SKILL HANDBOOK

FOLDABLES HANDBOOK

REFERENCE HANDBOOK

GLOSSARY/ GLOSARIO

INDEX

Measure in SI

The metric system of measurement was developed in 1795. A modern form of the metric system, called the International System (SI), was adopted in 1960 and provides the standard measurements that all scientists around the world can understand.

The SI system is convenient because unit sizes vary by powers of 10. Prefixes are used to name units. Look at **Table 2** for some common SI prefixes and their meanings.

Table 2 Common SI Prefixes			
Prefix	**Symbol**	**Meaning**	
kilo-	k	1,000	thousandth
hecto-	h	100	hundred
deka-	da	10	ten
deci-	d	0.1	tenth
centi-	c	0.01	hundreth
milli-	m	0.001	thousandth

Example

How many grams equal one kilogram?

Step 1 Find the prefix *kilo-* in **Table 2.**

Step 2 Using **Table 2,** determine the meaning of *kilo-*. According to the table, it means 1,000. When the prefix *kilo-* is added to a unit, it means that there are 1,000 of the units in a "kilounit."

Step 3 Apply the prefix to the units in the question. The units in the question are grams. There are 1,000 grams in a kilogram.

Practice Problem Is a milligram larger or smaller than a gram? How many of the smaller units equal one larger unit? What fraction of the larger unit does one smaller unit represent?

Dimensional Analysis

Convert SI Units In science, quantities such as length, mass, and time sometimes are measured using different units. A process called dimensional analysis can be used to change one unit of measure to another. This process involves multiplying your starting quantity and units by one or more conversion factors. A conversion factor is a ratio equal to one and can be made from any two equal quantities with different units. If 1,000 mL equal 1 L then two ratios can be made.

$$\frac{1,000 \text{ mL}}{1 \text{ L}} = \frac{1 \text{ L}}{1,000 \text{ mL}} = 1$$

One can convert between units in the SI system by using the equivalents in **Table 2** to make conversion factors.

Example

How many cm are in 4 m?

Step 1 Write conversion factors for the units given. From **Table 2,** you know that 100 cm = 1 m. The conversion factors are

$$\frac{100 \text{ cm}}{1 \text{ m}} \text{ and } \frac{1 \text{ m}}{100 \text{ cm}}$$

Step 2 Decide which conversion factor to use. Select the factor that has the units you are converting from (m) in the denominator and the units you are converting to (cm) in the numerator.

$$\frac{100 \text{ cm}}{1 \text{ m}}$$

Step 3 Multiply the starting quantity and units by the conversion factor. Cancel the starting units with the units in the denominator. There are 400 cm in 4 m.

$$4 \text{ m} = \frac{100 \text{ cm}}{1 \text{ m}} = 400 \text{ cm}$$

Practice Problem How many milligrams are in one kilogram? (Hint: You will need to use two conversion factors from **Table 2.**)

Table 3 Unit System Equivalents

Type of Measurement	Equivalent
Length	1 in = 2.54 cm 1 yd = 0.91 m 1 mi = 1.61 km
Mass and weight*	1 oz = 28.35 g 1 lb = 0.45 kg 1 ton (short) = 0.91 tonnes (metric tons) 1 lb = 4.45 N
Volume	$1\ in^3 = 16.39\ cm^3$ 1 qt = 0.95 L 1 gal = 3.78 L
Area	$1\ in^2 = 6.45\ cm^2$ $1\ yd^2 = 0.83\ m^2$ $1\ mi^2 = 2.59\ km^2$ 1 acre = 0.40 hectares
Temperature	$^\circ C = \frac{(^\circ F - 32)}{1.8}$ $K = {^\circ C} + 273$

*Weight is measured in standard Earth gravity.

Convert Between Unit Systems Table 3 gives a list of equivalents that can be used to convert between English and SI units.

Example

If a meterstick has a length of 100 cm, how long is the meterstick in inches?

Step 1 Write the conversion factors for the units given. From **Table 3,** 1 in = 2.54 cm.

$$\frac{1\ in}{2.54\ cm} \quad and \quad \frac{2.54\ cm}{1\ in}$$

Step 2 Determine which conversion factor to use. You are converting from cm to in. Use the conversion factor with cm on the bottom.

$$\frac{1\ in}{2.54\ cm}$$

Step 3 Multiply the starting quantity and units by the conversion factor. Cancel the starting units with the units in the denominator. Round your answer to the nearest tenth.

$$100\ \cancel{cm} \times \frac{1\ in}{2.54\ \cancel{cm}} = 39.37\ in$$

The meterstick is about 39.4 in long.

Practice Problem 1 A book has a mass of 5 lb. What is the mass of the book in kg?

Practice Problem 2 Use the equivalent for in and cm (1 in = 2.54 cm) to show how $1\ in^3 \approx 16.39\ cm^3$.

SCIENCE SKILL HANDBOOK

MATH SKILL HANDBOOK

FOLDABLES HANDBOOK

REFERENCE HANDBOOK

GLOSSARY/ GLOSARIO

INDEX

Precision and Significant Digits

When you make a measurement, the value you record depends on the precision of the measuring instrument. This precision is represented by the number of significant digits recorded in the measurement. When counting the number of significant digits, all digits are counted except zeros at the end of a number with no decimal point such as 2,050, and zeros at the beginning of a decimal such as 0.03020. When adding or subtracting numbers with different precision, round the answer to the smallest number of decimal places of any number in the sum or difference. When multiplying or dividing, the answer is rounded to the smallest number of significant digits of any number being multiplied or divided.

Example

The lengths 5.28 and 5.2 are measured in meters. Find the sum of these lengths and record your answer using the correct number of significant digits.

Step 1 Find the sum.

5.28 m	2 digits after the decimal
+ 5.2 m	1 digit after the decimal
10.48 m	

Step 2 Round to one digit after the decimal because the least number of digits after the decimal of the numbers being added is 1.

The sum is 10.5 m.

Practice Problem 1 How many significant digits are in the measurement 7,071,301 m? How many significant digits are in the measurement 0.003010 g?

Practice Problem 2 Multiply 5.28 and 5.2 using the rule for multiplying and dividing. Record the answer using the correct number of significant digits.

Scientific Notation

Many times numbers used in science are very small or very large. Because these numbers are difficult to work with scientists use scientific notation. To write numbers in scientific notation, move the decimal point until only one non-zero digit remains on the left. Then count the number of places you moved the decimal point and use that number as a power of ten. For example, the average distance from the Sun to Mars is 227,800,000,000 m. In scientific notation, this distance is 2.278×10^{11} m. Because you moved the decimal point to the left, the number is a positive power of ten.

The mass of an electron is about 0.000 000 000 000 000 000 000 000 000 000 911 kg. Expressed in scientific notation, this mass is 9.11×10^{-31} kg. Because the decimal point was moved to the right, the number is a negative power of ten.

Example

Earth is 149,600,000 km from the Sun. Express this in scientific notation.

Step 1 Move the decimal point until one non-zero digit remains on the left.

1.496 000 00

Step 2 Count the number of decimal places you have moved. In this case, eight.

Step 2 Show that number as a power of ten, 10^8.

Earth is 1.496×10^8 km from the Sun.

Practice Problem 1 How many significant digits are in 149,600,000 km? How many significant digits are in 1.496×10^8 km?

Practice Problem 2 Parts used in a high performance car must be measured to 7×10^{-6} m. Express this number as a decimal.

Practice Problem 3 A CD is spinning at 539 revolutions per minute. Express this number in scientific notation.

Make and Use Graphs

Data in tables can be displayed in a graph—a visual representation of data. Common graph types include line graphs, bar graphs, and circle graphs.

Line Graph A line graph shows a relationship between two variables that change continuously. The independent variable is changed and is plotted on the x-axis. The dependent variable is observed, and is plotted on the *y*-axis.

Example

Draw a line graph of the data below from a cyclist in a long-distance race.

Table 4 Bicycle Race Data	
Time (h)	**Distance (km)**
0	0
1	8
2	16
3	24
4	32
5	40

Step 1 Determine the x-axis and y-axis variables. Time varies independently of distance and is plotted on the x-axis. Distance is dependent on time and is plotted on the y-axis.

Step 2 Determine the scale of each axis. The x-axis data ranges from 0 to 5. The y-axis data ranges from 0 to 50.

Step 3 Using graph paper, draw and label the axes. Include units in the labels.

Step 4 Draw a point at the intersection of the time value on the x-axis and corresponding distance value on the y-axis. Connect the points and label the graph with a title, as shown in **Figure 8**.

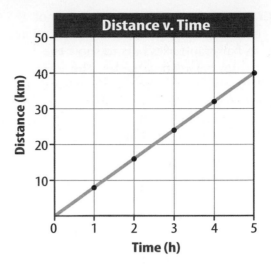

Figure 8 This line graph shows the relationship between distance and time during a bicycle ride.

Practice Problem A puppy's shoulder height is measured during the first year of her life. The following measurements were collected: (3 mo, 52 cm), (6 mo, 72 cm), (9 mo, 83 cm), (12 mo, 86 cm). Graph this data.

Find a Slope The slope of a straight line is the ratio of the vertical change, rise, to the horizontal change, run.

$$\text{Slope} = \frac{\text{vertical change (rise)}}{\text{horizontal change (run)}} = \frac{\text{change in } y}{\text{change in } x}$$

Example

Find the slope of the graph in **Figure 8**.

Step 1 You know that the slope is the change in y divided by the change in x.
$$\text{Slope} = \frac{\text{change in } y}{\text{change in } x}$$

Step 2 Determine the data points you will be using. For a straight line, choose the two sets of points that are the farthest apart.
$$\text{Slope} = \frac{(40 - 0)\ \text{km}}{(5 - 0)\ \text{h}}$$

Step 3 Find the change in y and x.
$$\text{Slope} = \frac{40\ \text{km}}{5\ \text{h}}$$

Step 4 Divide the change in y by the change in x.
$$\text{Slope} = \frac{8\ \text{km}}{\text{h}}$$

The slope of the graph is 8 km/h.

SCIENCE SKILL HANDBOOK

MATH SKILL HANDBOOK

FOLDABLES HANDBOOK

REFERENCE HANDBOOK

GLOSSARY/ GLOSARIO

INDEX

SCIENCE SKILL HANDBOOK

MATH SKILL HANDBOOK

FOLDABLES HANDBOOK

REFERENCE HANDBOOK

GLOSSARY/ GLOSARIO

INDEX

Bar Graph To compare data that does not change continuously you might choose a bar graph. A bar graph uses bars to show the relationships between variables. The *x*-axis variable is divided into parts. The parts can be numbers such as years, or a category such as a type of animal. The *y*-axis is a number and increases continuously along the axis.

Example

A recycling center collects 4.0 kg of aluminum on Monday, 1.0 kg on Wednesday, and 2.0 kg on Friday. Create a bar graph of this data.

Step 1 Select the *x*-axis and *y*-axis variables. The measured numbers (the masses of aluminum) should be placed on the *y*-axis. The variable divided into parts (collection days) is placed on the *x*-axis.

Step 2 Create a graph grid like you would for a line graph. Include labels and units.

Step 3 For each measured number, draw a vertical bar above the *x*-axis value up to the *y*-axis value. For the first data point, draw a vertical bar above Monday up to 4.0 kg.

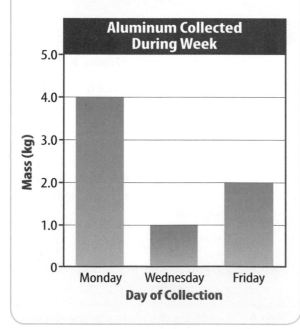

Practice Problem Draw a bar graph of the gases in air: 78% nitrogen, 21% oxygen, 1% other gases.

Circle Graph To display data as parts of a whole, you might use a circle graph. A circle graph is a circle divided into sections that represent the relative size of each piece of data. The entire circle represents 100%, half represents 50%, and so on.

Example

Air is made up of 78% nitrogen, 21% oxygen, and 1% other gases. Display the composition of air in a circle graph.

Step 1 Multiply each percent by 360° and divide by 100 to find the angle of each section in the circle.

$$78\% \times \frac{360°}{100} = 280.8°$$

$$21\% \times \frac{360°}{100} = 75.6°$$

$$1\% \times \frac{360°}{100} = 3.6°$$

Step 2 Use a compass to draw a circle and to mark the center of the circle. Draw a straight line from the center to the edge of the circle.

Step 3 Use a protractor and the angles you calculated to divide the circle into parts. Place the center of the protractor over the center of the circle and line the base of the protractor over the straight line.

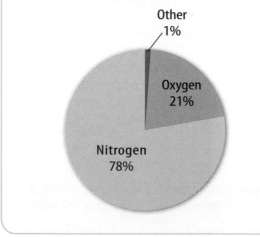

Practice Problem Draw a circle graph to represent the amount of aluminum collected during the week shown in the bar graph to the left.

Student Study Guides & Instructions
By Dinah Zike

1. You will find suggestions for Study Guides, also known as Foldables or books, in each chapter lesson and as a final project. Look at the end of the chapter to determine the project format and glue the Foldables in place as you progress through the chapter lessons.

2. Creating the Foldables or books is simple and easy to do by using copy paper, art paper, and Internet printouts. Photocopies of maps, diagrams, or your own illustrations may also be used for some of the Foldables. Notebook paper is the most common source of material for study guides and 83% of all Foldables are created from it. When folded to make books, notebook paper Foldables easily fit into 11" × 17" or 12" × 18" chapter projects with space left over. Foldables made using photocopy paper are slightly larger and they fit into Projects, but snugly. Use the least amount of glue, tape, and staples needed to assemble the Foldables.

3. Seven of the Foldables can be made using either small or large paper. When 11" × 17" or 12" × 18" paper are used, these become projects for housing smaller Foldables. Project format boxes are located within the instructions to remind you of this option.

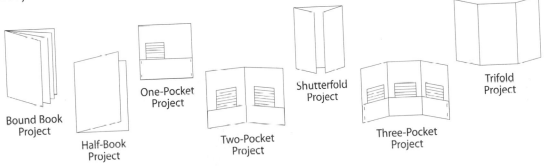

Bound Book Project

Half-Book Project

One-Pocket Project

Two-Pocket Project

Shutterfold Project

Three-Pocket Project

Trifold Project

4. Use one-gallon self-locking plastic bags to store your projects. Place strips of two-inch clear tape along the left, long side of the bag and punch holes through the taped edge. Cut the bottom corners off the bag so it will not hold air. Store this Project Portfolio inside a three-hole binder. To store a large collection of project bags, use a giant laundry-soap box. Holes can be punched in some of the Foldable Projects so they can be stored in a three-hole binder without using a plastic bag. Punch holes in the pocket books before gluing or stapling the pocket.

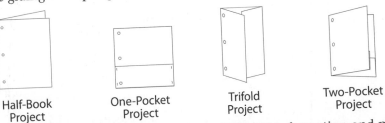

Half-Book Project

One-Pocket Project

Trifold Project

Two-Pocket Project

5. Maximize the use of the projects by collecting additional information and placing it on the back of the project and other unused spaces of the large Foldables.

SCIENCE SKILL HANDBOOK

MATH SKILL HANDBOOK

FOLDABLES HANDBOOK

REFERENCE HANDBOOK

GLOSSARY/ GLOSARIO

INDEX

Half-Book Foldable® By Dinah Zike

Step 1 Fold a sheet of notebook or copy paper in half.

Label the exterior tab and use the inside space to write information.

PROJECT FORMAT
Use 11" × 17" or 12" × 18" paper on the horizontal axis to make a large project book.

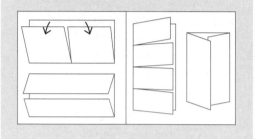

Variations

Paper can be folded vertically, like a *hamburger* or horizontally, like a *hotdog*.

A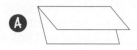

B

C Half-books can be folded so that one side is ½ inch longer than the other side. A title or question can be written on the extended tab.

- -

Worksheet Foldable or Folded Book® By Dinah Zike

Step 1 Make a half-book (see above) using work sheets, Internet print-outs, diagrams, or maps.

Step 2 Fold it in half again.

Variations

A This folded sheet as a small book with two pages can be used for comparing and contrasting, cause and effect, or other skills.

B When the sheet of paper is open, the four sections can be used separately or used collectively to show sequences or steps.

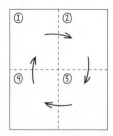

SCIENCE SKILL HANDBOOK

MATH SKILL HANDBOOK

FOLDABLES HANDBOOK

REFERENCE HANDBOOK

GLOSSARY/ GLOSARIO

INDEX

Two-Tab and Concept-Map Foldable® By Dinah Zike

Step 1 Fold a sheet of notebook or copy paper in half vertically or horizontally.

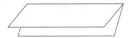

Step 2 Fold it in half again, as shown.

Step 3 Unfold once and cut along the fold line or valley of the top flap to make two flaps.

Variations

A Concept maps can be made by leaving a ½ inch tab at the top when folding the paper in half. Use arrows and labels to relate topics to the primary concept.

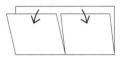

B Use two sheets of paper to make multiple page tab books. Glue or staple books together at the top fold.

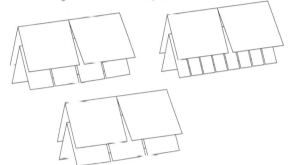

- -

Three-Quarter Foldable® By Dinah Zike

Step 1 Make a two-tab book (see above) and cut the left tab off at the top of the fold line.

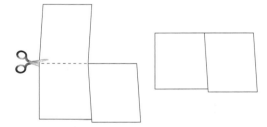

Variations

A Use this book to draw a diagram or a map on the exposed left tab. Write questions about the illustration on the top right tab and provide complete answers on the space under the tab.

B Compose a self-test using multiple choice answers for your questions. Include the correct answer with three wrong responses. The correct answers can be written on the back of the book or upside down on the bottom of the inside page.

SCIENCE SKILL HANDBOOK

MATH SKILL HANDBOOK

FOLDABLES HANDBOOK

REFERENCE HANDBOOK

GLOSSARY/ GLOSARIO

INDEX

SCIENCE SKILL HANDBOOK

MATH SKILL HANDBOOK

FOLDABLES HANDBOOK

REFERENCE HANDBOOK

GLOSSARY/ GLOSARIO

INDEX

Three-Tab Foldable® By Dinah Zike

Step 1 Fold a sheet of paper in half horizontally.

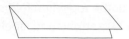

Step 2 Fold into thirds.

Step 3 Unfold and cut along the folds of the top flap to make three sections.

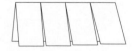

Variations

A Before cutting the three tabs draw a Venn diagram across the front of the book.

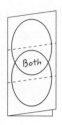

B Make a space to use for titles or concept maps by leaving a ½ inch tab at the top when folding the paper in half.

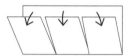

Four-Tab Foldable® By Dinah Zike

Step 1 Fold a sheet of paper in half horizontally.

Step 2 Fold in half and then fold each half as shown below.

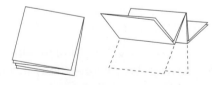

Step 3 Unfold and cut along the fold lines of the top flap to make four tabs.

Variations

A Make a space to use for titles or concept maps by leaving a ½ inch tab at the top when folding the paper in half.

B Use the book on the vertical axis, with or without an extended tab.

Folding Fifths for a Foldable® By Dinah Zike

Step 1 Fold a sheet of paper in half horizontally.

Step 2 Fold again so one-third of the paper is exposed and two-thirds are covered.

Step 3 Fold the two-thirds section in half.

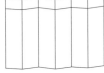

Step 4 Fold the one-third section, a single thickness, back-ward to make a fold line.

Variations

A Unfold and cut along the fold lines to make five tabs.

B Make a five-tab book with a ½ inch tab at the top (see two-tab instructions).

C Use 11″ × 17″ or 12″ × 18″ paper and fold into fifths for a five-column and/or row table or chart.

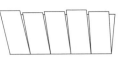

. . . .

Folded Table or Chart, and Trifold Foldable® By Dinah Zike

Step 1 Fold a sheet of paper in the required number of vertical columns for the table or chart.

Step 2 Fold the horizontal rows needed for the table or chart.

PROJECT FORMAT
Use 11″ × 17″ or 12″ × 18″ paper and fold it to make a large trifold project book or larger tables and charts.

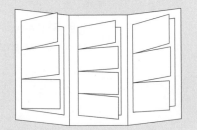

Variations

A Make a trifold by folding the paper into thirds vertically or horizontally.

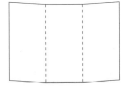

B Make a trifold book. Unfold it and draw a Venn diagram on the inside.

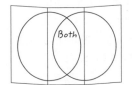

SCIENCE SKILL HANDBOOK

MATH SKILL HANDBOOK

FOLDABLES HANDBOOK

REFERENCE HANDBOOK

GLOSSARY/ GLOSARIO

INDEX

SCIENCE SKILL HANDBOOK

MATH SKILL HANDBOOK

FOLDABLES HANDBOOK

REFERENCE HANDBOOK

GLOSSARY/ GLOSARIO

INDEX

Two or Three-Pockets Foldable® By Dinah Zike

Step 1 Fold up the long side of a horizontal sheet of paper about 5 cm.

Step 2 Fold the paper in half.

Step 3 Open the paper and glue or staple the outer edges to make two compartments.

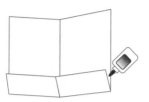

Variations

A Make a multi-page booklet by gluing several pocket books together.

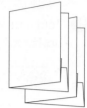

B Make a three-pocket book by using a trifold (see previous instructions).

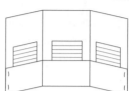

PROJECT FORMAT
Use 11" × 17" or 12" × 18" paper and fold it horizontally to make a large multi-pocket project.

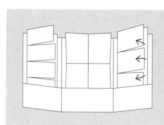

Matchbook Foldable® By Dinah Zike

Step 1 Fold a sheet of paper almost in half and make the back edge about 1–2 cm longer than the front edge.

Step 2 Find the midpoint of the shorter flap.

Step 3 Open the paper and cut the short side along the fold lines making two tabs.

Step 4 Close the book and fold the tab over the short side.

Variations

A Make a single-tab matchbook by skipping Steps 2 and 3.

B Make two smaller matchbooks by cutting the single-tab matchbook in half.

Shutterfold Foldable® By Dinah Zike

Step 1 Begin as if you were folding a vertical sheet of paper in half, but instead of creasing the paper, pinch it to show the midpoint.

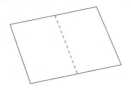

PROJECT FORMAT
Use 11" × 17" or 12" × 18" paper and fold it to make a large shutterfold project.

Step 2 Fold the top and bottom to the middle and crease the folds.

Variations

A Use the shutterfold on the horizontal axis.

B Create a center tab by leaving .5–2 cm between the flaps in Step 2.

Four-Door Foldable® By Dinah Zike

Step 1 Make a shutterfold (see above).

Step 2 Fold the sheet of paper in half.

Step 3 Open the last fold and cut along the inside fold lines to make four tabs.

Variations

A Use the four-door book on the opposite axis.

B Create a center tab by leaving .5–2 cm between the flaps in Step 1.

SCIENCE SKILL HANDBOOK

MATH SKILL HANDBOOK

FOLDABLES HANDBOOK

REFERENCE HANDBOOK

GLOSSARY/ GLOSARIO

INDEX

SCIENCE SKILL HANDBOOK

MATH SKILL HANDBOOK

FOLDABLES HANDBOOK

REFERENCE HANDBOOK

GLOSSARY/ GLOSARIO

INDEX

Bound Book Foldable® By Dinah Zike

Step 1 Fold three sheets of paper in half. Place the papers in a stack, leaving about .5 cm between each top fold. Mark all three sheets about 3 cm from the outer edges.

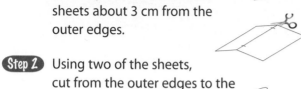

Step 2 Using two of the sheets, cut from the outer edges to the marked spots on each side. On the other sheet, cut between the marked spots.

Step 3 Take the two sheets from Step 1 and slide them through the cut in the third sheet to make a 12-page book.

Step 4 Fold the bound pages in half to form a book.

Variation

A Use two sheets of paper to make an eight-page book, or increase the number of pages by using more than three sheets.

PROJECT FORMAT

Use two or more sheets of 11" × 17" or 12" × 18" paper and fold it to make a large bound book project.

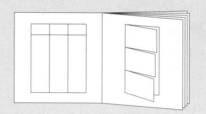

Accordian Foldable® By Dinah Zike

Step 1 Fold the selected paper in half vertically, like a *hamburger*.

Step 2 Cut each sheet of folded paper in half along the fold lines.

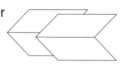

Step 3 Fold each half-sheet almost in half, leaving a 2 cm tab at the top.

Step 4 Fold the top tab over the short side, then fold it in the opposite direction.

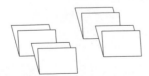

Variations

A Glue the straight edge of one paper inside the tab of another sheet. Leave a tab at the end of the book to add more pages.

B Tape the straight edge of one paper to the tab of another sheet, or just tape the straight edges of nonfolded paper end to end to make an accordian.

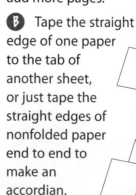

C Use whole sheets of paper to make a large accordian.

Layered Foldable® By Dinah Zike

Step 1 Stack two sheets of paper about 1–2 cm apart. Keep the right and left edges even.

Step 2 Fold up the bottom edges to to form four tabs. Crease the fold to hold the tabs in place.

Step 3 Staple along the folded edge, or open and glue the papers together at the fold line.

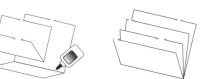

Variations

A Rotate the book so the fold is at the top or to the side.

B Extend the book by using more than two sheets of paper.

Envelope Foldable® By Dinah Zike

Step 1 Fold a sheet of paper into a *taco*. Cut off the tab at the top.

Step 2 Open the *taco* and fold it the opposite way making another *taco* and X-fold pattern on the sheet of paper.

Step 3 Cut a map, illustration or diagram to fit the inside of the envelope.

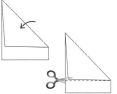

Step 4 Use the outside tabs for labels and inside tabs for writing information.

Variations

A Use 11″ × 17″ or 12″ × 18″ paper to make a large envelope.

B Cut off the points of the four tabs to make a window in the middle of the book.

SCIENCE SKILL HANDBOOK

MATH SKILL HANDBOOK

FOLDABLES HANDBOOK

REFERENCE HANDBOOK

GLOSSARY/ GLOSARIO

INDEX

Sentence Strip Foldable® By Dinah Zike

Step 1 Fold two sheets of paper in half vertically, like a *hamburger*.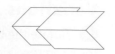

Step 2 Unfold and cut along fold lines making four half sheets.

Step 3 Fold each half sheet in half horizontally, like a *hotdog*.

Step 4 Stack folded horizontal sheets evenly and staple together on the left side.

Step 5 Open the top flap of the first sentence strip and make a cut about 2 cm from the stapled edge to the fold line. This forms a flap that can be raisied and lowered. Repeat this step for each sentence strip.

Variations

A Expand this book by using more than two sheets of paper.

B Use whole sheets of paper to make large books.

Pyramid Foldable® By Dinah Zike

Step 1 Fold a sheet of paper into a *taco*. Crease the fold line, but do not cut it off.

Step 2 Open the folded sheet and refold it like a *taco* in the opposite direction to create an X-fold pattern.

Step 3 Cut one fold line as shown, stopping at the center of the X-fold to make a flap.

Step 4 Outline the fold lines of the X-fold. Label the three front sections and use the inside spaces for notes. Use the tab for the title.

Step 5 Glue the tab into a project book or notebook. Use the space under the pyramid for other information.

Step 6 To display the pyramid, fold the flap under and secure with a paper clip, if needed.

SCIENCE SKILL HANDBOOK

MATH SKILL HANDBOOK

FOLDABLES HANDBOOK

REFERENCE HANDBOOK

GLOSSARY/ GLOSARIO

INDEX

Single-Pocket or One-Pocket Foldable® By Dinah Zike

Step 1 Using a large piece of paper on a vertical axis, fold the bottom edge of the paper upwards, about 5 cm.

Step 2 Glue or staple the outer edges to make a large pocket.

PROJECT FORMAT

Use 11" × 17" or 12" × 18" paper and fold it vertically or horizontally to make a large pocket project.

Variations

A Make the one-pocket project using the paper on the horizontal axis.

B To store materials securely inside, fold the top of the paper almost to the center, leaving about 2–4 cm between the paper edges. Slip the Foldables through the opening and under the top and bottom pockets.

- -

Multi-Tab Foldable® By Dinah Zike

Step 1 Fold a sheet of notebook paper in half like a *hotdog*.

Step 2 Open the paper and on one side cut every third line. This makes ten tabs on wide ruled notebook paper and twelve tabs on college ruled.

Step 3 Label the tabs on the front side and use the inside space for definitions, or other information.

Variation

A Make a tab for a title by folding the paper so the holes remain uncovered. This allows the notebook Foldable to be stored in a three-hole binder.

SCIENCE SKILL HANDBOOK

MATH SKILL HANDBOOK

FOLDABLES HANDBOOK

REFERENCE HANDBOOK

GLOSSARY/ GLOSARIO

INDEX

PERIODIC TABLE OF THE ELEMENTS

Element — Hydrogen
Atomic number — 1
Symbol — H
Atomic mass — 1.01
State of matter

🎈 Gas
💧 Liquid
⬜ Solid
⊙ Synthetic

A column in the periodic table is called a **group**.

A row in the periodic table is called a **period**.

1

1 Hydrogen 1 H 1.01 🎈

2 Lithium 3 Li 6.94 | Beryllium 4 Be 9.01

3 Sodium 11 Na 22.99 | Magnesium 12 Mg 24.31

	1	2	3	4	5	6	7	8	9
4			Scandium 21 Sc 44.96	Titanium 22 Ti 47.87	Vanadium 23 V 50.94	Chromium 24 Cr 52.00	Manganese 25 Mn 54.94	Iron 26 Fe 55.85	Cobalt 27 Co 58.93
5			Yttrium 39 Y 88.91	Zirconium 40 Zr 91.22	Niobium 41 Nb 92.91	Molybdenum 42 Mo 95.96	Technetium 43 Tc (98) ⊙	Ruthenium 44 Ru 101.07	Rhodium 45 Rh 102.91
6			Lanthanum 57 La 138.91	Hafnium 72 Hf 178.49	Tantalum 73 Ta 180.95	Tungsten 74 W 183.84	Rhenium 75 Re 186.21	Osmium 76 Os 190.23	Iridium 77 Ir 192.22
7			Actinium 89 Ac (227)	Rutherfordium 104 Rf (267) ⊙	Dubnium 105 Db (268) ⊙	Seaborgium 106 Sg (271) ⊙	Bohrium 107 Bh (272) ⊙	Hassium 108 Hs (270) ⊙	Meitnerium 109 Mt (276) ⊙

Potassium 19 K 39.10 | Calcium 20 Ca 40.08
Rubidium 37 Rb 85.47 | Strontium 38 Sr 87.62
Cesium 55 Cs 132.91 | Barium 56 Ba 137.33
Francium 87 Fr (223) | Radium 88 Ra (226)

The number in parentheses is the mass number of the longest lived isotope for that element.

Lanthanide series

Cerium 58 Ce 140.12	Praseodymium 59 Pr 140.91	Neodymium 60 Nd 144.24	Promethium 61 Pm (145) ⊙	Samarium 62 Sm 150.36	Europium 63 Eu 151.96

Actinide series

Thorium 90 Th 232.04	Protactinium 91 Pa 231.04	Uranium 92 U 238.03	Neptunium 93 Np (237) ⊙	Plutonium 94 Pu (244) ⊙	Americium 95 Am (243) ⊙

SCIENCE SKILL HANDBOOK
MATH SKILL HANDBOOK
FOLDABLES HANDBOOK
REFERENCE HANDBOOK
GLOSSARY/GLOSARIO
INDEX

Legend:
- Metal
- Metalloid
- Nonmetal
- Recently discovered

	13	14	15	16	17	18
						Helium 2 He 4.00
	Boron 5 B 10.81	Carbon 6 C 12.01	Nitrogen 7 N 14.01	Oxygen 8 O 16.00	Fluorine 9 F 19.00	Neon 10 Ne 20.18

10	11	12	13	14	15	16	17	18
			Aluminum 13 Al 26.98	Silicon 14 Si 28.09	Phosphorus 15 P 30.97	Sulfur 16 S 32.07	Chlorine 17 Cl 35.45	Argon 18 Ar 39.95
Nickel 28 Ni 58.69	Copper 29 Cu 63.55	Zinc 30 Zn 65.38	Gallium 31 Ga 69.72	Germanium 32 Ge 72.64	Arsenic 33 As 74.92	Selenium 34 Se 78.96	Bromine 35 Br 79.90	Krypton 36 Kr 83.80
Palladium 46 Pd 106.42	Silver 47 Ag 107.87	Cadmium 48 Cd 112.41	Indium 49 In 114.82	Tin 50 Sn 118.71	Antimony 51 Sb 121.76	Tellurium 52 Te 127.60	Iodine 53 I 126.90	Xenon 54 Xe 131.29
Platinum 78 Pt 195.08	Gold 79 Au 196.97	Mercury 80 Hg 200.59	Thallium 81 Tl 204.38	Lead 82 Pb 207.20	Bismuth 83 Bi 208.98	Polonium 84 Po (209)	Astatine 85 At (210)	Radon 86 Rn (222)
Darmstadtium 110 Ds (281)	Roentgenium 111 Rg (280)	Copernicium 112 Cn (285)	Ununtrium * 113 Uut (284)	Ununquadium * 114 Uuq (289)	Ununpentium * 115 Uup (288)	Ununhexium * 116 Uuh (293)		Ununoctium * 118 Uuo (294)

* The names and symbols for elements 113–116 and 118 are temporary. Final names will be selected when the elements' discoveries are verified.

Gadolinium 64 Gd 157.25	Terbium 65 Tb 158.93	Dysprosium 66 Dy 162.50	Holmium 67 Ho 164.93	Erbium 68 Er 167.26	Thulium 69 Tm 168.93	Ytterbium 70 Yb 173.05	Lutetium 71 Lu 174.97
Curium 96 Cm (247)	Berkelium 97 Bk (247)	Californium 98 Cf (251)	Einsteinium 99 Es (252)	Fermium 100 Fm (257)	Mendelevium 101 Md (258)	Nobelium 102 No (259)	Lawrencium 103 Lr (262)

SCIENCE SKILL HANDBOOK

MATH SKILL HANDBOOK

FOLDABLES HANDBOOK

REFERENCE HANDBOOK

GLOSSARY/ GLOSARIO

INDEX

Topographic Map Symbols

Topographic Map Symbols

━━━━━	Primary highway, hard surface	⌁⌁⌁	Index contour
▰▰▰	Secondary highway, hard surface	⋯⋯⋯	Supplementary contour
═══════	Light-duty road, hard or improved surface	⌁⌁	Intermediate contour
=========	Unimproved road	⬭	Depression contours
++++++	Railroad: single track		
+++++	Railroad: multiple track	━ ━ ━	Boundaries: national
+++++	Railroads in juxtaposition	━ ━ ━	State
		━ ━ ‥	County, parish, municipal
▪▃▄▅	Buildings	━ ━ ━	Civil township, precinct, town, barrio
♪♪ ⊞ cem	Schools, church, and cemetery	━ ‥ ━ ‥	Incorporated city, village, town, hamlet
▪▭ ▨▨	Buildings (barn, warehouse, etc.)	‥ ━ ‥ ━ ‥	Reservation, national or state
∘ ∘	Wells other than water (labeled as to type)	━━━━━	Small park, cemetery, airport, etc.
●●● ⊘	Tanks: oil, water, etc. (labeled only if water)	━ ‥ ━ ‥	Land grant
⊙ ⚐	Located or landmark object; windmill	━━━━━	Township or range line, U.S. land survey
⚒ ×	Open pit, mine, or quarry; prospect	━ ━ ━	Township or range line, approximate location
	Marsh (swamp)		
	Wooded marsh	⌁⌁	Perennial streams
	Woods or brushwood	→←	Elevated aqueduct
	Vineyard	∘ ∿	Water well and spring
	Land subject to controlled inundation	⌁⊬	Small rapids
	Submerged marsh	⌁	Large rapids
	Mangrove	▨▨▨	Intermittent lake
	Orchard	⌁ ⌁ ⌁	Intermittent stream
	Scrub	→==== ←	Aqueduct tunnel
	Urban area		Glacier
		⌁⊬	Small falls
x7369	Spot elevation	▨▨	Large falls
670	Water elevation		Dry lake bed

Rocks

Rocks

Rock Type	Rock Name	Characteristics
Igneous (intrusive)	Granite	Large mineral grains of quartz, feldspar, hornblende, and mica. Usually light in color.
	Diorite	Large mineral grains of feldspar, hornblende, and mica. Less quartz than granite. Intermediate in color.
	Gabbro	Large mineral grains of feldspar, augite, and olivine. No quartz. Dark in color.
Igneous (extrusive)	Rhyolite	Small mineral grains of quartz, feldspar, hornblende, and mica, or no visible grains. Light in color.
	Andesite	Small mineral grains of feldspar, hornblende, and mica or no visible grains. Intermediate in color.
	Basalt	Small mineral grains of feldspar, augite, and possibly olivine or no visible grains. No quartz. Dark in color.
	Obsidian	Glassy texture. No visible grains. Volcanic glass. Fracture looks like broken glass.
	Pumice	Frothy texture. Floats in water. Usually light in color.
Sedimentary (detrital)	Conglomerate	Coarse grained. Gravel or pebble-size grains.
	Sandstone	Sand-sized grains 1/16 to 2 mm.
	Siltstone	Grains are smaller than sand but larger than clay.
	Shale	Smallest grains. Often dark in color. Usually platy.
Sedimentary (chemical or organic)	Limestone	Major mineral is calcite. Usually forms in oceans and lakes. Often contains fossils.
	Coal	Forms in swampy areas. Compacted layers of organic material, mainly plant remains.
Sedimentary (chemical)	Rock Salt	Commonly forms by the evaporation of seawater.
Metamorphic (foliated)	Gneiss	Banding due to alternate layers of different minerals, of different colors. Parent rock often is granite.
	Schist	Parallel arrangement of sheetlike minerals, mainly micas. Forms from different parent rocks.
	Phyllite	Shiny or silky appearance. May look wrinkled. Common parent rocks are shale and slate.
	Slate	Harder, denser, and shinier than shale. Common parent rock is shale.
Metamorphic (nonfoliated)	Marble	Calcite or dolomite. Common parent rock is limestone.
	Soapstone	Mainly of talc. Soft with greasy feel.
	Quartzite	Hard with interlocking quartz crystals. Common parent rock is sandstone.

SCIENCE SKILL HANDBOOK

MATH SKILL HANDBOOK

FOLDABLES HANDBOOK

REFERENCE HANDBOOK

GLOSSARY/ GLOSARIO

INDEX

Minerals

Science Skill Handbook

Math Skill Handbook

Foldables Handbook

Reference Handbook

Glossary/ Glosario

Index

Minerals

Mineral (formula)	Color	Streak	Hardness Pattern	Breakage Properties	Uses and Other
Graphite (C)	black to gray	black to gray	1–1.5	basal cleavage (scales)	pencil lead, lubricants for locks, rods to control some small nuclear reactions, battery poles
Galena (PbS)	gray	gray to black	2.5	cubic cleavage perfect	source of lead, used for pipes, shields for X rays, fishing equipment sinkers
Hematite (Fe_2O_3)	black or reddish-brown	reddish-brown	5.5–6.5	irregular fracture	source of iron; converted to pig iron, made into steel
Magnetite (Fe_3O_4)	black	black	6	conchoidal fracture	source of iron, attracts a magnet
Pyrite (FeS_2)	light, brassy, yellow	greenish-black	6–6.5	uneven fracture	fool's gold
Talc ($Mg_3 Si_4O_{10} (OH)_2$)	white, greenish	white	1	cleavage in one direction	used for talcum powder, sculptures, paper, and tabletops
Gypsum ($CaSO_4 \cdot 2H_2O$)	colorless, gray, white, brown	white	2	basal cleavage	used in plaster of paris and dry wall for building construction
Sphalerite (ZnS)	brown, reddish-brown, greenish	light to dark brown	3.5–4	cleavage in six directions	main ore of zinc; used in paints, dyes, and medicine
Muscovite ($KAl_3Si_3 O_{10}(OH)_2$)	white, light gray, yellow, rose, green	colorless	2–2.5	basal cleavage	occurs in large, flexible plates; used as an insulator in electrical equipment, lubricant
Biotite ($K(Mg,Fe)_3 (AlSi_3O_{10}) (OH)_2$)	black to dark brown	colorless	2.5–3	basal cleavage	occurs in large, flexible plates
Halite (NaCl)	colorless, red, white, blue	colorless	2.5	cubic cleavage	salt; soluble in water; a preservative

Minerals

Mineral (formula)	Color	Streak	Hardness	Breakage Pattern	Uses and Other Properties
Calcite ($CaCO_3$)	colorless, white, pale blue	colorless, white	3	cleavage in three directions	fizzes when HCl is added; used in cements and other building materials
Dolomite ($CaMg(CO_3)_2$)	colorless, white, pink, green, gray, black	white	3.5–4	cleavage in three directions	concrete and cement; used as an ornamental building stone
Fluorite (CaF_2)	colorless, white, blue, green, red, yellow, purple	colorless	4	cleavage in four directions	used in the manufacture of optical equipment; glows under ultraviolet light
Hornblende ($(CaNa)_{2-3}$ $(Mg,Al,$ $Fe)_5-(Al,Si)_2$ Si_6O_{22} $(OH)_2)$	green to black	gray to white	5–6	cleavage in two directions	will transmit light on thin edges; 6-sided cross section
Feldspar ($KAlSi_3O_8$) ($NaAl$ Si_3O_8), ($CaAl_2Si_2$ O_8)	colorless, white to gray, green	colorless	6	two cleavage planes meet at 90° angle	used in the manufacture of ceramics
Augite ((Ca,Na) (Mg,Fe,Al) $(Al,Si)_2 O_6$)	black	colorless	6	cleavage in two directions	square or 8-sided cross section
Olivine ($(Mg,Fe)_2$ SiO_4)	olive, green	none	6.5–7	conchoidal fracture	gemstones, refractory sand
Quartz (SiO_2)	colorless, various colors	none	7	conchoidal fracture	used in glass manufacture, electronic equipment, radios, computers, watches, gemstones

SCIENCE SKILL HANDBOOK

MATH SKILL HANDBOOK

FOLDABLES HANDBOOK

REFERENCE HANDBOOK

GLOSSARY/ GLOSARIO

INDEX

Weather Map Symbols

SCIENCE SKILL HANDBOOK

MATH SKILL HANDBOOK

FOLDABLES HANDBOOK

REFERENCE HANDBOOK

GLOSSARY/ GLOSARIO

INDEX

Sample Station Model

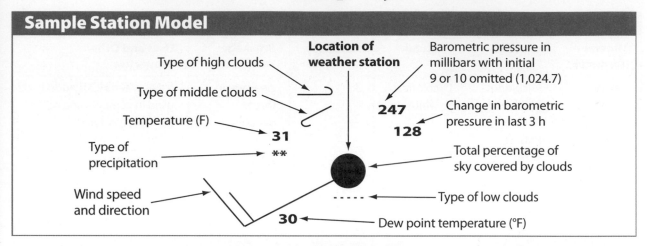

Type of high clouds

Type of middle clouds

Temperature (F) → **31**

Type of precipitation → **

Wind speed and direction

Location of weather station

Barometric pressure in millibars with initial 9 or 10 omitted (1,024.7)

247

Change in barometric pressure in last 3 h

128

Total percentage of sky covered by clouds

Type of low clouds

30 ← Dew point temperature (°F)

Sample Plotted Report at Each Station

Precipitation		Wind Speed and Direction		Sky Coverage		Some Types of High Clouds	
☰	Fog	◯	0 calm	◯	No cover	⌐	Scattered cirrus
★	Snow	╱	1–2 knots	◐	1/10 or less	⌐ɔ	Dense cirrus in patches
●	Rain	↘	3–7 knots	◕	2/10 to 3/10	⌐_ɔ	Veil of cirrus covering entire sky
⊼	Thunderstorm	↘	8–12 knots	◑	4/10	⌐ɔ	Cirrus not covering entire sky
'	Drizzle	↘	13–17 knots	◑	–		
▽	Showers	↘	18–22 knots	◕	6/10		
		↘	23–27 knots	◕	7/10		
		↘	48–52 knots	◑	Overcast with openings		
		1 knot = 1.852 km/h		●	Completely overcast		

Some Types of Middle Clouds		Some Types of Low Clouds		Fronts and Pressure Systems	
∠	Thin altostratus layer	⌒	Cumulus of fair weather	Ⓗ or High Ⓛ or Low	Center of high- or low-pressure system
⫽	Thick altostratus layer	⌣	Stratocumulus	▲▲▲▲	Cold front
⌒	Thin altostratus in patches	-----	Fractocumulus of bad weather	●●●●	Warm front
⌣	Thin altostratus in bands	—	Stratus of fair weather	▲●▲●	Occluded front
				●▲●▲	Stationary front

Use and Care of a Microscope

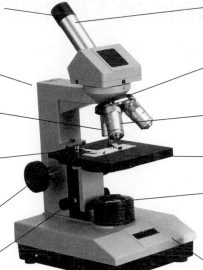

Eyepiece Contains magnifying lenses you look through.

Arm Supports the body tube.

Low-power objective Contains the lens with the lowest power magnification.

Stage clips Hold the microscope slide in place.

Coarse adjustment Focuses the image under low power.

Fine adjustment Sharpens the image under high magnification.

Body tube Connects the eyepiece to the revolving nosepiece.

Revolving nosepiece Holds and turns the objectives into viewing position.

High-power objective Contains the lens with the highest magnification.

Stage Supports the microscope slide.

Light source Provides light that passes upward through the diaphragm, the specimen, and the lenses.

Base Provides support for the microscope.

Caring for a Microscope

1. Always carry the microscope holding the arm with one hand and supporting the base with the other hand.
2. Don't touch the lenses with your fingers.
3. The coarse adjustment knob is used only when looking through the lowest-power objective lens. The fine adjustment knob is used when the high-power objective is in place.
4. Cover the microscope when you store it.

Using a Microscope

1. Place the microscope on a flat surface that is clear of objects. The arm should be toward you.
2. Look through the eyepiece. Adjust the diaphragm so light comes through the opening in the stage.
3. Place a slide on the stage so the specimen is in the field of view. Hold it firmly in place by using the stage clips.

4. Always focus with the coarse adjustment and the low-power objective lens first. After the object is in focus on low power, turn the nosepiece until the high-power objective is in place. Use ONLY the fine adjustment to focus with the high-power objective lens.

Making a Wet-Mount Slide

1. Carefully place the item you want to look at in the center of a clean, glass slide. Make sure the sample is thin enough for light to pass through.
2. Use a dropper to place one or two drops of water on the sample.
3. Hold a clean coverslip by the edges and place it at one edge of the water. Slowly lower the coverslip onto the water until it lies flat.
4. If you have too much water or a lot of air bubbles, touch the edge of a paper towel to the edge of the coverslip to draw off extra water and draw out unwanted air.

SCIENCE SKILL HANDBOOK

MATH SKILL HANDBOOK

FOLDABLES HANDBOOK

REFERENCE HANDBOOK

GLOSSARY/ GLOSARIO

INDEX

SCIENCE SKILL HANDBOOK
MATH SKILL HANDBOOK
FOLDABLES HANDBOOK
REFERENCE HANDBOOK
GLOSSARY/ GLOSARIO
INDEX

Diversity of Life: Classification of Living Organisms

A six-kingdom system of classification of organisms is used today. Two kingdoms—Kingdom Archaebacteria and Kingdom Eubacteria—contain organisms that do not have a nucleus and that lack membrane-bound structures in the cytoplasm of their cells. The members of the other four kingdoms have a cell or cells that contain a nucleus and structures in the cytoplasm, some of which are surrounded by membranes. These kingdoms are Kingdom Protista, Kingdom Fungi, Kingdom Plantae, and Kingdom Animalia.

Kingdom Archaebacteria

one-celled; some absorb food from their surroundings; some are photosynthetic; some are chemosynthetic; many are found in extremely harsh environments including salt ponds, hot springs, swamps, and deep-sea hydrothermal vents

Kingdom Eubacteria

one-celled; most absorb food from their surroundings; some are photosynthetic; some are chemosynthetic; many are parasites; many are round, spiral, or rod-shaped; some form colonies

Kingdom Protista

Phylum Euglenophyta one-celled; photosynthetic or take in food; most have one flagellum; euglenoids

Kingdom Eubacteria
Bacillus anthracis

Phylum Chlorophyta
Desmids

Phylum Bacillariophyta one-celled; photosynthetic; have unique double shells made of silica; diatoms

Phylum Dinoflagellata one-celled; photosynthetic; contain red pigments; have two flagella; dinoflagellates

Phylum Chlorophyta one-celled, many-celled, or colonies; photosynthetic; contain chlorophyll; live on land, in freshwater, or salt water; green algae

Phylum Rhodophyta most are many-celled; photosynthetic; contain red pigments; most live in deep, saltwater environments; red algae

Phylum Phaeophyta most are many-celled; photosynthetic; contain brown pigments; most live in saltwater environments; brown algae

Phylum Rhizopoda one-celled; take in food; are free-living or parasitic; move by means of pseudopods; amoebas

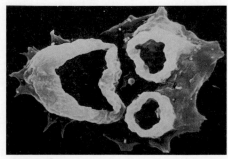

Amoeba

Phylum Zoomastigina one-celled; take in food; free-living or parasitic; have one or more flagella; zoomastigotes

Phylum Ciliophora one-celled; take in food; have large numbers of cilia; ciliates

Phylum Sporozoa one-celled; take in food; have no means of movement; are parasites in animals; sporozoans

Phylum Myxomycota
Slime mold

Phyla Myxomycota and Acrasiomycota one- or many-celled; absorb food; change form during life cycle; cellular and plasmodial slime molds

Phylum Oomycota many-celled; are either parasites or decomposers; live in freshwater or salt water; water molds, rusts and downy mildews

Kingdom Fungi

Phylum Zygomycota many-celled; absorb food; spores are produced in sporangia; zygote fungi; bread mold

Phylum Ascomycota one- and many-celled; absorb food; spores produced in asci; sac fungi; yeast

Phylum Basidiomycota many-celled; absorb food; spores produced in basidia; club fungi; mushrooms

Phylum Deuteromycota members with unknown reproductive structures; imperfect fungi; *Penicillium*

Phylum Mycophycota organisms formed by symbiotic relationship between an ascomycote or a basidiomycote and green alga or cyanobacterium; lichens

Phylum Oomycota
Phytophthora infestans

Lichens

SCIENCE SKILL HANDBOOK

MATH SKILL HANDBOOK

FOLDABLES HANDBOOK

REFERENCE HANDBOOK

GLOSSARY/ GLOSARIO

INDEX

SCIENCE SKILL HANDBOOK

MATH SKILL HANDBOOK

FOLDABLES HANDBOOK

REFERENCE HANDBOOK

GLOSSARY/ GLOSARIO

INDEX

Kingdom Plantae

Divisions Bryophyta (mosses), **Anthocerophyta** (hornworts), **Hepaticophyta** (liverworts), **Psilophyta** (whisk ferns) many-celled non-vascular plants; reproduce by spores produced in capsules; green; grow in moist, land environments

Division Lycophyta many-celled vascular plants; spores are produced in conelike structures; live on land; are photosynthetic; club mosses

Division Arthrophyta vascular plants; ribbed and jointed stems; scalelike leaves; spores produced in conelike structures; horsetails

Division Pterophyta vascular plants; leaves called fronds; spores produced in clusters of sporangia called sori; live on land or in water; ferns

Division Ginkgophyta deciduous trees; only one living species; have fan-shaped leaves with branching veins and fleshy cones with seeds; ginkgoes

Division Cycadophyta palmlike plants; have large, featherlike leaves; produces seeds in cones; cycads

Division Coniferophyta deciduous or evergreen; trees or shrubs; have needlelike or scalelike leaves; seeds produced in cones; conifers

Division Anthophyta
Tomato plant

Phylum Platyhelminthes
Flatworm

Division Gnetophyta shrubs or woody vines; seeds are produced in cones; division contains only three genera; gnetum

Division Anthophyta dominant group of plants; flowering plants; have fruits with seeds

Kingdom Animalia

Phylum Porifera aquatic organisms that lack true tissues and organs; are asymmetrical and sessile; sponges

Phylum Cnidaria radially symmetrical organisms; have a digestive cavity with one opening; most have tentacles armed with stinging cells; live in aquatic environments singly or in colonies; includes jellyfish, corals, hydra, and sea anemones

Phylum Platyhelminthes bilaterally symmetrical worms; have flattened bodies; digestive system has one opening; parasitic and free-living species; flatworms

Division Bryophyta
Liverwort

Phylum Chordata

Phylum Nematoda round, bilaterally symmetrical body; have digestive system with two openings; free-living forms and parasitic forms; roundworms

Phylum Mollusca soft-bodied animals, many with a hard shell and soft foot or footlike appendage; a mantle covers the soft body; aquatic and terrestrial species; includes clams, snails, squid, and octopuses

Phylum Annelida bilaterally symmetrical worms; have round, segmented bodies; terrestrial and aquatic species; includes earthworms, leeches, and marine polychaetes

Phylum Arthropoda largest animal group; have hard exoskeletons, segmented bodies, and pairs of jointed appendages; land and aquatic species; includes insects, crustaceans, and spiders

Phylum Echinodermata marine organisms; have spiny or leathery skin and a water-vascular system with tube feet; are radially symmetrical; includes sea stars, sand dollars, and sea urchins

Phylum Chordata organisms with internal skeletons and specialized body systems; most have paired appendages; all at some time have a notochord, nerve cord, gill slits, and a post-anal tail; include fish, amphibians, reptiles, birds, and mammals

SCIENCE SKILL HANDBOOK

MATH SKILL HANDBOOK

FOLDABLES HANDBOOK

REFERENCE HANDBOOK

GLOSSARY/ GLOSARIO

INDEX

Glossary/Glosario

Cómo usar el glosario en español:
1. Busca el término en inglés que desees encontrar.
2. El término en español, junto con la definición, se encuentran en la columna de la derecha.

Pronunciation Key

Use the following key to help you sound out words in the glossary.

a . . . . back (BAK)	ew . . . . food (FEWD)
ay . . . . day (DAY)	yoo . . . . pure (PYOOR)
ah . . . . father (FAH thur)	yew . . . . few (FYEW)
ow . . . . flower (FLOW ur)	uh . . . . comma (CAH muh)
ar . . . . car (CAR)	u (+ con) . . . . rub (RUB)
e . . . . less (LES)	sh . . . . shelf (SHELF)
ee . . . . leaf (LEEF)	ch . . . . nature (NAY chur)
ih . . . . trip (TRIHP)	g . . . . gift (GIHFT)
i (i + com + e) idea (i DEE uh)	j . . . . gem (JEM)
oh . . . . go (GOH)	ing . . . . sing (SING)
aw . . . . soft (SAWFT)	zh . . . . vision (VIH zhun)
or . . . . orbit (OR buht)	k . . . . cake (KAYK)
oy . . . . coin (COYN)	s . . . . seed, cent (SEED, SENT)
oo . . . . foot (FOOT)	z . . . . zone, raise (ZOHN, RAYZ)

| English | Ⓐ | Español |

asteroid/binomial nomenclature

asteroide/nomenclatura binomial

asteroid: a small, rocky object that orbits the Sun. (p. 109)

astronomical unit: the average distance from Earth to the Sun—about 150 million km. (p. 110)

autotroph (AW tuh trohf): an organism that converts light energy to usable energy. (p. 154)

asteroide: objeto pequeño y rocoso que orbita el Sol. (pág. 109)

unidad astronómica: distancia media entre la Tierra y el Sol, aproximadamente 150 millones de km. (pág. 110)

autotrófo: organismo que convierte la energía lumínica en energía útil. (pág. 154)

Ⓑ

binomial nomenclature (bi NOH mee ul • NOH mun klay chur): a naming system that gives each organism a two-word scientific name. (p. 156)

nomenclatura binomial: sistema de nombrar que le da a cada organismo un nombre científico de dos palabras. (pág. 156)

SCIENCE SKILL HANDBOOK

MATH SKILL HANDBOOK

FOLDABLES HANDBOOK

REFERENCE HANDBOOK

GLOSSARY/ GLOSARIO

INDEX

biome: a geographic area on Earth that contains ecosystems with similar biotic and abiotic features. (p. 205)

biosphere (BI uh sfihr): the parts of Earth and the surrounding atmosphere where there is life. (p. 205)

biotic potential: the potential growth of a population if it could grow in perfect conditions with no limiting factors. (p. 208)

birthrate: the number of offspring produced by a population over a given time period. (p. 213)

bioma: área geográfica en la Tierra que contiene ecosistemas con características bióticas y abióticas similares. (pág. 205)

biosfera: partes de la Tierra y de la atmósfera que la rodea donde hay vida. (pág. 205)

potencial biótico: crecimiento potencial de una población si esta puede crecer en condiciones perfectas sin factores limitantes. (pág. 208)

tasa de nacimientos: número de crías que tiene una población durante un período de tiempo dado. (pág. 213)

C

carrying capacity: the largest number of individuals of one species that an ecosystem can support over time. (p. 209)

chemical change: a change in matter in which the substances that make up the matter change into other substances with different chemical and physical properties. (p. 24)

chemical property: the ability or inability of a substance to combine with or change into one or more new substances. (p. 15)

climax community: a stable community that no longer goes through major ecological changes. (p. 225)

comet: a small, rocky and icy object that orbits the Sun. (p. 109)

commensalism: a symbiotic relationship that benefits one species but does not harm or benefit the other. (p. 228)

community: all the populations living in an ecosystem at the same time. (p. 206)

competition: the demand for resources, such as food, water, and shelter, in short supply in a community. (p. 207)

consumer: an organism that cannot make its own food and gets energy by eating other organisms. (p. 224)

coral reef: an underwater structure made from outside skeletons of tiny, soft-bodied animals called coral. (p. 221)

capacidad de carga: número mayor de individuos de una especie que un medioambiente puede mantener. (pág. 209)

cambio químico: cambio de la materia en el cual las sustancias que componen la materia se transforman en otras sustancias con propiedades químicas y físicas diferentes. (pág. 24)

propiedad química: capacidad o incapacidad de una sustancia para combinarse con una o más sustancias o transformarse en una o más sustancias. (pág. 15)

comunidad clímax: comunidad estable que ya no sufrirá mayores cambios ecológicos. (pág. 225)

cometa: objeto pequeño, rocoso y helado que orbita el Sol. (pág. 109)

comensalismo: relación simbiótica que beneficia a una especie pero no causa daño ni beneficia a la otra. (pág. 228)

comunidad: todas las poblaciones que viven en un ecosistema, al mismo tiempo. (pág. 206)

competición: demanda de recursos, tales como alimento, agua y refugio, cuyo suministro es escaso en una comunidad. (pág. 207)

consumidor: organismo que no puede hacer sus propios alimentos y obtiene energía comiendo otros organismos. (pág. 224)

arrecife de coral: estructura bajo el agua formada por exoesqueletos de animales diminutos y de cuerpo blando. (pág. 221)

critical thinking: comparing what you already know with information you are given in order to decide whether you agree with it. (p. NOS 8)

cytoplasm: the liquid part of a cell inside the cell membrane; contains salts and other molecules. (p. 164)

pensamiento crítico: comparación que se hace cuando se sabe algo acerca de información nueva, y se decide si se está o no de acuerdo con ella. (pág. NOS 8)

citoplasma: fluido en el interior de una célula que contiene sales y otras moléculas. (pág. 164)

D

death rate: the number of individuals in a population that die over a given time period. (p. 213)

density: the mass per unit volume of a substance. (p. 13)

dependent variable: the factor a scientist observes or measures during an experiment. (p. NOS 19)

description: a spoken or written summary of observations. (p. NOS 10)

desert: a biome that receives very little rain. (p. 206)

tasa de mortalidad: número de individuos que mueren en una población en un período de tiempo dado. (pág. 213)

densidad: cantidad de masa por unidad de volumen de una sustancia. (pág. 13)

variable dependiente: factor que el científico observa o mide durante un experimento. (pág. NOS 19)

descripción: resumen oral o escrito de las observaciones. (pág. NOS 10)

desierto: bioma que recibe muy poca lluvia. (pág. 206)

E

ecological succession: the process of one ecological community gradually changing into another. (p. 225)

electric energy: energy carried by an electric current. (p. 45)

endangered species: a species whose population is at risk of extinction. (p. 215)

energy: the ability to cause change. (p. 41)

equinox: when Earth's rotation axis is tilted neither toward nor away from the Sun. (p. 77)

estuary (ES chuh wer ee): a coastal area where freshwater from rivers and streams mixes with salt water from seas or oceans. (p. 219)

eukaryotic (yew ker ee AH tihk) cell: a cell that has a nucleus and other membrane-bound organelles. (p. 162)

eutrophication (yoo troh fuh KAY shun): the process of a body of water becoming nutrient-rich. (p. 228)

explanation: an interpretation of observations. (p. NOS 10)

sucesión ecológica: proceso en el que una comunidad ecológica cambia gradualmente en otra. (pág. 225)

energía eléctrica: energía transportada por una corriente eléctrica. (pág. 45)

especie en peligro: especie cuya población se encuentra en riesgo de extinción. (pág. 215)

energía: capacidad de ocasionar cambio. (pág. 41)

equinoccio: cuando el eje de rotación de la Tierra se inclina sin acercarse ni alejarse del Sol. (pág. 77)

estuario: zona costera donde el agua dulce de los ríos y arroyos se mezcla con el agua salada de los mares y los océanos. (pág. 219)

célula eucariótica: célula que tiene un núcleo y otros organelos limitados por una membrana. (pág. 162)

eutrofización: proceso por el cual un cuerpo de agua se vuelve rico en nutrientes. (pág. 228)

explicación: interpretación de las observaciones. (pág. NOS 10)

extinct species: a species that has died out and no individuals are left. (p. 215)

especie extinta: especie que ha dejado de existir y no quedan individuos de ella. (pág. 215)

F

friction: a contact force that resists the sliding motion of two surfaces that are touching. (p. 51)

fricción: fuerza que resiste el movimiento de dos superficies que están en contacto. (pág. 51)

G

Galilean moons: the four largest of Jupiter's 63 moons; discovered by Galileo. (p. 125)

lunas de Galileo: las cuatro lunas más grandes de las 63 lunas de Júpiter; descubiertas por Galileo. (pág. 125)

gas: matter that has no definite volume and no definite shape. (p. 10)

gas: materia que no tiene volumen ni forma definidos. (pág. 10)

grassland: a biome where grasses are the dominant plants. (p. 207)

pradera: bioma donde los pastos son las plantas dominantes. (pág. 207)

greenhouse effect: the natural process that occurs when certain gases in the atmosphere absorb and reradiate thermal energy from the Sun. (p. 117)

efecto invernadero: proceso natural que ocurre cuando ciertos gases en la atmósfera absorben y vuelven a irradiar la energía térmica del Sol. (pág. 117)

H

habitat: the place within an ecosystem where an organism lives; provides the biotic and abiotic factors an organism needs to survive and reproduce. (pp. 155, 223)

hábitat: lugar en un ecosistema donde vive un organismo; proporciona los factores bióticos y abióticos de un organismo necesita para sobrevivir y reproducirse. (pág. 155, 223)

heterotroph (HE tuh roh trohf): an organism that obtains energy from other organisms. (p. 154)

heterótrofo: organismo que obtiene energía de otros organismos. (pág. 154)

hypothesis: a possible explanation for an observation that can be tested by scientific investigations. (p. NOS 4)

hipótesis: explicación posible de una observación que se puede probar por medio de investigaciones científicas. (pág. NOS 4)

I

impact crater: a round depression formed on the surface of a planet, moon, or other space object by the impact of a meteorite. (p. 134)

cráter de impacto: depresión redonda formada en la superficie de un planeta, luna u otro objeto espacial debido al impacto de un meteorito. (pág. 134)

independent variable: the factor that is changed by the investigator to observe how it affects a dependent variable. (p. NOS 15)

variable independiente: factor que el investigador cambia para observar cómo afecta la variable dependiente. (pág. NOS 15)

inference: a logical explanation of an observation that is drawn from prior knowledge or experience. (p. NOS 4)

inferencia: explicación lógica de una observación que se extrae de un conocimiento previo o experiencia. (pág. NOS 4)

SCIENCE SKILL HANDBOOK

MATH SKILL HANDBOOK

FOLDABLES HANDBOOK

REFERENCE HANDBOOK

GLOSSARY/ GLOSARIO

INDEX

International System of Units (SI): the internationally accepted system of measurement. (p. NOS 10)

intertidal zone: the ocean shore between the lowest low tide and the highest high tide. (p. 221)

Sistema Internacional de Unidades (SI): sistema de medidas aceptado internacionalmente. (pág. NOS 10)

zona intermareal: playa en medio de la marea baja más baja y la marea alta más alta. (pág. 221)

kinetic (kuh NEH tik) energy: energy due to motion. (p. 42)

energía cinética: energía debida al movimiento. (pág. 42)

law of conservation of energy: law that states that energy can be transformed from one form to another, but it cannot be created or destroyed. (p. 50)

law of conservation of mass: law that states that the total mass of the reactants before a chemical reaction is the same as the total mass of the products after the chemical reaction. (p. 27)

limiting factor: a factor that can limit the growth of a population. (p. 207)

liquid: matter with a definite volume but no definite shape. (p. 10)

lunar eclipse: an occurrence during which the Moon moves into Earth's shadow. (p. 92)

ley de la conservación de la energía: ley que plantea que la energía puede transformarse de una forma a otra, pero no puede crearse ni destruirse. (pág. 50)

ley de la conservación de la masa: ley que plantea que la masa total de los reactivos antes de una reacción química es la misma que la masa total de los productos después de la reacción química. (pág. 27)

factor limitante: factor que puede limitar el crecimiento de una población. (pág. 207)

líquido: materia con volumen definido y forma indefinida. (pág. 10)

eclipse lunar: ocurrencia durante la cual la Luna se mueve hacia la zona de sombra de la Tierra. (pág. 92)

maria (MAR ee uh): the large, dark, flat areas on the Moon. (p. 82)

mass: the amount of matter in an object. (p. 12)

mechanical energy: sum of the potential energy and the kinetic energy in a system. (p. 45)

meteor: a meteoroid that has entered Earth's atmosphere and produces a streak of light. (p. 134)

meteorite: a meteoroid that strikes a planet or a moon. (p. 134)

meteoroid: a small rocky particle that moves through space. (p. 134)

migration: the instinctive, seasonal movement of a population of organisms from one place to another. (p. 216)

mares: áreas extensas, oscuras y planas en la Luna. (pág. 82)

masa: cantidad de materia en un objeto. (pág. 12)

energía mecánica: suma de la energía potencial y la energía cinética en un sistema. (pág. 45)

meteoro: meteorito que ha entrado a la atmósfera de la Tierra y produce un haz de luz. (pág. 134)

meteorito: meteoroide que impacta un planeta o una luna. (pág. 134)

meteoroide: partícula rocosa pequeña que se mueve por el espacio. (pág. 134)

migración: movimiento instintivo de temporada de una población de organismos de un lugar a otro. (pág. 216)

SCIENCE SKILL HANDBOOK

MATH SKILL HANDBOOK

FOLDABLES HANDBOOK

REFERENCE HANDBOOK

GLOSSARY/ GLOSARIO

INDEX

mitochondrion (mi tuh KAHN dree ahn): an organelle that breaks down food and releases energy. (p. 165)

mutualism: a symbiotic relationship in which both organisms benefit. (p. 227)

niche (NICH): the way a species interacts with abiotic and biotic factors to obtain food, find shelter, and fulfill other needs. (p. 223)

nuclear energy: energy stored in and released from the nucleus of an atom. (p. 45)

observation: the act of using one or more of your senses to gather information and take note of what occurs. (p. NOS 4)

orbit: the path an object follows as it moves around another object. (p. 72)

parasitism: a symbiotic relationship in which one organism benefits and the other is harmed. (p. 228)

penumbra: the lighter part of a shadow where light is partially blocked. (p. 89)

period of revolution: the time it takes an object to travel once around the Sun. (p. 110)

period of rotation: the time it takes an object to complete one rotation. (p. 110)

phase: the lit part of the Moon or a planet that can be seen from Earth. (p. 84)

photoperiodism: a plant's response to the number of hours of darkness in its environment. (p. 190)

photosynthesis (foh toh SIHN thuh sus): a series of chemical reactions that convert light energy, water, and carbon dioxide into the food-energy molecule glucose and give off oxygen. (p. 180)

mitocondria: organelo que descompone el alimento y libera energía. (pág. 165)

mutualismo: relación simbiótica en la cual los dos organismos se benefician. (pág. 227)

nicho: forma de una especie interacciona con los factores abióticos y bióticos para obtener comida, encontrar refugio, y satisfacer otras necesidades. (pág. 223)

energía nuclear: energía almacenada en y liberada por el núcleo de un átomo. (pág. 45)

observación: acción de usar uno o más sentidos para reunir información y tomar notar de lo que ocurre. (pág. NOS 4)

órbita: trayectoria que un objeto sigue a medida que se mueve alrededor de otro objeto. (pág. 72)

parasitismo: relación simbiótica en la cual se perjudica organismo se beneficia y el otro. (pág. 228)

penumbra: parte más clara de una sombra donde la luz se bloquea parcialmente. (pág. 89)

período de revolución: tiempo que gasta un objeto en dar una vuelta alrededor del Sol. (pág. 110)

período de rotación: tiempo que gasta un objeto para completar una rotación. (pág. 110)

fase: parte iluminada de la Luna o de un planeta que se ve desde la Tierra. (pág. 84)

fotoperiodismo: respuesta de una planta al número de horas de oscuridad en su medioambiente. (pág. 190)

fotosíntesis: serie de reacciones químicas que convierte la energía lumínica, el agua y el dióxido de carbono en glucosa, una molécula de energía alimentaria, y producen oxígeno. (pág. 180)

SCIENCE SKILL HANDBOOK

MATH SKILL HANDBOOK

FOLDABLES HANDBOOK

REFERENCE HANDBOOK

GLOSSARY/GLOSARIO

INDEX

physical change: a change in the size, shape, form, or state of matter that does not change the matter's identity. (p. 22)

physical property: a characteristic of matter that you can observe or measure without changing the identity of the matter. (p. 12)

pioneer species: the first species that colonizes new or undisturbed land. (p. 226)

plant hormone: a substance that acts as a chemical messenger within a plant. (p. 191)

population: all the organisms of the same species that live in the same area at the same time. (p. 206)

population density: the size of a population compared to the amount of space available. (p. 208)

potential (puh TEN chul) energy: stored energy due to the interactions between objects or particles. (p. 42)

prediction: a statement of what will happen next in a sequence of events. (p. NOS 4)

producer: an organism that uses an outside energy source, such as the Sun, and produces its own food. (p. 224)

prokaryotic (pro kayr ee AH tihk) cell: a cell that does not have a nucleus or other membrane-bound organelles. (p. 162)

cambio físico: cambio en el tamaño, la forma o estado de la materia en el que no cambia la identidad de la materia. (pág. 22)

propiedad física: característica de la materia que puede observarse o medirse sin cambiar la identidad de la materia. (pág. 12)

especie pionera: primera especie que coloniza tierra nueva o tierra virgen. (pág. 226)

fitohormona: sustancia que actúa como mensajero químico dentro de una planta. (pág. 191)

población: todos los organismos de la misma especie que viven en la misma área al mismo tiempo. (pág. 206)

densidad poblacional: tamaño de una población comparado con la cantidad de espacio disponible. (pág. 208)

energía potencia: energía almacenada debido a las interacciones entre objetos o partículas. (pág. 42)

predicción: afirmación de lo que ocurrirá después en una secuencia de eventos. (pág. NOS 4)

productor: organismo que utiliza una fuente de energía exterior, como el Sol, y produce sus propios alimentos. (pág. 224)

célula procariota: célula que no tiene núcleo ni otros organelos limitados por una membrana. (pág. 162)

R

radiant energy: energy carried by an electromagnetic wave. (p. 45)

revolution: the orbit of one object around another object. (p. 72)

rotation: the spin of an object around its axis. (p. 73)

rotation axis: the line on which an object rotates. (p. 73)

energía radiante: energía que transporta una onda electromagnética. (pág. 45)

revolución: movimiento de un objeto alrededor de otro objeto. (pág. 72)

rotación: movimiento giratorio de un objeto sobre su eje. (pág. 73)

eje de rotación: línea sobre la cual un objeto rota. (pág. 73)

S

salinity (say LIH nuh tee): a measure of the mass of dissolved salts in a mass of water. (p. 215)

salinidad: medida de la masa de sales disueltas en una masa de agua. (pág. 215)

science: the investigation and exploration of natural events and of the new information that results from those investigations. (p. NOS 2)

scientific law: a rule that describes a pattern in nature. (p. NOS 7)

scientific theory: an explanation of observations or events that is based on knowledge gained from many observations and investigations. (p. NOS 7)

significant digits: the number of digits in a measurement that are known with a certain degree of reliability. (p. NOS 12)

solar eclipse: an occurrence during which the Moon's shadow appears on Earth's surface. (p. 90)

solid: matter that has a definite shape and a definite volume. (p. 10)

solstice: when Earth's rotation axis is tilted directly toward or away from the Sun. (p. 77)

solubility (sahl yuh BIH luh tee): the maximum amount of solute that can dissolve in a given amount of solvent at a given temperature and pressure. (p. 14)

sound energy: energy carried by sound waves. (p. 45)

stimulus: any change in an organism's environment that causes a response. (p. 187)

symbiosis (sihm bee OH sus): a close, long-term relationship between two species that usually involves an exchange of food or energy. (p. 227)

ciencia: la investigación y exploración de los eventos naturales y de la información nueva que es el resultado de estas investigaciones. (pág. NOS 2)

ley científica: regla que describe un patrón dado en la naturaleza. (pág. NOS 7)

teoría científica: explicación de observaciones o eventos con base en conocimiento obtenido de muchas observaciones e investigaciones. (pág. NOS 7)

cifras significativas: número de dígitos que se conoce con cierto grado de fiabilidad en una medida. (pág. NOS 12)

eclipse solar: acontecimiento durante el cual la sombra de la Luna aparece sobre la superficie de la Tierra. (pág. 90)

sólido: materia con forma y volumen definidos. (pág. 10)

solsticio: cuando el eje de rotación de la Tierra se inclina acercándose o alejándose del Sol. (pág. 77)

solubilidad: cantidad máxima de soluto que puede disolverse en una cantidad dada de solvente a temperatura y presión dadas. (pág. 14)

energía sonora: energía que transportan las ondas sonoras. (pág. 45)

estímulo: cualquier cambio en el medioambiente de un organismo que causa una respuesta. (pág. 187)

simbiosis: relación intrínseca a largo plazo entre dos especies que generalmente involucra intercambio de alimento o energía. (pág. 227)

T

taiga (TI guh): a forest biome consisting mostly of cone-bearing evergreen trees. (p. 211)

taxon: a group of organisms. (p. 157)

technology: the practical use of scientific knowledge, especially for industrial or commercial use. (p. NOS 6)

temperate: the term describing any region of Earth between the tropics and the polar circles. (p. 209)

taiga: bioma de bosque constituido en su mayoría por coníferas perennes. (pág. 211)

taxón: grupo de organismos. (pág. 157)

tecnología: uso práctico del conocimiento científico, especialmente para uso industrial o comercial. (pág. NOS 6)

temperatura: término que describe cualquier región de la Tierra entre los trópicos y los círculos polares. (pág. 209)

SCIENCE SKILL HANDBOOK

MATH SKILL HANDBOOK

FOLDABLES HANDBOOK

REFERENCE HANDBOOK

GLOSSARY/GLOSARIO

INDEX

SCIENCE SKILL HANDBOOK

MATH SKILL HANDBOOK

FOLDABLES HANDBOOK

REFERENCE HANDBOOK

GLOSSARY/GLOSARIO

INDEX

terrestrial planets: Earth and the other inner planets that are closest to the Sun including Mercury, Venus, and Mars. (p. 115)

thermal energy: the sum of the kinetic energy and the potential energy of the particles that make up an object. (p. 45)

threatened species: a species at risk, but not yet endangered. (p. 215)

tide: the periodic rise and fall of the ocean's surface caused by the gravitational force between Earth and the Moon, and Earth and the Sun. (p. 93)

tropism: plant growth toward or away from an external stimulus. (p. 188)

tundra (TUN druh): a biome that is cold, dry, and treeless. (p. 211)

planetas terrestres: la Tierra y otros planetas interiores que están más cerca del Sol, incluidos Mercurio, Venus y Marte. (pág. 115)

energía térmica: suma de la energía cinética y potencial de las partículas que componen un objeto. (pág. 45)

especie amenazada: especie en riesgo, pero que todavía no está en peligro. (pág. 215)

marea: ascenso y descenso periódico de la superficie del océano causados por la fuerza gravitacional entre la Tierra y la Luna, y entre la Tierra y el Sol. (pág. 93)

tropismo: crecimiento de una planta hacia o alejado de un estímulo externo. (pág. 188)

tundra: bioma frío, seco y sin árboles. (pág. 211)

U

umbra: the central, darker part of a shadow where light is totally blocked. (p. 89)

umbra: parte central más oscura de una sombra donde la luz está completamente bloqueada. (pág. 89)

V

variable: any factor that can have more than one value. (p. NOS 19)

volume: the amount of space a sample of matter occupies. (p. 10)

variable: cualquier factor que tenga más de un valor. (pág. NOS 19)

volumen: cantidad de espacio que ocupa la materia. (pág. 10)

W

waning phases: phases of the Moon during which less of the Moon's near side is lit each night. (p. 84)

waxing phases: phases of the Moon during which more of the Moon's near side is lit each night. (p. 84)

wetland: an aquatic ecosystem that has a thin layer of water covering soil that is wet most of the time. (p. 218)

work: the amount of energy used as a force moves an object over a distance. (p. 44)

fases menguantes: fases de la Luna durante las cuales el lado cercano de la Luna está menos iluminado cada noche. (pág. 84)

fases crecientes: fases de la Luna durante las cuales el lado cercano de la Luna está más iluminado cada noche. (pág. 84)

humedal: ecosistema acuático que tiene una capa delgada de suelo cubierto de agua que permanece húmedo la mayor parte del tiempo. (pág. 218)

trabajo: cantidad de energía usada como fuerza que mueve un objeto a cierta distancia. (pág. 44)

Index

Italic numbers = illustration/photo **Bold numbers = vocabulary term**
lab = indicates entry is used in a lab on this page

A

Abiotic factors
in aquatic ecosystems, 239
Academic Vocabulary, NOS 11,
26, 74,152, 182, 217. *See also*
Vocabulary
Accretion hypothesis
explanation of, 113
Altiplano flamingos, 211. *See also*
Flamingos
Amoebas
explanation of, 152
Anemometer, NOS 20, *NOS 20*
Apollo Space Program, 87
Aquatic ecosystems
estuary, 255, **255**
explanation of, 251
freshwater, 251 *lab*, 252, 252–253, *253*
ocean, 251 *lab*, *256*, 256–257, *257*
wetland, 254, **254**
Aquatic succession
explanation of, 264, *264*
Arengo, Felicity, 211
Armstrong, Neil, 87
Asexual reproduction
explanation of, 153
Asteroids
explanation of, **109**, *109*, 132
formation of, 113, 131 *lab*
Astronauts, 87
Astronomical unit (AU)
explanation of, **110**
Astrophysicists
explanation of, 129
Atmosphere
of Earth, 118
ATP (adenosine triphosphate), 182,
183
explanation of, 165
Autotrophs
explanation of, 154, **154**
Auxins
explanation of, 191, *191*

B

Bacteria
characteristics of, 161 *lab*
as chemoautotrophs, 154
explanation of, 152, 162
photosynthesis in, 183
Beakers, NOS 18, *NOS 18*
Big Idea, NOS 2, NOS 32, 6, 32, 38, 58,
68, 98, 104, 138, 148, 170, 176,
196, 202, 232, 238, 268
Review, NOS 33, 35, 61, 101, 141,
173, 199, 235, 271

Binoculars, NOS 20, *NOS 20*
Binomial nomenclature
explanation of, 156, *156*
Biodiversity
in deserts, 242
in estuaries, 255
in freshwater ecosystems, 252, 253
in grasslands, 243
in oceans, 256, 257
in taiga, 247
in temperate deciduous forests, 246
in temperate rain forests, 245
in tropical rain forests, 244
in tundra, 247
in wetlands, 254
Biomes. *See also* **Aquatic ecosystems;
Ecosystems; Land biomes**
explanation of, 241, **241**
modeling of, 266–267 *lab*
Biosphere
ecological systems and, 205
example of, 206, *206*
explanation of, 203, 205
Biotic potential,
explanation of, 208
Birthrate,
explanation of, 213
population size and, 221 *lab*
Boiling point
explanation of, 14
separation by, *17*
Boxer crabs, 227, *227*
Brumbaugh, Dan, 259

C

Callisto, 125
Canis, 157
Carbohydrates
in cells, 162
energy from, 154
explanation of, 152
produced by photosynthesis, 165
Carbon dioxide
deforestation and, 185
energy use and, 55
as greenhouse gas, 185
in plants, 179, 180, 181, *181*, 183, *183*
on Venus, 117
Careers in Science, 113, 129, 159, 211
Carnations, 190, *190*
Carnivores
method of obtaining energy by, 224
Carrying capacity
of Earth, 217
explanation of, 209
Cassini orbiter, 126
Cell membrane
explanation of, 163, *163*

Cell wall
explanation of, 163, *163*
Cells
activities of, 164
cytoplasm in, 164
explanation of, 153, 161
macromolecules in, 152, 162
storage in, 166, *166*
substances in, 162, 164
types of, 162
Cellular respiration
energy release during, 182
explanation of, 182, 183
importance of, 182
observation of, 182 *lab*
photosynthesis v., 183, *183*
Ceres
discovery of, 131
as dwarf planet, 131, 132, *132*
explanation of, 109, *109*, 129, *131*
Chapter Review, NOS 32–NOS 33,
34–35, 60–61, 100–101, 140–141,
172–173, 198–199, 234–235,
270–271
Chemical change
energy and, 26, *26*
explanation of, **24**
physical change v., 28, *28*
signs of, *24*, 24–25, *25*
Chemical energy
light energy converted to, 154
use of, 52, 53, *53*
Chemical potential energy, 43
Chemical properties
categories of, 15
explanation of, 15
observation of, 21 *lab*
Chemical stimuli
plant responses to, *191*, 191–192,
192
Chemoautotrophs
explanation of, 154
Chlorophyll
distribution of, 205, *205*
explanation of, 181, *181*
Chloroplasts
explanation of, 165, 180, *180*, 181
Chondrite meteorites
explanation of, 113
Chondrules
explanation of, 113
Classes
explanation of, 157
Climate
in China, 241 *lab*
Climate change
carbon dioxide in atmosphere and,
55
deforestation and, 185

Science Skill Handbook · Math Skill Handbook · Foldables Handbook · Reference Handbook · Glossary/Glosario · Index

SCIENCE SKILL HANDBOOK

MATH SKILL HANDBOOK

FOLDABLES HANDBOOK

REFERENCE HANDBOOK

GLOSSARY/ GLOSARIO

INDEX

SCIENCE SKILL HANDBOOK

MATH SKILL HANDBOOK

FOLDABLES HANDBOOK

REFERENCE HANDBOOK

GLOSSARY/ GLOSARIO

INDEX

SCIENCE SKILL HANDBOOK

MATH SKILL HANDBOOK

FOLDABLES HANDBOOK

REFERENCE HANDBOOK

GLOSSARY/ GLOSARIO

INDEX

Credits

Art Acknowledgments: MCA+, Argosy, Cindy Shaw, Mapping Specialists Ltd.

Photo Credits